ANATOMY&PHYSIOLOGY
Laboratory Manual

NINTH EDITION

KEVIN T. PATTON, PhD
Professor of Human Anatomy & Physiology Instruction
New York Chiropractic College
Seneca Falls, New York

Professor Emeritus of Life Sciences
St. Charles Community College
Cottleville, Missouri

Assistant Professor of Physiology (retired)
St. Louis University Medical School
St. Louis, Missouri

LEAD CONTRIBUTOR
STEVEN R. WOOD, MS, MA
Professor of Anatomy and Physiology (adjunct)
Lone Star Community College – University Park
Houston, Texas

Professor of Biological Sciences (retired)
Florida State College at Jacksonville
Open Campus – Deerwood Center
Jacksonville, Florida

CONTRIBUTOR
DANIEL J. MATUSIAK, EdD
Adjunct Professor
St. Charles Community College
Cottleville, Missouri

Life Science Teacher
St. Dominic High School
O'Fallon, Missouri

ELSEVIER

ELSEVIER

3251 Riverport Lane
St. Louis, Missouri 63043

ANATOMY & PHYSIOLOGY LABORATORY MANUAL, NINTH EDITION   ISBN: 978-0-323-35224-6

Notices

International Standard Book Number: 978-0-323-35224-6

Executive Content Strategist: Kellie White
Content Development Manager: Billie Sharp
Content Development Specialist: Joe Gramlich
Content Coordinator: Samantha Taylor
Publishing Services Manager: Jeff Patterson
Senior Project Manager: Clay S. Broeker
Cover Designer: Brian Salisbury

Printed in the United States of America

Last digit is the print number: 9 8 7 6 5 4 3

Working together
to grow libraries in
developing countries

www.elsevier.com • www.bookaid.org

Contents

Preface

Anatomy and physiology laboratory courses provide the essential hands-on learning opportunities required for a thorough understanding of the human body. This manual contains a series of 55 exercises that provide several guided explorations of human structure and function to accompany any standard human anatomy and physiology textbook. These activities include:

☐ **Labeling exercises** provide opportunities to identify important structures learned in the laboratory and lecture portions of the course. Once completed, they provide guidance to laboratory examinations of models and specimens. Students are encouraged to write out the labels so that the terms are more easily learned.

☐ **Coloring exercises** are becoming the most popular and effective way for many learners to grasp the essential spatial relationships of anatomical structures. This manual contains an accurate and comprehensive collection of anatomy and physiology coloring plates.

☐ **Dissection of anatomical models** and examination of charts are an integral part of any beginning anatomy and physiology laboratory experience. This manual's instructions give valuable guidance for the effective use of models and charts.

☐ **Dissection of fresh and preserved specimens** of tissues, organs, and whole organisms enhances student appreciation of anatomical and functional relationships. Examination of tissues and organs such as those from sheep and cows is suggested in specific exercises throughout this manual. The rat, the cat, and the fetal pig are offered as options for many of the more comprehensive dissection activities. The last unit offers a guide to a live or taped demonstration with a prosected human cadaver.

☐ **Physiological experiments** emphasizing a variety of functional processes of the human body offer students immediate and dramatic examples of physiological concepts. When possible, these activities center around examination of the student's own physiological processes.

☐ **Content and concept review** questions and fill-in tables in each Lab Report and throughout the text encourage students to reinforce and apply their knowledge of human structure and function.

☐ **Modern anatomical imaging** techniques such as computed tomography (CT), magnetic resonance imaging (MRI), and ultrasonography are introduced where appropriate. In each special presentation of imaging technology, students are challenged to interpret actual images of the human body.

☐ **Practical applications** to exercise and athletics, clinical situations, and everyday experiences increase student motivation and place important concepts in a useful context. Each practical example includes application questions that encourage students to think about how concepts apply to the situation described.

This laboratory manual offers other features that enhance learning and ensure a safe and effective laboratory experience:

☐ **A full color design** enhances the learning experience by making the material in the lab manual easier to navigate and easier to use.

☐ **Learning objectives** presented at the beginning of each exercise offer a framework for learning.

☐ **Complete lists of materials** for each exercise give the students and instructor a handy reference for efficient setup of laboratory activities.

☐ **Boxed hints** provide students with special tips on handling specimens, using equipment, and otherwise managing their laboratory activities.

☐ **Safety tips** are highlighted in special boxes to remind students of potential hazards such as fire, chemical spills, cuts, and biological contamination.

☐ **Numerous illustrations** of proper procedures complement the text's complete description of laboratory activities. All anatomical illustrations include a handy compass rosette to orient students to anatomical directions and to reinforce development of spatial perspective.

The design of this laboratory package not only makes the laboratory course fun and effective for the student, but it also provides essential support for the instructor and lab preparation technician. Here are some examples of elements designed to aid instruction and preparation:

☐ **A comprehensive instruction and preparation guide** is provided to each adopting instructor. The guide contains a complete set of hints and special notes and instructions for each laboratory exercise. The guide provides a list of materials broken down by exercise and a comprehensive list of all materials suggested for the course. Substitutions and special sources are given where appropriate. Lists of solution-preparation guidelines and other aids are found throughout the guide. Reproducible handouts to supplement certain exercises are also provided in the guide.

☐ **Modular organization of laboratory exercises** allows their use in virtually any order required by the needs of individual courses. Comprehensive cross-references in the instruction and preparation guide alert instructors about other lab exercises that may involve similar material. For example, Exercise 33: Hormones may be more appropriately done near the reproductive system exercises in some courses.

☐ **Complete instructions for lab activities** are given to the student, freeing the instructor to interact with laboratory students on an individual basis rather than spending a great deal of time introducing the lab procedure to the whole class.

□ **Easy-to-evaluate Lab Report formats** allow instructors to check student work or assign grades in an efficient manner. The Instructor's Guide provides correct answers to objective questions in each Lab Report.

Thanks to Steve Wood for his excellent contributions to—and coordination of—this revision. I also appreciate the support and contributions by my friends and colleagues Dan Matusiak and Suzanne Hembrough, who have provided innumerable practical hints, suggestions, and content over the years. Dr. Gary Thibodeau, as always, provided valuable advice and good cheer. I also thank Elsevier's editorial and production staff for their constant support and encouragement as well as their professional savvy. My sincerest thanks to everyone involved.

Kevin T. Patton

I wish to sincerely express my thanks to Dr. Kevin Patton for his support of my efforts in this edition. Further, I am grateful to the Elsevier team for their insight as we worked on enhancing the Lab Manual. Finally, a special word of thanks is extended to Kellie White, Joe Gramlich, Bridget Healy, and Clay Broeker for providing me the opportunity to participate in this revision. Their counsel throughout this project was greatly appreciated.

Steven R. Wood

Welcome to Anatomy and Physiology Laboratory

Anatomy and physiology laboratory challenges you to learn a great deal about human structure and function in a rather informal, practical atmosphere. Despite its informality as a learning situation, laboratory work requires some appreciation of the scientific method in general, and of laboratory policy and procedure in particular. Read this introductory section carefully. It will introduce you to laboratory science and will give you tips on how to complete this course with great success.

THE SCIENTIFIC METHOD

The scientific method is merely a systematic approach to discovery. From its early days as a discipline, science has relied on this very simple, logical method for gaining an understanding of the universe. The basics of the scientific method can be summarized as a set of steps that are followed in scientific discovery:

Hypothesis. First, one makes a tentative explanation, called a hypothesis, about some aspect of nature. A hypothesis is a reasonable guess based on previous informal observations or on previously tested explanations.

Initial experimentation. After a hypothesis has been proposed, it must be tested. The testing of a hypothesis is called experimentation. Scientific experiments are designed to be as simple as possible, to avoid the possibility of errors. Often, experimental controls are used to ensure that the test situation itself is not affecting the results. For example, if a new cancer drug is being tested, half the test subjects will get the drug and half the subjects will be given a harmless substitute. The group getting the drug is called the test group, and the group getting the placebo is called the control group. If both groups improve, or if only the control group improves, the drug's effectiveness hasn't been proven. If the test group improves, but the control group doesn't, the hypothesis that the drug works is tentatively accepted as true. Experimentation requires accurate measurement and recording of data.

Interpretation and conclusion. After an experiment, or series of experiments, the researcher analyzes all of the experimental data. If the results support the original hypothesis, it is tentatively accepted as true, and the researcher moves on to the next step. If the data do not support the hypothesis, the researcher tentatively rejects the hypothesis. If an experimental error is suspected, the hypothesis may not be rejected but retested. Knowing which hypotheses are untrue is almost as valuable as knowing which are true. Every rejected hypothesis brings the scientific community a little closer to the truth.

Replication. This step in the scientific method is the one least appreciated by nonscientists. After a hypothesis is tested and accepted, it is retested over and over to make sure that it is true. Because researchers often make minor mistakes in the design or execution of experiments, it is important that other scientists verify the original work. Usually, initial research experiments and their results are published in scientific journals so that others in the same field of research can benefit from them and verify them. If experimental results cannot be replicated (re-created) by other scientists, the hypothesis is not widely accepted. If a hypothesis withstands this rigorous retesting, the level of confidence in the hypothesis increases. A hypothesis that has gained a high level of confidence is called a theory or law.

The "facts" presented in this course are merely the latest theories of how the body is built and how it functions. As methods of imaging the body and measuring functional processes improve, we find new data that cause us to replace old theories with newer ones.

MEASUREMENT AND DATA COLLECTION

Scientific experimentation is valid only when data are accurately measured and accurately recorded. In this lab course, you will be invited from time to time to execute various experiments. Your results will be meaningful only if you are careful to measure and record your results properly.

In this manual, as in nearly all scientific works, only the metric system of measurement is used. The metric system is useful for two important reasons: it is commonly used throughout the world, and metric units are easily converted because they are all based on units of 10. The metric system is often referred to as the SI or International System.

Do not worry about being able to convert metric units to United States (English) units or vice versa. You will rarely, if ever, be required to do that type of unit conversion in this course. It is more important that you learn to "think in metric," without regard to equivalent units in another system.

In this course, you will use metric units to measure time, temperature, length, volume, mass, and pressure. Each of these measurable characteristics has a basic metric unit that can be increased or decreased by factors of 10 as needed. For example, the basic unit of measuring length is the meter. The meter is a useful unit in measuring the height of an elephant, 2 to 3 meters, but not in measuring the distance to the moon. Units a thousand times larger, kilometers, are used instead. Likewise, the diameter of a bacterial cell is measured in micrometers, which are one-millionth of a meter. Different-sized metric units can be converted back and forth by multiplying or dividing by factors of 10.

The tables in this section give the basic units and common alternate units for time, temperature, length, volume, mass, and pressure.

The abbreviations of metric units are given in parentheses. Note that they do not have a period (.) after them. Be careful to notice whether they are capital (uppercase) letters.

Accurate measurement means using units of measurement correctly, but it also means using measuring devices accurately. If you are not familiar with reading the markings on metric rulers, balances, thermometers, and other common measuring devices, ask your instructor to demonstrate.

TIME

Basic unit: second (sec)

0.000001 second = microsecond (μsec)

0.001 second = millisecond (msec)

60 seconds = minute (min)

3600 seconds = hour (hr)

TEMPERATURE

Basic unit: degree Celsius (° C)

No alternate units are commonly used.

LENGTH

Basic unit: meter (m)

0.000000001 meter = nanometer (nm)

0.000001 meter = micrometer (μm)

0.001 meter = millimeter (mm)

0.01 meter = centimeter (cm)

1000 meters = kilometer (km)

VOLUME

Basic unit: liter (l or L)

0.001 liter = milliliter (ml)*

0.01 liter = centiliter (cl)

0.1 liter = deciliter (dl)

*milliliters = cubic centimeters (cc)

MASS

Basic unit: gram (g)

0.001 gram = milligram (mg)

0.01 gram = centigram (cg)

1000 grams = kilogram (kg)

PRESSURE

Basic unit: millimeters of mercury (mm Hg)

No alternate units are commonly used.

HOW TO DISSECT

The term anatomy literally means "to cut apart," so it is no wonder that dissections are commonly done in anatomy lab courses. Dissection activities recommended in this manual are not proposed without recognition of humane concerns. The purpose of these dissections is to instruct in a way that no other method can duplicate. The specimens called for are usually from animals raised specifically to be euthanized and used as resources. For health professionals, dissection of anatomical preparations is a necessary prerequisite to working with living bodies.

The goal of any dissection exercise is the exploration of anatomical relationships. Proper dissection requires patience and skill. Some students slice and hack away at their specimens; others hardly touch them. Good technique lies somewhere between these two extremes. Organs should be separated from one another only enough to see surrounding structures. Rarely should structures be cut or removed. The instructions given in this manual state when, where, and how cuts should be made.

Each dissection activity in this manual offers safety advice concerning proper handling of the dissection specimens. Protective gloves, lab coat, and eyewear are recommended. Always be careful when using dissection tools; severe injuries can result from their careless use.

Figure A shows some commonly used dissection instruments. A brief discussion of each is in order here:

☐ **1. Scalpel or knife.** The scalpel is probably the instrument most overused by beginners in an anatomy lab course. This tool should rarely be used and only when you want to cut all the way through a specimen. A pathology knife, or butcher knife, is a much more useful tool.

☐ **2. Scissors.** Scissors are probably the most underused dissection tool. Whenever you are tempted to use a scalpel for cutting, try the scissors first. Often, your results will be much better and you will not have damaged important underlying parts.

☐ **3. Probes.** You may want to have several types of probes. Both dull and sharp probes (dissecting needles) are useful in separating tissues, exploring cavities, tracing blood vessels, and pointing to structures.

☐ **4. Forceps.** Forceps are one of the handiest dissection tools. They can be used to grasp small objects, to separate structures, to point to structures, to explore cavities, and to pull on structures.

☐ **5. Ruler.** Your metric ruler should be marked in both centimeters and millimeters. It is useful in measuring organs and in many nondissection lab activities.

☐ **6. Dissection pins.** These are standard, heavy-duty straight pins. Dissection pins are useful in pinning membranes and other structures to a dissection board to keep them temporarily out of the way.

☐ **7. Dissection tray.** There are many varieties and shapes of dissection trays, and your instructor will recommend the best for your situation. Dissection trays help organize the dissection activity by keeping everything together, and they protect the lab table surface. Some types can also be used for storing your specimen for later study.

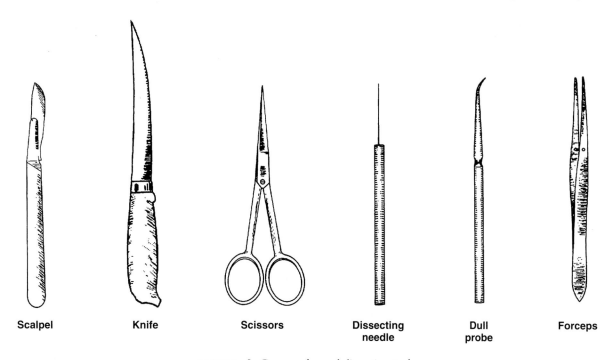

FIGURE A Commonly used dissection tools.

USING THIS MANUAL

The format of each Lab Exercise is self-explanatory. After some brief introductory remarks, each exercise begins with a section entitled "Before You Begin." This section recommends that before starting any lab activity you should:

❏ Read the appropriate chapter(s) in the textbook you are using for this course.

❏ Set your learning goals so that you know what important concepts you should be trying to learn.

❏ Prepare your materials so that your lab activity will run smoothly.

❏ Read the entire activity before starting. In this way, you will not be surprised (and therefore unprepared) for any step in the procedure.

❏ Each exercise contains one or more activities. Your instructor may suggest that you do all the activities in an exercise or only one. Each activity includes some or all of these helpful features:

❏ Large, bold step numbers help you keep your place as your eyes move back and forth between the manual and your lab setup. Each step number is preceded by a check-box (❏) that you can use to check off each step as it is completed.

   ☑ **1.** Find these structures on your specimen:
      ☑ head
      ☑ neck
      ☑ torso

   ☑ **2.** Carefully open the ventral body cavity of your specimen.

   ☑ **3.** Locate the following in the ventral body cavity of your specimen:
      ☑ stomach
      ☑ spleen
      ☑ liver

❏ The following features highlight useful information for completing the activities safely and successfully:

  HINT boxes – offer valuable information and dissection techniques.

 SAFETY FIRST boxes – draw attention to important safety concerns pertaining to the lab activities.

LANDMARK CHARACTERISTICS boxes – provide helpful advice for identifying specimens.

❏ Anatomical dissection illustrations and photographs are identified with a colored tab running the length of the page for quick and easy reference.

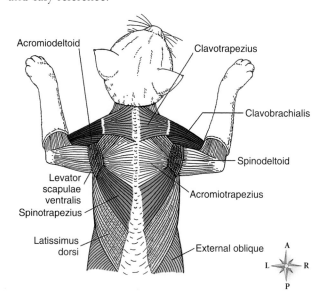

☐ Labeling exercises encourage you to apply your knowledge of human anatomy in a practical test. Long label lines allow you room to write the name of the structure directly on the illustration. When each figure is completely labeled, the terms should be transferred to the Lab Report so that the instructor can check your work.

colors; otherwise many parts will look the same. If you use pens, make sure they won't bleed through the paper. If you use pencils, you may want to insert a piece of plain paper into your manual over each completed coloring plate so that the colors do not rub off on the facing page. The materials list in the first exercise reminds you to bring colored pens or pencils to your work area, but it is assumed that you will have these for all the lab exercises.

☐ Each exercise ends with a Lab Report. The report includes handy tables and sketching areas for you to record your laboratory observations and results. Where appropriate, the Lab Report also presents objective and subjective questions for you to answer. Some of these questions drill you on your knowledge of important terms, whereas others ask you to use your basic knowledge to interpret, organize, or otherwise process basic facts to ensure that you understand conceptual relationships. A number of highlighted practical application boxes in the exercise itself often ask you to apply your basic knowledge in this way. These questions, along with practice in making scientific observations, help you develop your scientific reasoning skills.

SAFETY FIRST!

As already mentioned, numerous boxed safety tips appear throughout this manual. Entitled "SAFETY FIRST," their large letters and urgent tone are meant to call your attention to potential hazards in the laboratory. Before beginning the course, it is essential that you learn some basic laboratory safety policies:

☐ Always use care and common sense in the laboratory.
☐ Check the labels of all chemicals for safety warnings before using them. If the container does not have a safety label, consult the instructor.
☐ Wear protective gear if you are handling dangerous materials.
☐ Plan ahead about what to do if a spill occurs. If you spill a dangerous substance on your body, you may have to remove your clothing. If your lab has a safety shower, stand under it and pull the ring (see Figure B).
☐ Avoid using materials to which you have a known sensitivity.
☐ Locate first aid equipment in the laboratory and familiarize yourself with its use.

☐ The coloring exercise has been cited by educators and students as being an effective method for learning anatomy. By using multiple senses to trace and highlight shapes and relationships, you reinforce your knowledge of the human form. Each coloring plate is like a paint-by-number activity. Each label has a small red number that corresponds to a red number on the illustration itself. Use a colored pen or pencil (not a crayon) to write the term over the outline letters of the label. This will reinforce your familiarity with the term and its correct spelling and makes the label a "color code" so you can later find the structure by its color. After filling in the label, use the same color to shade in the matching structure in the illustration. Use contrasting colors so that parts next to one another can be easily distinguished. Do not attempt to color everything in realistic

☐ Confirm all directions, procedures, and other information with your instructor before each activity. Mark changes or additions in this manual, crossing out any printed information that does not apply to you.

☐ Locate the nearest medical help and identify the easiest and fastest way to access it (for example, phoning an ambulance).

☐ Locate the fire safety equipment in your lab and familiarize yourself with its use. Locate the nearest fire alarm box and identify the recommended primary and alternative fire exit routes.

Important Safety Information

(Use the spaces that follow to write important safety information.)

Location of first aid box:

Emergency medical help:

Fire extinguisher location:

Fire extinguisher type:

Fire alarm box location:

Primary escape route:

Alternate escape route:

Weather safety shelter:

Important notes:

☐ Always follow the directions and safety advice provided with equipment and supplies, even if they are different than those given in this manual. Injuries often result from the misuse of equipment.

☐ Remember that absolutely no eating, drinking, or smoking is allowed in the laboratory.

☐ To avoid injury or contamination, properly dispose of or clean and store all lab equipment and supplies before vacating the laboratory. Wash your hands thoroughly on entering and leaving a biological laboratory.

☐ Always supervise experiments or demonstrations in progress. Never leave a laboratory experiment unattended.

HOW TO STUDY FOR LAB QUIZZES

Tips for effective studying could fill several volumes. Instead of an entire work on studying, this section presents a few tips that many students have found to be particularly helpful in the anatomy and physiology laboratory course. As with any list of study tips, you will find some more useful to you than others. You will find many additional tips and practical advice in the *Survival Guide for Anatomy & Physiology* (2nd ed.), published by Elsevier, and at *theAPstudent.org*.

☐ Identify the type of quizzes you will encounter. Written quizzes may involve multiple choice, matching, or other objective questions. Written quizzes may also have subjective short answer or essay questions in which you must interpret or restate concepts. Figures may be offered for labeling. Practical tests may involve stations at which specimens have been placed. You may be asked to perform a procedure or answer a question about the specimen while at each station. You may have an individualized practical quiz in which the instructor will ask you questions or watch you perform a procedure individually. Many lab courses involve online quizzes, lab reports, or other graded activities. Ask your instructor for some sample questions if you do not understand how an upcoming quiz is constructed. Knowing the manner in which you will be evaluated is important to designing your study strategy.

☐ Organize a study group (which may be the same as your lab group) to meet several times before a quiz to help each other with the material. Such groups can also operate by phone, email, discussion forums, or social media such as chat or group video. Quizzing each other is a useful technique.

☐ Spend many brief sessions reviewing specimens and other lab work, rather than one or two long sessions just before the quiz. Ask your instructor if there are open lab times or a learning center at which you can review models or specimens. Try to find online resources to help you practice.

☐ Study actively. Do not just sit and look at your study materials; do some hands-on activities with them. Make flash cards on paper or online to quiz yourself. Set up your own practical exam, and then take it. Sketch specimens and models again. Draw a "concept map" in which you draw boxes or pictures connected in a logical way. This will help you organize concepts in your mind.

☐ Use all of your resources. Your account at *evolve.elsevier.com* has learning resources. Campus libraries and learning centers often offer the services of specialists who can help you sharpen your study skills. They can show you examples of concept maps and flash cards. Your instructor has successfully completed laboratory courses and has helped numerous previous students in this course, so ask your instructor for study tips. Use the course textbook and the study aids in the textbook to help you learn the lab material.

Chemical Safety

Safety shower

Pull

Eyewash
(hold eyelids open)

Safety goggles

Protective gloves

Fire Safety

1. Pull pin
2. Aim
3. Squeeze handles together

Fire extinguisher

Fire blanket
(wrap yourself as you pull it out)

FIGURE B Commonly used chemical and fire safety equipment.

The Student Laboratory

The laboratory portion of the typical anatomy and physiology course is in some ways a unique beast. Here are a few ideas on how to make the student laboratory the best possible experience:

- **Safety is always first!** Scientists are sticklers for safety. They never take a step into the lab without every possible safety precaution being in place. A mistake in the lab, even a student lab, can cause serious injury or even death. Far too many preventable injuries occur in student labs. So PLEASE heed all of the safety precautions printed in your lab manuals, posted in your labs, and articulated or published by your school or professor or both. In addition, use common sense.

- **Use the "field method" for identifying anatomical structures.** Roger Tory Peterson, the famous naturalist and birder, developed a method for field identification of birds that has since been used for everything from identifying sparrows to spotting enemy aircraft. The Peterson method focuses on "field marks," the one or two characteristics that distinguish particular birds or airplanes from similar birds or airplanes. Simply approach tissues, bones, bone markings, muscles, and other structures that you need to identify in lab courses as you would animals in the field. Focus on the one or two characteristics that make one tissue different from all others. Peterson's method also makes use of range maps that show where different birds are likely to be found. Do the same with lab specimens. Where are adductor muscles likely to be found? On the inside of limbs. So where would you start looking for adductor longus? Use a little tip from field geography, too. It might take you all day to find the Mississippi River on a map if you have no clue what a river is. When learning bone markings, how can you find the supraorbital foramen when you have no idea what a foramen is? Study types of things, like types of muscles, types of bones, and so on, before studying the specific examples assigned to you.

- **Remember that the laboratory is a playground.** That doesn't mean you should just goof around for no good reason. It does mean that labs are intended to be fun, hands-on opportunities to play with specimens, models, and experimental equipment. Therefore, approach it that way. Don't just try to get by with the minimum activity. If you linger and look a little deeper, or turn the model around this way, then another way, you'll find a deeper understanding of what you were supposed to find as well as the connections that help you draw concepts together into the *big picture*. Kinesthetic (tactile) learners will especially benefit from this aspect of the lab course—often in ways that bring home points from the lecture or discussion portions of the course.

- **Use flash cards.** Flash cards are especially useful in certain lab activities. Many students like to draw pictures of lab specimens on one side of a card and its name or description on the other side. You might even bring a camera to take photos of your dissections so that you can use them to make flash cards! Your cell phone may have a camera, so use it as a learning tool in lab!

- **Use mnemonic devices.** Archeologists have recently uncovered evidence that mnemonic devices were used by the ancient Greeks thousands of years ago in their famous schools. You may have seen one of those memory experts that can spout off all the names on a page in the phone book using mnemonic devices. Mnemonic devices are little sayings or mental images you use to help you remember a concept. For example, the acronym IPMAT has been used by generations of students to help them learn the phases of the cell cycle: interphase, prophase, metaphase, anaphase, and telophase. The mnemonic sentence "On old Olympus's tiny tops, a friendly Viking grew vines and hops," is a mnemonic for learning the names, in order, of the 12 pairs of cranial nerves. (You can find the names in Table 24-1.) The sillier the phrase or mental image you use, or the more ribald, the easier it is to remember and the more useful it is as a memory aid.

- **Dissect like an artist.** Some of the best anatomists have in fact also been great artists. Artistic finesse in pulling apart structures without destroying them or removing them from their relative position in the body is far more effective than simply hacking away. Your goal should be to find structures so that you can understand how the body is constructed.

  You don't have to be a great sketch artist. However, you should *sketch a lot*. Draw everything! Don't sweat and slave over creating a masterpiece, even if you're capable. (Wait until after lab and work on your masterpiece on the weekend.) However, do take enough time that you can recognize key features later on when you use your sketches to study. In addition, label as much as you can. A sketch without any labels is pretty useless, except maybe as a coaster.

The Student Laboratory—cont'd

Come to the lab prepared. Read what you will be doing in lab before you do it. If you don't come prepared, then half the time in the lab will be spent just trying to figure out what to do. The other half of your time will be spent trying to rush through the activity without any appreciation of the concepts behind it. Preparation also means reading the portions of the textbook that relate to the lab activity. Preparation is probably the greatest key to using the student lab to its greatest potential.

☐ **Use many resources.** When you're trying to find anatomical specimens or interpret results from a physiology demonstration or experiment, don't rely solely on your textbook and lab manual. Often your specimen will not look like the picture in these books. No organ or tissue looks exactly like any other. Therefore, find out where you can purchase or borrow a lab atlas, anatomy atlas, histology book, and other useful resources. In addition, many useful resources for the anatomy and physiology lab can be found on the Internet. (You can use a search engine to find them.)

Photo and Illustration Credits

Figure 3-1: Courtesy VEE GEE Scientific.

Figure 6-3: Courtesy Dennis Strete. **Figure 6-4:** From Young B: *Wheater's functional histology*, ed 6, Philadelphia, 2014, Churchill Livingstone.

Figures 7-4, 7-8: Courtesy Ed Reschke. **Figure 7-5:** From Tallitsch R, Guastafelli R: *Histology: An identification manual*, St. Louis, 2009, Mosby. **Figures 7-6, 7-9:** Courtesy Dennis Strete. **Figures 7-7, 7-10:** From Young B: *Wheater's functional histology*, ed 6, Philadelphia, 2014, Churchill Livingstone.

Figures 8-4, 8-5, 8-6, 8-7, 8-8, 8-9, 8-10, 8-11, 8-12: Courtesy Dennis Strete.

Figures 9-1, 9-2: Courtesy Ed Reschke. **Figure 9-3:** Courtesy Dennis Strete. **Figure 9-4:** From Gartner LP, Hiatt JL: *Color textbook of histology*, ed 3, Philadelphia, 2007, Saunders.

Figure 10-1, A: From Erlandsen SL, Magney JM: *Color atlas of histology*, St. Louis, 1992, Mosby.

Figure 11-3: From Gartner LP, Hiatt JL: *Color textbook of histology*, ed 3, Philadelphia, 2007, Saunders.

Figures 12-2, 12-3, 12-4, 12-5: From Abrahams P, Marks S, Hutchings R: *McMinn's color atlas of the head and neck anatomy*, ed 4, Philadelphia, 2010, Mosby.

Figures 13-5, 13-6: From Muscolino JE: *Kinesiology: The skeletal system and muscle function*, ed 2, St. Louis, 2011, Mosby.

Figure 14-1: Courtesy Vidic B, Suarez FR: *Photographic atlas of the human body*, St. Louis, 1984, Mosby. **Figure 14-2, A, B:** From Muscolino JE: *Kinesiology: The skeletal system and muscle function*, ed 2, St. Louis, 2011, Mosby.

Figure 15-2: Courtesy Vidic B, Suarez FR: *Photographic atlas of the human body*, St. Louis, 1984, Mosby. **Figure 15-3, A, B:** From Muscolino JE: *Kinesiology: The skeletal system and muscle function*, ed 2, St. Louis, 2011, Mosby.

Figure 17-3: From Muscolino JE: *Kinesiology: The skeletal system and muscle function*, ed 2, St. Louis, 2011, Mosby.

Figure 27-3: Courtesy Ed Reschke

Figure 32-3, A: From Kierszenbaum A: *Histology and cell biology*, Philadelphia, 2002, Mosby. **Figure 32-3, B, C:** Courtesy Ed Reschke. **Figure 32-3, D:** From Erlandsen SL, Magney JM: *Color atlas of histology*, St. Louis, 1992, Mosby.

Figure 34-6: Courtesy Biomedical Polymers.

Figure 39-1, B: Courtesy Photo Science Library. **Figure 39-1 C, D, E:** Courtesy Ed Reschke.

Figure 49-2: From Brunzel NA: *Fundamentals of urine and body fluid analysis*, ed 2, Philadelphia, 2004, Saunders

Figure 50-4: From Brunzel NA: *Fundamentals of urine and body fluid analysis*, ed 2, Philadelphia, 2004, Saunders.

Figure 55-5: Courtesy Vidic B, Suarez FR: *Photographic atlas of the human body*, St. Louis, 1984, Mosby.

1

Organization of the Body

Many explorers use maps, figures, and photographs to help orient themselves to the terrain to be explored. The anatomist uses maps, figures, and photos to explore the body and its parts. The use of maps and other aids to find a geographical position is called *orienteering* and is a useful analogy to human anatomical study. At the beginning of this exercise, you will learn how anatomical "maps" and models are read. Later in this exercise, you will become familiar with the major body systems and some of their organs so that you will be comfortable with the "lay of the land" in the human body.

BEFORE YOU BEGIN

☐ Read the appropriate chapter in your textbook.
☐ Set your learning goals.
☐ When you finish this exercise, you should be able to:
   ☐ use anatomical terms correctly.
   ☐ discuss the nature of an anatomical section.
   ☐ describe the basic plan of the human body.
   ☐ identify the major body cavities.
   ☐ list the major systems of the body, their principal organs, and their primary functions.
☐ Prepare your materials:
   ☐ dissectible human torso model (or comparable charts)
   ☐ models or figures showing different anatomical sections
   ☐ computer setup with human dissection program (optional)
☐ Read the directions and safety tips for this exercise carefully before starting any procedure.

Study TIPS

Learning and comprehending the material in this lab are important to your success in anatomy and physiology. These terms will be used extensively throughout the course. Use all of the available resources (textbook, colored illustrations, Brief Atlas, the *A&P Survival Guide*, flash cards, etc.) to review the terms. During this lab, use **Table 1-1** and the illustrations, and with a lab partner work together in either labeling a torso chart or quizzing each other by identifying the various directional terms, planes and sections, body cavities, and body regions.

A. PLANES AND SECTIONS

All terms describing the anatomy of organisms assume that the body is in the classic anatomical position. For the human, that means standing, facing the viewer. The hands are held down along the side of the trunk, with the palms facing forward. It is often useful to show a figure of a *sectioned* human body or organ. A "section" refers to a part cut along a plane. A plane is a geometrical concept referring to an imagined flat surface.

> **Hint** The anatomical position of a four-legged animal, such as a rat, cat, or fetal pig, is standing on all four limbs, head facing forward. See Exercise 2 for an example. •

The term *cross section (c.s.),* for example, refers to a part cut crosswise. A *longitudinal section (l.s.)* is a cut made lengthwise. These terms are useful only in limited circumstances because they do not really identify whether the cuts are made top to bottom, front to back, or side to side. The following three anatomical planes are used to describe sections of the body:

☐ 1 **Sagittal plane**—A sagittal plane extends from front to back and top to bottom, dividing the body into left and right portions. A *midsagittal plane* refers to a sagittal plane that divides the body into exactly equal left and right portions.
☐ 2 **Frontal plane**—The frontal plane, also called a *coronal plane,* divides the body into front and back portions.
☐ 3 **Horizontal plane**—Also called a *transverse plane,* the horizontal plane divides the body into top and bottom portions.

Using the models or figures provided, find at least three examples of each of the sections described **(Figure 1-1)**. For each, ask yourself what perspective the section gives that a section cut along a different plane does not give.

B. ANATOMICAL DIRECTIONS

To locate structures within a body, you must use *directional terms.* Actually, you use these kinds of terms all the time—for example, *left, right, up, down, north, south.*

☐ 1 Review the directional terms given in Table 1-1. Notice that they are grouped in relative pairs. Each member of a pair is the opposite, or complement, of the other member of the pair. For example, *right* is the opposite direction of *left.*
To make the reading of anatomical figures a little easier, an *anatomical compass* is used throughout this lab manual, just as it is in the textbook. On many figures, you will notice a small compass rosette similar to those on geographical maps. Rather than being labeled N, S, E, and W, the

anatomical rosette is labeled with abbreviated anatomical directions.

☐   2 Review this list of directional terms and abbreviations:

- ☐ A = Anterior
- ☐ D = Distal
- ☐ I = Inferior
- ☐ L (opposite R) = Left
- ☐ L (opposite M) = Lateral
- ☐ M = Medial
- ☐ P (opposite A) = Posterior
- ☐ P (opposite D) = Proximal
- ☐ R = Right
- ☐ S = Superior

☐   3 Review the examples of how the anatomical compass is used in illustrations by looking at **Figure 1-2, *A, B, F, G***. Test your knowledge of directions and the use of the anatomical compass by labeling the rosettes given in Figure 1-2, *C, D, E, H, I, J*.

TABLE 1-1   Directional Terms

DIRECTIONAL TERM	DEFINITION	EXAMPLE OF USAGE
Left	To the left of the body (not your left, the subject's)	The stomach is to the *left* of the liver.
Right	To the right of the body or structure being studied	The *right* kidney is damaged.
Lateral	Toward the side; away from the midsagittal plane	The eyes are *lateral* to the nose.
Medial	Toward the midsagittal plane; away from the side	The eyes are *medial* to the ears.
Anterior	Toward the front of the body	The nose is on the *anterior* of the head.
Posterior	Toward the back (rear) of the body	The heel is *posterior* to the toes.
Superior	Toward the top of the body	The shoulders are *superior* to the hips.
Inferior	Toward the bottom of the body	The stomach is *inferior* to the heart.
Dorsal	Along (or toward) the vertebral surface of the body	Her scar is along the *dorsal* surface.
Ventral	Along (toward) the belly surface of the body	The navel is on the *ventral* surface.
Caudad (caudal)	Toward the tail (four-legged animals)	The neck is *caudad* to the skull.
Cephalad	Toward the head (four-legged animals)	The neck is *cephalad* to the tail.
Proximal	Toward the trunk (describes relative position in a limb or other appendage)	This joint is *proximal* to the toenail.
Distal	Away from the trunk or point of attachment	The hand is *distal* to the elbow.
Visceral	Toward an internal organ; away from the outer wall (describes positions inside a body cavity)	This organ is covered with the *visceral* layer of the membrane.
Parietal	Toward the wall; away from internal structures	The abdominal cavity is lined with the *parietal* peritoneal membrane.
Deep	Toward the inside of a part; away from the surface	The thigh muscles are *deep* to the skin.
Superficial	Toward the surface of a part; away from the inside	The skin is a *superficial* organ.
Medullary	Refers to an inner region, or *medulla*	The *medullary* portion of the organ contains nerve tissue.
Cortical	Refers to an outer region, or *cortex*	The *cortical* area produces hormones.

Coloring Exercises: Planes and Directions

Use colored pens or pencils to shade in both the figure and the labels. Each red numeral in the figure corresponds to a matching red numeral following the appropriate label.

Planes
SAGITTAL₁
MIDSAGITTAL₂
FRONTAL₃
HORIZONTAL₄

Directions
LATERAL₅
MEDIAL₆
ANTERIOR₇
POSTERIOR₈
SUPERIOR₉
INFERIOR₁₀
PROXIMAL₁₁
DISTAL₁₂

FIGURE 1-1

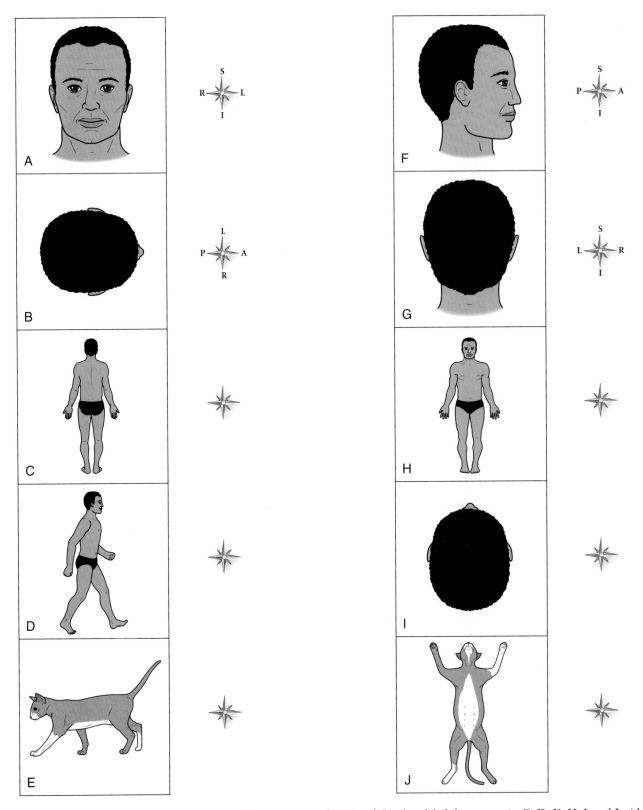

FIGURE 1-2 Look at the examples of labeling anatomical directions (**A** and **B**, **F** and **G**); then label the rosettes in **C**, **D**, **E**, **H**, **I**, and **J** with the appropriate letters: S, I, A, P, L, and R.

C. BODY CAVITIES AND REGIONS

The inside of the human body contains the viscera, or internal organs. The viscera are found in any of a number of cavities (spaces) within the body **(Figure 1-3)**. The two principal groups of body cavities are the dorsal body cavities and the ventral body cavities. Because these spaces are so large, they are sometimes subdivided into smaller units.

☐ 1 Using a dissectible torso model, find these divisions of the dorsal body cavities (and the organs within):

☐ **Cranial cavities**—Within the skull. Organ: *brain*

☐ **Spinal cavities**—Within the vertebral column. Organ: *spinal cord*

☐ 2 Using the torso model, find these divisions and organs of the ventral body cavities:

☐ **Thoracic cavity**—Within the rib cage

☐ **Pleural cavities**—Left one-third and right one-third of the thoracic cavity. Organ: *lung*

☐ **Mediastinum**—Middle one-third of thorax. Organs: *heart, trachea, esophagus*

☐ **Abdominopelvic cavity**—From the diaphragm to the bottom of the trunk

☐ **Abdominal cavity**—From the diaphragm to the rim of the pelvic bones. Organs: *stomach, liver, most of the intestines, pancreas, spleen, kidneys*

☐ **Pelvic cavity**—From the pelvic rim to the floor of the trunk. Organs: *portions of the intestines, ovaries, uterus, urinary bladder*

☐ 3 Because the abdominopelvic cavity is so large and contains so many different organs, it is often convenient to subdivide it into nine abdominopelvic regions **(Figure 1-4)**. The regions are bounded by a grid made by imagining two horizontal planes (one just below the ribs, the other just above the hip bones) and two sagittal planes (each just medial to a nipple). This arrangement forms a 3-D, tic-tac-toe grid in the abdominopelvic cavity. Identify the approximate locations of each of the nine regions on a model of the human torso:

☐ **Right hypochondriac region**—Top right region (*hypochondriac* means "below [rib] cartilage")

☐ **Epigastric region**—Top middle region (*epigastric* means "near the stomach")

☐ **Left hypochondriac region**—Top left region

☐ **Right lumbar region**—Middle right region (*lumbar* refers to lumbar vertebrae in lower back)

☐ **Umbilical region**—Central region (*umbilical* refers to the umbilicus, or navel)

☐ **Left lumbar region**—Middle left region (*lumbar* refers to lumbar vertebrae in lower back)

☐ **Right iliac region**—Lower right region (*iliac* refers to ilium, the bowl-like part of the hip bone)

FIGURE 1-3 Label the names of the body cavities on the lines provided and on the blanks in the Lab Report at the end of this exercise.

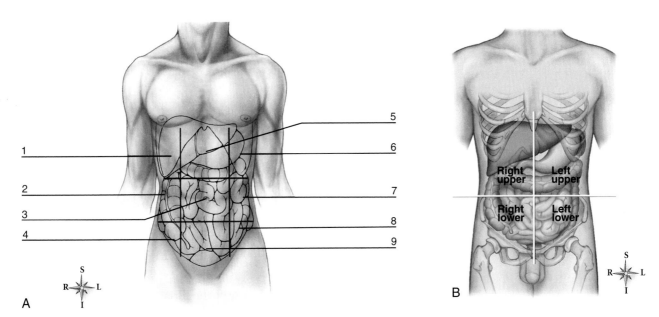

FIGURE 1-4 A, Label on the lines provided and on the blanks in the Lab Report the nine regions of the abdominopelvic cavity. **B**, Four quadrants of the abdominopelvic cavity.

☐ **Hypogastric region**—Lower middle region (*hypogastric* means "below the stomach")
☐ **Left iliac region**—Lower left region

D. SURFACE REGIONS

There are hundreds of terms that describe specific locations on the surface of the human body. These names are useful not only for identifying surface features but also the underlying muscles, bones, nerves, and blood vessels. In this activity, locate regions named by a few of the more common terms.

☐ 1 Locate the following surface regions on the anterior aspect of a human model or **Figure 1-5**:
  ☐ **Abdominal**—Area overlying the abdominal cavity
  ☐ **Antebrachial**—Forearm
  ☐ **Axillary**—Armpit
  ☐ **Brachial**—Upper arm
  ☐ **Buccal**—Cheek (side of mouth)
  ☐ **Carpal**—Wrist
  ☐ **Cervical**—Neck
  ☐ **Coxal**—Hip
  ☐ **Cubital**—Anterior of elbow
  ☐ **Femoral**—Thigh
  ☐ **Mental**—Chin

☐ **Orbital**—Eye
☐ **Patellar**—Anterior knee joint
☐ **Pubic**—Lower front of trunk, between thighs
☐ **Tarsal**—Ankle
☐ **Thoracic**—Chest
☐ **Tibial**—Anterior leg (shin)

☐ 2 Identify these regions on the posterior aspect of your subject:
  ☐ **Cervical**—Neck
  ☐ **Flank**—Lateral region
  ☐ **Gluteal**—Buttocks
  ☐ **Lumbar**—Lower back
  ☐ **Occipital**—Posterior of head
  ☐ **Popliteal**—Posterior knee joint
  ☐ **Scapular**—Shoulder blade
  ☐ **Sural**—Calf
  ☐ **Thoracic**—Upper back

E. BODY SYSTEMS

As you know, the human organism is composed of organ groups called *systems*. The organs of a system work together in an organized manner to accomplish the function(s) of the system. As an introduction to human body systems, study **Table 1-2**. Each of the systems will be discussed in more detail later in this course.

1 _____

2 _____

3 _____

4 _____

5 _____

6 _____

7 _____

8 _____

9 _____

10 _____

11 _____

12 _____

13 _____

14 _____

15 _____

16 _____

17 _____

18 _____

19 _____

20 _____

21 _____

22 _____

23 _____

24 _____

25 _____

26 _____

FIGURE 1-5 Label these figures using the regional terms listed in activity D and on the blanks in the Lab Report at the end of this exercise.

T A B L E   1 - 2   **Body Systems**

ORGAN SYSTEM	PRINCIPAL ORGANS	PRIMARY FUNCTION(S)
Integumentary	Skin	Protection, temperature regulation, sensation
Skeletal	Bones, ligaments	Support, protection, movement, mineral/fat storage, blood production
Muscular	Skeletal muscle, tendons	Movement, posture, heat production
Nervous	Brain, spinal cord, nerves, sensory organs	Control/regulation/coordination of other systems, sensation, memory
Endocrine	Pituitary gland, adrenals, pancreas	Control/regulation of other systems, thyroid, parathyroids, other glands
Cardiovascular	Heart, arteries, veins, capillaries	Exchange and transport of materials
Lymphatic	Lymph nodes, lymphatic vessels, spleen	Immunity, fluid balance, thymus, tonsils
Respiratory	Lungs, bronchial tree, trachea, larynx	Gas exchange, acid-base balance nasal cavity
Digestive	Stomach, intestines, esophagus, liver, mouth, pancreas	Breakdown and absorption of nutrients, elimination of waste
Urinary	Kidneys, ureters, bladder, urethra	Excretion of waste, fluid and electrolyte balance, acid-base balance
Reproductive male	Testes, vas deferens, prostate, seminal vesicles, penis	Continuation of genes (reproduction)
Reproductive female	Ovaries, fallopian tubes, uterus, vagina	Reproduction, nurturing of offspring

Name: _____ Date: _____ Section: _____

LAB REPORT 1
Organization of the Body

Figure 1-3 (from p. 5)

1. _____
2. _____
3. _____
4. _____
5. _____
6. _____
7. _____
8. _____
9. _____

Figure 1-4 (from p. 6)

1. _____
2. _____
3. _____
4. _____
5. _____
6. _____
7. _____
8. _____
9. _____

Multiple Choice

1. _____
2. _____
3. _____
4. _____
5. _____
6. _____

Figure 1-5 (from p. 7)

1. _____
2. _____
3. _____
4. _____

Multiple Choice (only one response is correct in each item)

1. An anatomist cuts a cadaver (preserved body) with a large saw in a way that divides the cadaver into equal left and right halves. The cut is along a _?_ plane.
   a. sagittal
   b. midsagittal
   c. frontal
   d. horizontal
   e. a and b are correct

2. In many study skulls, the top of the skull can be removed so that inner features can be seen. Along which plane should one cut to open the top of a human study skull?
   a. sagittal
   b. coronal
   c. horizontal
   d. frontal
   e. b and d are correct

3. A surgeon makes an incision medially from the left axillary region, turning inferiorly at the midline and proceeding to the pubic region. The path of the cut can be mapped on the patient's chest as:
   a. ⌐ b. + c. ∟ d. ¬ e. – f. /

4. Which of these regions contains the spleen?
   a. epigastric
   b. hypogastric
   c. left hypochondriac
   d. right hypochondriac
   e. right lumbar

5. Soccer players often wear shin protectors, which shield the _?_ region of each leg.
   a. femoral
   b. tibial
   c. popliteal
   d. cortical
   e. gluteal

6. Control and regulation of other systems are primary functions of the _?_.
   a. nervous system
   b. cardiovascular system
   c. endocrine system
   d. urinary system
   e. a and c are correct

5. _____

6. _____

7. _____

8. _____

9. _____

10. _____

11. _____

12. _____

13. _____

14. _____

15. _____

16. _____

17. _____

18. _____

19. _____

20. _____

21. _____

22. _____

23. _____

24. _____

25. _____

26. _____

Fill-in

1. _____

2. _____

3. _____

4. _____

5. _____

6. _____

7. _____

8. _____

9. _____

10. _____

11. _____

12. _____

Fill-in (give the correct anatomical term for each item below)

1. The head is _?_ to the feet.

2. The liver is part of the _?_ system.

3. A leg amputation is likely to involve a _?_ cut, or section, through bone.

4. My lower back, or _?_, is sore.

5. The first finger is _?_ to the hand, no matter which position it is in.

6. The popliteal vein is found in the _?_.

7. The heart is _?_ to the right lung.

8. The shoulder is _?_ to the elbow, no matter how one's arm is held.

9. The skin is _?_ relative to the skeleton.

10. Adipose tissue is often just _?_ to the skin.

11. An occipital scar is on the back of the _?_.

12. The thoracic wall is lined with the _?_ layer of the double-layered pleural membrane.

Sketch (make a rough sketch of a human figure in the position indicated by the compass rosette and label)

Dissection: The Whole Body

This exercise may be used as either an introduction to vertebrate anatomy or as a synthesis activity to conclude the laboratory course. Succeeding exercises in this manual concentrate on organs or systems one by one. This exercise begins the study of the body with an overview of everything together in an exploration of the entire vertebrate body. Because the vertebrate body plan is similar among species, another lab animal specimen (e.g., fetal pig, rabbit) could be substituted.

> **Hint** ▸ In a short course, a well-preserved specimen can be used from time to time throughout your studies. If you will be looking at your dissected specimen for the next several months, make sure that it is kept in the appropriate container under conditions suggested by your instructor. •

BEFORE YOU BEGIN

- ☐ Set your learning goals. When you finish this exercise, you should be able to:
  - ☐ perform a whole-body dissection of a vertebrate animal.
  - ☐ identify the major anatomical features of the vertebrate body in a dissected specimen.
- ☐ Prepare your materials:
  - ☐ preserved (plain or double-injected) or freshly killed lab rat (or similar vertebrate)
  - ☐ dissection tools and trays
  - ☐ mounted rat skeleton (optional)
  - ☐ storage container (if preserved specimen is to be reused)
  - ☐ computer setup with a program to simulate dissection of a human body (optional)
- ☐ Read the directions and safety tips for this exercise *carefully* before starting any procedure.

> **⊘ safety first**
> Observe the usual precautions when working with a preserved or fresh specimen. Heed the safety advice accompanying preservatives used with your specimen. Use protective gloves and safety eyewear while handling your specimen. Avoid injury with dissection tools. Dispose of your specimen as instructed. •

Study TIPS

As you complete this dissection, refer to an illustration or atlas of the human body. Use the illustration or atlas to locate and compare the various external and internal structures with your preserved specimen. Since the vertebrate body plan among species is very similar, this may help you to understand the structure of the human body.

A. EXTERNAL ASPECT

Examine the external aspect of your specimen.

- ☐ **1** Determine the anatomical orientation of the specimen. Which direction is anterior? Posterior? Which direction is ventral? Dorsal? Identify sagittal, transverse, and frontal planes in your specimen **(Figure 2-1, A)**.
- ☐ **2** Identify these externally visible features:
  - ☐ **Pinna (auricle)**
  - ☐ **External nares (nostrils)**
  - ☐ **Vibrissae (whiskers)**
  - ☐ **Incisors**
  - ☐ **Integument**
  - ☐ **Forelimbs**
  - ☐ **Hindlimbs**
  - ☐ **Thoracic region**
  - ☐ **Abdominal region**
  - ☐ **Nipples**
  - ☐ **Anus**
  - ☐ **Tail**
- ☐ **3** Determine the sex of your specimen by examining the external genitals:
  - ☐ **Female**—Immediately anterior to the anus, on the ventral surface, is the **vulva** with an opening to the **vagina.** Anterior to the vulva is the **clitoris** with the **urethral** opening.
  - ☐ **Male**—The **scrotum** containing the **testes** is immediately anterior to the anus, perhaps even hiding the anus from view. Near the anterior edge of the scrotum is the **penis** with its prepuce, or skinfold covering. Locate the opening of the **urethra** in the penis.

> **Hint** ▸ A complete set of anatomical sketches of the rat are found in the Anatomical Atlas of the Rat **(Figures 2-1 to 2-7)**. •

B. SKIN, BONES, AND MUSCLES

☐ 1 Remove most of the skin from your specimen by following this procedure:

    ☐ Place the animal in the tray with its ventral surface facing you.

    ☐ Pull up on the skin over the sternum and puncture it with the tip of a scissors. Slide the bottom tip of the scissors into the **subcutaneous** area under the skin.

    ☐ Begin cutting along the lines indicated in Figure 2-2. Be careful not to cut into the skeletal muscles under the skin.

    ☐ With your forceps, pull the two flaps of skin over the neck away from the animal's body. Notice the **areolar tissue** under the skin that is pulled apart as you remove the skin. Pull the flaps of skin over the abdomen and over the **groin** area away in a similar fashion.

    ☐ Turn the animal over so the dorsum is facing you.

    ☐ If you made all the cuts properly, you should be able to pull the skin off the back in one complete piece. Sometimes it helps if you scrape at the loose connective tissue under the skin with your scalpel as you peel away the skin. The skinning process is difficult unless you have patience and proceed slowly.

☐ 2 Examine the skin, identifying these features:

    ☐ **Dermis**—The thick inner layer of the skin

    ☐ **Epidermis**—The thinner outer layer of the skin with *hair* (fur)

☐ 3 Explore the shape of the skinned rat body. How many **bones** of the rat's skeleton can you see or palpate (feel)? If you have a mounted rat skeleton available, identify as many of the bones of the skeleton as you can. If you become stumped, refer to Figure 2-3, A, in the rat atlas. Notice the similarity between the rat's skeletal plan and that of the human.

☐ 4 Observe the rat's musculature. Some of the external muscles of the torso can be separated from one another for easier viewing. Slide a probe into the loose connective tissue joining adjacent muscles and run the probe along their margins. Using Figures 2-3 and 2-4 as guides, try to identify the major superficial muscles of the rat's body.

C. CARDIOVASCULAR STRUCTURES

☐ 1 Open the **ventral body cavity** by cutting into its muscular wall in a manner similar to your earlier cut into the skin. Cut flaps in the neck, abdomen, and groin areas as you did with the skin, but do not cut all the way around to the back. Be careful not to damage any **visceral organs** with your scissors as you cut. Fold back the flaps, and either anchor them with pins or remove them.

☐ 2 Locate the **heart** near the middle of the **thoracic cavity** in the **mediastinum.** Can you identify the four chambers?

☐ 3 If you have a double-injected preserved specimen, the **arteries** are filled with red latex and the **veins** are filled with blue latex. If not, the arteries can usually be distinguished from veins because they are stiffer and lighter in color than veins. Locate the **aorta**, the large artery leaving the heart and

arching posteriorly. Trace the branches of the aorta, naming them if you can. Use Figure 2-5, A, if you need help.

☐ 4 Locate the **anterior vena cava** where it drains into the heart. This is analogous to the superior vena cava in the human. Follow its tributary veins and identify them with the help of Figure 2-5, B. Locate the **posterior vena cava** and trace its tributaries.

> **Hint**   Once you have cut into the ventral body cavity, you may be tempted to cut and remove organs. It is important that you keep everything as intact as possible. You may pull organs to one side or another to view deeper structures, but avoid making cuts.   •

D. VISCERA

The viscera, or major internal organs, can be seen within the ventral body cavity. Use Figures 2-6 and 2-7 to guide you in locating the following:

☐ 1 Locate some of these features of the lower **respiratory system:**

    ☐ **Larynx**

    ☐ **Trachea**

    ☐ **Primary bronchi**

    ☐ **Lungs** (Can you distinguish the parietal and visceral pleurae?)

    ☐ **Diaphragm**

☐ 2 Locate these structures of the **digestive system:**

    ☐ **Submandibular salivary glands**

    ☐ **Esophagus**

    ☐ **Stomach**

    ☐ **Liver**

    ☐ **Pancreas**

    ☐ **Small intestine**

    ☐ **Mesentery**

    ☐ **Cecum** (This structure is very large in the rat and does not have an appendix as does the human cecum.)

    ☐ **Colon**

☐ 3 Locate these **lymphatic** organs:

    ☐ **Spleen**

    ☐ **Thymus** (The thymus may be small or not visible in older animals.)

☐ 4 Locate these features of the **urinary system:**

    ☐ **Kidney**

    ☐ **Ureter**

    ☐ **Urinary bladder**

    ☐ **Urethra**

☐ 5 Try to locate these **endocrine glands** in your specimen:

    ☐ **Thyroid gland**

    ☐ **Thymus gland**

    ☐ **Pancreas**

    ☐ **Adrenal glands**

    ☐ **Testes**

    ☐ **Ovaries**

☐ 6 Identify these structures associated with the **male reproductive system:**

☐ Testes
☐ Epididymis
☐ **Ductus (vas) deferens**
☐ **Seminal vesicle**
☐ **Prostate gland**
☐ **Penis**

☐ 7 Find these **female reproductive system** structures:
☐ Ovaries
☐ **Uterine tubes**
☐ **Uterus** (Notice that the rat uterus has a Y shape, with a right and left uterine horn.)
☐ **Vagina**

☐ 8 If your specimen is a pregnant female, open the uterus *very carefully* and identify these structures:

☐ **Amniotic sac**—This is a fluid-filled cushion for each embryo.
☐ **Embryo**—Examine the structure of the embryo. Do you think that it is in a late stage or an early stage of development?
☐ **Umbilical cord**—Can you distinguish the umbilical vessels?
☐ **Placenta**—It is attached to the uterine lining.

Hint ▶ Unless your lab group has both male and female specimens, you may want to temporarily trade specimens with a group that has a rat of a different sex than yours. By doing so, you will be able to find the features of both reproductive systems.   •

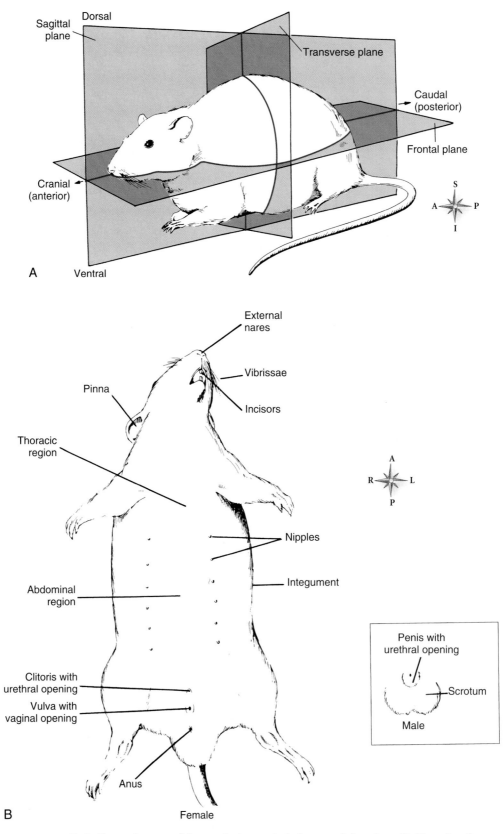

FIGURE 2-1 External aspect of the rat. **A,** Anatomical planes and directions. **B,** Ventral surface.

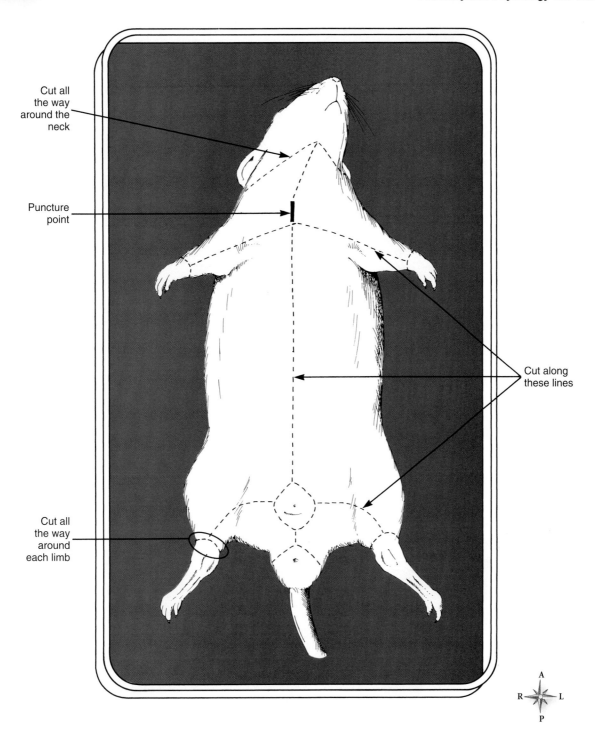

FIGURE 2-2 Directions for cutting the skin of the rat.

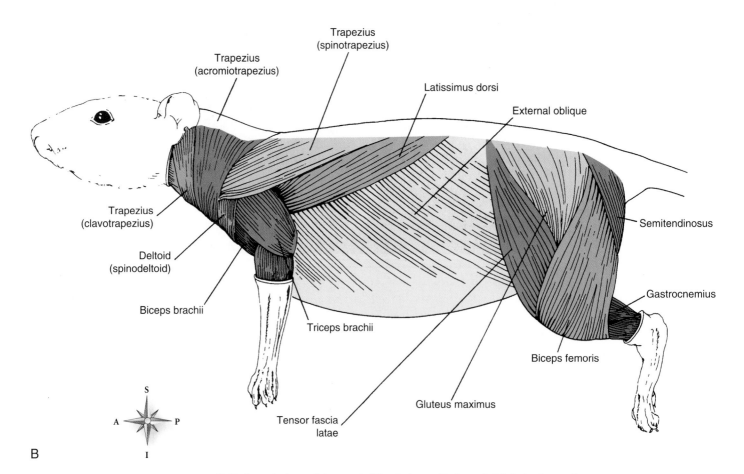

FIGURE 2-3 Lateral views of the rat. **A**, The skeleton. **B**, Superficial skeletal muscles.

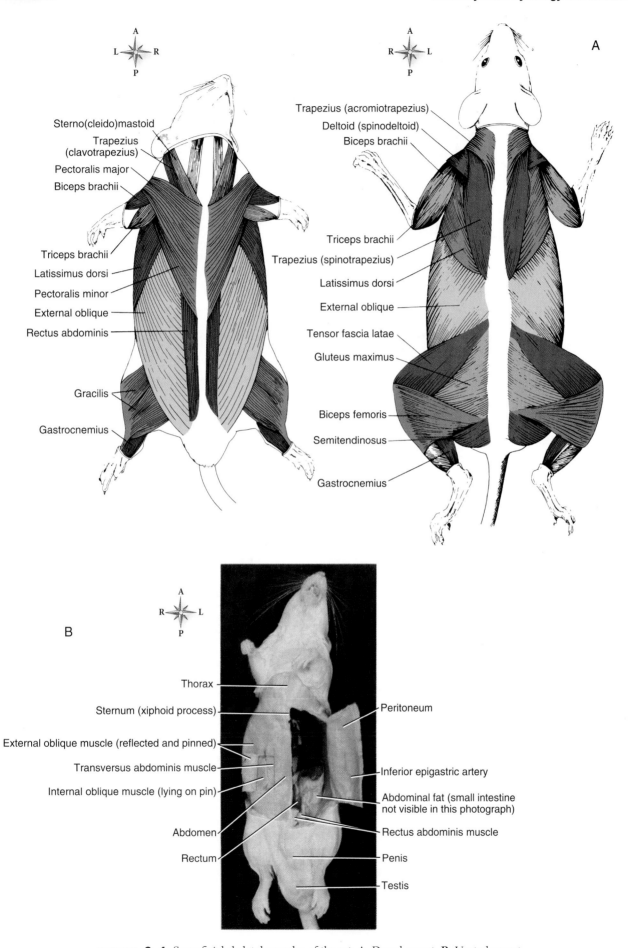

FIGURE 2-4 Superficial skeletal muscles of the rat. **A**, Dorsal aspect. **B**, Ventral aspect.

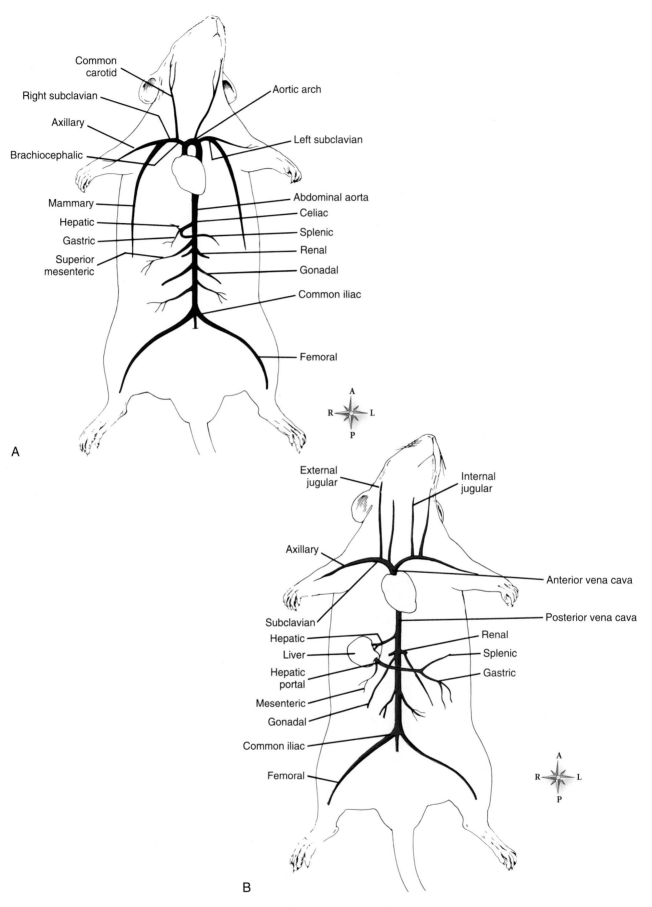

FIGURE 2-5 The rat's systemic circulation. **A,** Major systemic arteries. **B,** Major systemic veins.

FIGURE 2-6 Ventral body cavity of the rat.

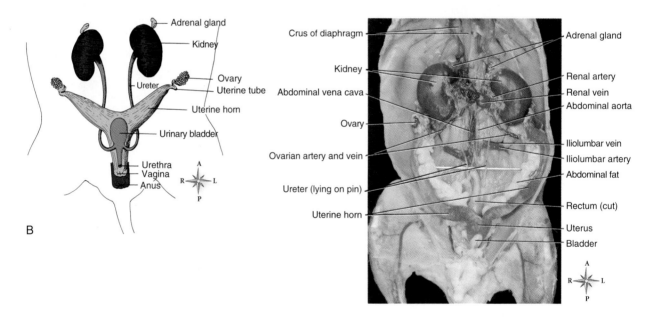

FIGURE 2-7 Pelvic body cavity of the rat. **A**, Male. **B**, Female.

Name: _____ Date: _____ Section: _____

Dissection: The Whole Body

Rat Dissection Checklist

☐ **External aspect**
  ☐ pinna (auricle)
  ☐ external naris (nostril)
  ☐ vibrissae (whiskers)
  ☐ incisors
  ☐ integument
  ☐ forelimbs
  ☐ hindlimbs
  ☐ thoracic region
  ☐ abdominal region
  ☐ nipples
  ☐ anus
  ☐ tail
  ☐ sex: female
  ☐ vulva
  ☐ vagina
  ☐ clitoris
  ☐ urethral opening
  ☐ sex: male
  ☐ scrotum (testes within)
  ☐ penis
  ☐ prepuce (foreskin)
  ☐ urethral opening
☐ **Skin, bones, and muscles**
  ☐ subcutaneous areolar tissue
  ☐ dermis
  ☐ epidermis, fur
  ☐ axial skeleton
  ☐ cranial bones
  ☐ facial bones
  ☐ cervical vertebrae
  ☐ thoracic vertebrae
  ☐ lumbar vertebrae
  ☐ sacral vertebrae
  ☐ caudal vertebrae
  ☐ ribs
  ☐ sternum
  ☐ appendicular skeleton
  ☐ scapula
  ☐ clavicle
  ☐ humerus
  ☐ radius
  ☐ ulna
  ☐ carpal bones
  ☐ metacarpal bones
  ☐ phalanges of the forelimb

☐ coxal bone
☐ femur
☐ patella
☐ tibia
☐ fibula
☐ tarsal bones
☐ metatarsal bones
☐ phalanges of the hindlimb
☐ head, neck, and shoulder muscles
☐ sternomastoid (human: sternocleidomastoid)
☐ clavotrapezius (human: trapezius)
☐ acromiotrapezius (human: trapezius)
☐ spinotrapezius (human: trapezius)
☐ spinodeltoid (human: deltoid)
☐ biceps brachii
☐ triceps brachii
☐ latissimus dorsi
☐ abdominal and hindlimb muscles
☐ external oblique
☐ rectus abdominis
☐ tensor fascia latae
☐ gluteus maximus
☐ biceps femoris
☐ semitendinosus
☐ gastrocnemius
☐ gracilis
☐ **Cardiovascular structures**
  ☐ heart
  ☐ left and right atria
  ☐ left and right ventricles
  ☐ aorta
  ☐ major aortic branches
  ☐ common carotid arteries
  ☐ brachiocephalic artery
  ☐ left subclavian artery
  ☐ celiac artery (trunk)
  ☐ superior mesenteric artery
  ☐ renal arteries
  ☐ gonadal arteries
  ☐ common iliac arteries
  ☐ anterior vena cava (human: superior vena cava)
  ☐ subclavian veins
  ☐ posterior vena cava (human: inferior vena cava)
  ☐ hepatic vein
  ☐ renal veins
  ☐ common iliac veins
  ☐ hepatic portal vein

☐ **Viscera**
  ☐ respiratory structures
  ☐ larynx
  ☐ trachea
  ☐ primary bronchi
  ☐ lungs
  ☐ pleurae
  ☐ diaphragm
  ☐ digestive structures
  ☐ submandibular salivary glands
  ☐ esophagus
  ☐ stomach
  ☐ liver
  ☐ pancreas
  ☐ small intestine
  ☐ mesentery
  ☐ cecum
  ☐ colon
  ☐ lymphatic organs
  ☐ spleen
  ☐ thymus (if visible)
  ☐ urinary structures
  ☐ kidney
  ☐ ureter
  ☐ urinary bladder

☐ urethra
☐ endocrine glands
☐ thyroid gland
☐ thymus gland
☐ pancreas
☐ adrenal glands
☐ testes
☐ ovaries
☐ male reproductive organs
☐ testes
☐ epididymis
☐ ductus (vas) deferens
☐ seminal vesicles
☐ prostate gland
☐ penis
☐ female reproductive organs
☐ ovaries
☐ uterine tubes (oviducts)
☐ uterus
☐ vagina
☐ pregnant uterus
☐ amniotic sac
☐ embryo (or fetus)
☐ umbilical cord
☐ placenta

The Microscope

In the seventeenth century, the amateur Dutch scientist Anton van Leeuwenhoek used one of the first microscopes to discover a whole new world of living organisms. Using a single lens, or **simple microscope**, he observed tiny organisms in pond water and scrapings from his own teeth. Robert Hooke, an English scientist, discovered that larger organisms had small microscopic subunits that he called boxes or *cells*. Ever since this early era of discovery, biological microscopy has been essential in the study of living organisms.

The microscopes used in this course are **compound microscopes**, made of a set of lenses. They are more powerful and more complex than those used by van Leeuwenhoek and Hooke. This exercise introduces you to the use and care of the standard compound microscope.

BEFORE YOU BEGIN

- ☐ Read the appropriate chapter in your textbook.
- ☐ Set your learning goals. When you finish this exercise, you should be able to:
  - ☐ identify each major part of a compound light microscope and describe its function
  - ☐ determine total magnification at different settings
  - ☐ use a microscope to observe prepared specimens
  - ☐ prepare a wet-mount slide
  - ☐ stain microscopic specimens
  - ☐ record microscopic observations accurately
- ☐ Prepare your materials:
  - ☐ compound light microscope
  - ☐ prepared microslides: *newsprint "e," three colored threads*
  - ☐ clean slides
  - ☐ coverslips
  - ☐ paper wipes
  - ☐ methylene blue stain
  - ☐ flat toothpicks
  - ☐ Read the directions and safety tips for this exercise *carefully* before starting any procedure.

Study TIPS

To become proficient in the use of the microscope, take advantage of this lab activity and any "open labs" that may be offered. Obviously, the more you use the microscope, the better you will become in focusing and examining specimens. With your instructor's permission, you may want to extend this lab activity by examining other specimens (hair, cloth fibers, etc.).

Proper identification of the various parts of the microscope is important to its proper use and care. Obtain an unlabeled copy of a microscope photo. Your instructor may have an unlabeled copy of a microscope photo, or you may want to photocopy the photo of the microscope **(Figure 3-1)** and delete the labels. You can also use your cell phone to photograph the microscope and later print the photo and label it. Quiz yourself by taking this blank photo and labeling the parts of the microscope.

A. PARTS OF THE MICROSCOPE

- ☐ 1 Obtain a compound light microscope and identify each of the structures described in the following.

> **Hint** Because not all microscope models are alike, some of the structures described may be different on your scope. Refer to Figure 3-1 for help in this exercise. •

- ☐ 2 The set of lenses closest to your eye is the **ocular**, or eyepiece. The ocular magnifies an image by the factor indicated on the ocular's barrel, usually 10×. If the factor is 10×, the image is magnified 10 times. If the factor is 5×, the image is magnified 5 times.
- ☐ 3 The **body tube** holds the ocular in place. Although called a *tube*, it may be more like a box in some models.
- ☐ 4 At the bottom of the body tube is the **revolving nosepiece**. A turretlike circular mechanism rotates so that different lenses can be selected. *Always rotate* the nosepiece by holding the outside of the revolving disk; *never* push on the lens barrels.
- ☐ 5 Each of the lens sets attached to the revolving nosepiece is an **objective**. As with the ocular, each objective is marked with its magnification factor. Microscopes may have any or all of the following objectives:
  - ☐ 4× (scanning objective) is used for initial location of the specimen. Some scopes have 3.2× or 3.5× scanning objectives. List the factor on your scope's scanning objective here. _____
  - ☐ 10× (low-power objective) may also be used for initial location of the specimen. It is also used for observing specimens that do not need greater magnification.

FIGURE 3-1 Important parts of the typical modern compound light microscope.

- ☐ 40× (high-dry objective) is used for specimens requiring greater magnification. This objective is called *dry* because it does not require the use of oil, as other high-power objectives do. Some scopes have 43× or 45× high-dry objectives. List the factor on your scope's high-dry objective here. _____
- ☐ 100× (high-oil objective) is used for magnification of extremely small specimens, such as bacterial cells. It must be immersed in oil, so it is called the *high-oil* objective. This objective will not be used in this course.
- ☐ In this manual, *low power* will refer to use of the 10× objective, and *high power* will refer to use of the 40× objective.

☐ 6 **Total magnification** is determined by multiplying the power of the ocular by the power of the objective in use. Thus, when using a 10× ocular and the low-power objective, total magnification is 100× (10 × 10 = 100). List all ocular and objective combinations, and then determine all the total magnifications possible on your scope and record them in the Lab Report.

☐ 7 The specimen is usually mounted on a glass or plastic **microscope slide** that rests on the stage, a platform just below the objective. The stage has a hole so that light can pass through the specimen from below. If the stage has an adjustable bracket that moves the slide around mechanically, the stage is called a **mechanical stage.** If not, the slide is held by **stage clips** and must be moved by hand.

☐ 8 Below the stage is a high-intensity **lamp**. Light rays from the lamp travel through a hole in the stage, through the specimen mounted on a slide, and then through the objective and ocular, to the eye.

☐ 9 A **condenser**, a lens that concentrates light, may be found between the lamp and the stage.

☐ 10 Sometimes the light from the lamp is too strong to see the specimen clearly. The light level may be reduced by adjusting the lamp intensity (if possible). Light intensity may also be adjusted by adjusting the **diaphragm** just below the stage **(Figure 3-2)**. A *disk diaphragm* is a rotating disk with holes of different diameters. An *iris diaphragm* is made of overlapping slivers of metal in a pattern resembling the iris flower, as does the iris of the human eye. Like the iris of the eye, the iris diaphragm can dilate or constrict its opening. You can change the amount of light passing to the specimen by rotating the edge of the disk diaphragm or by rotating the lever projecting from the iris diaphragm.

☐ 11 The entire upper assembly of the microscope is held in an upright position by a bar called the **arm**. The scope is supported by a square or horseshoe-shaped **base**. The arm may be connected to the base by a **pivot**, which allows the upper assembly to move into a more comfortable viewing position.

☐ 12 The **coarse-focus knobs** and **fine-focus knobs** are on the arm. These knobs adjust the distance between the stage and objective, thus focusing an image of the specimen. The fine-focus knob changes the distance very little, whereas the coarse-focus knob changes the distance greatly.

FIGURE 3-2 **A,** Disk diaphragm set at a large opening, then at a smaller opening. **B,** Iris diaphragm open, then partially closed.

B. USING THE MICROSCOPE

Skill in using the microscope is necessary for many of the exercises in this lab manual. Fortunately, learning to use the microscope is both easy and fun. Before beginning, acquaint yourself with these basic rules:

☐ Always carry the scope with two hands: one under the base and the other grasping the arm. Carry it in an upright position.

☐ Unwind the lamp cord carefully. Avoid damaging the parts around which it is coiled. Plug the cord into an outlet in a safe manner.

> **safety first**
>
> Be careful when plugging the power cord into the outlet. Always plug it into a receptacle at your station, taking care not to string it over a chair, across an aisle, or in any other dangerous position. Before you turn on the microscope, make sure that the light intensity dial is on the lowest setting. If the light intensity dial is on a high setting, the sudden voltage surge may burn out the lamp. •

☐ Make sure the stage and objective are at the farthest distance apart and that the *lowest-power objective is in position*. Start each new observation at low power.

☐ 1 Obtain a microscope slide with a newsprint letter "*e*" mounted on it. This is your practice specimen.

☐ 2 Place your slide carefully on the stage and secure it with stage clips or the brackets of the mechanical stage. Move the slide so that the "*e*" is centered in the stage's hole.

☐ 3 While looking from the side, use the coarse-focus knob to move the objective (still on low power) as close as possible to the slide.

☐ 4 Look through the ocular and use the coarse-focus knob to slowly move the objective and slide apart. When the image becomes clear, switch to the fine-focus knob to make the image even sharper. To avoid damaging the scope and slide, *never move the objective and stage toward each other while looking through the ocular.*

> **Hint** To avoid eyestrain and a possible headache, always keep both eyes open when viewing a specimen. With binocular scopes this is easy once you have adjusted the distance between oculars. However, it may take some practice if you are using a monocular scope. If you have trouble keeping both eyes open, try covering the unused eye with your hand. •

☐ 5 Adjust the light intensity, using the lamp controller or diaphragm, until the detail of the image is at its clearest.

☐ 6 Sketch the entire field of view in the space provided in the Lab Report. You'll see that the "*e*" is upside down and backward. This inversion occurs with all specimens.

> **Hint** Here are some rules for recording microscopic observations properly:
>
> • Label each sketch with the name of the specimen and what type of section it is.
> • Label each sketch with the total magnification.
> • Label as many parts of the sketch as you can. Labels should be orderly, never crossing lines with each other.
> • Sketches should be done with care, not with haste.

☐ 7 Center the part of the specimen that you wish to see more clearly and switch to a higher-power objective. Most scopes are **parfocal,** which means that the image remains focused when you change objectives. However, some minor adjustment with the fine focus is usually necessary. *Never adjust the coarse focus when using high power.*

☐ 8 Sketch the entire field that you see using the high-power (40× to 45×) objective.

☐ 9 When you remove the slide, make sure that the low-power objective is in viewing position and that the objective and stage are as far apart as possible.

☐ 10 Practice focusing at different depths by using a prepared slide of three crossed strands of colored thread. The strands (one red, one yellow, and one blue) cross at the same point. Determine which is on top, which is in the middle, and which is on the bottom. Report your results in the Lab Report.

☐ 11 When you have finished for the day, return the scope to its original configuration. The low-power objective should be in position. Make sure the slide has been removed.

> **Hint** If you can't see an image in your scope:
>
> • Make sure the lamp is on.
> • Make sure the diaphragm is open. The amount of light should be set low on low power and high on high power.
> • Check for obstructions in the light path.
> • Make sure the objective is seated properly.
> • Check to see if the specimen is centered.
> • Clean the lenses with lens paper and lens solution (not facial tissues or lab wipes).
>
> If the image seems to fade in and out:
>
> • Watch to see if the body tube or stage is shifting or dropping.
> • Make sure the scope doesn't require a rubber eyecup for proper viewing.
> • Make sure the specimen is not in a medium that obstructs viewing.
> • Check the lamp or cord for short circuits.
>
> If the image doesn't look like the figure in the book:
>
> • Get a different book (it may have a better figure).
> • Use your imagination.
> • Join the club (nobody else's specimen is identical to that in the book either).

C. PREPARING MICROSCOPIC SPECIMENS

We will often use prepared slides of human and other tissues in this course. However, occasionally we may be making our own specimens.

A **wet-mount** slide is a slide on which a wet specimen is placed, then covered with a **coverslip**. **Stains** are used to make a specimen, or some of its parts, more visible. Some require special techniques, but most stains can simply be added to the specimen and viewed. The usual method for preparing a stained wet-mount slide is described in **Figure 3-3** and in the following steps:

☐ **1** Obtain some skin cells by scraping the inner surface of your cheek with a clean, flat toothpick.

☐ **2** Wipe the scrapings on a clean microscope slide and put a small drop of *methylene blue* stain directly on the smear.

> ### ! safety first
> Use only fresh toothpicks, and dispose of used toothpicks immediately by placing them in the waste container indicated by your instructor. Take precautions to avoid the spread of disease through saliva. •

☐ **3** Place one edge of a coverslip on the slide next to the specimen, and then let it drop slowly on the specimen. This method prevents forming air bubbles.

☐ **4** Absorb any excess fluid around the edges of the coverslip with the edge of a paper wipe.

☐ **5** Locate some cells with the low-power objective, shift to high power, and sketch your observations in the Lab Report.

> ### 📌 landmark characteristics
> You are looking for scattered epithelial cells. Each cell will appear as a lightly stained, flat polygon or circle with a dark center. The dark center is the nucleus of the cell. Some cells may be separate, whereas others are clumped together.
>
> You may see a variety of other things in your specimen: bacteria, vegetable or meat fibers, and other matter. Don't worry; this is normal. Distinct dark circles with hollow centers that may be in motion are air bubbles. •

> **Hint** ▶ If your instructor wants you to learn how to use an oil-immersion objective, follow these directions. After focusing on high-dry, rotate the nosepiece *halfway* to the high-oil objective. Put a drop of immersion oil on the slide, and then rotate the high-oil objective into the oil drop. You may need to increase the lighting. When finished, clean the objective and other surfaces as your instructor directs. •

FIGURE 3-3 Staining a wet-mount specimen. **A,** Place the specimen on the slide. **B,** Add a small drop of stain. **C,** Drop the coverslip slowly to prevent air bubbles. **D,** Absorb excess fluid with a paper wipe.

Name: _____ Date: _____ Section: _____

LAB REPORT 3
The Microscope

Specimen: *newsprint "e"*
Total Magnification: _____

Does the "e" in the newsprint appear to be oriented the same way it is on the stage? Explain your observations.

Is the *diameter of field* the same when observing the specimen under high power and low power?

Which of the three colored threads in the prepared slide is on the bottom?

Which thread is on the top?

Specimen: *human cheek cells*
Total Magnification: _____

Specimen: *newsprint "e"*
Total Magnification: _____

What is the darkly stained region of each cell?

What advantage is gained by staining this specimen?

List all the possible ocular-objective combinations on your microscope and calculate the total magnification for each.

Power of Ocular	Power of Objective	Total Magnification
_____	_____	_____
_____	_____	_____
_____	_____	_____
_____	_____	_____

Fill-in

1. _____
2. _____
3. _____
4. _____
5. _____
6. _____
7. _____
8. _____

Multiple Choice

1. _____
2. _____
3. _____
4. _____
5. _____
6. _____
7. _____

Fill-in

1. A _?_ is a glass or plastic rectangle on which specimens are mounted.
2. A _?_ is at the base of the body tube, allowing selection of different objectives.
3. Below the stage is a high-intensity _?_ or other light source.
4. Different lens sets, or _?_, are attached to the revolving nosepiece.
5. If the stage has a bracket that moves the slide, it is called a(n) _?_ stage.
6. The _?_ allows the user to limit the amount of light from a steady light source.
7. The set of lenses closest to the viewer's eye is the _?_.
8. The _?_ is a lens under the stage that concentrates light.

Multiple Choice (only one choice is correct)

1. A microscope _?_ the image of a specimen.
   a. magnifies
   b. reverses
   c. reduces
   d. erases
   e. a and b are correct
2. The use of _?_ may make the specimen (or some of its parts) more visible.
   a. stain
   b. the diaphragm
   c. fine focus
   d. all of the above
   e. none of the above
3. If you select a 40× objective to use with a 5× ocular, the total magnification would be:
   a. 200×
   b. 45×
   c. 400×
   d. 405×
   e. none of the above
4. When you move a specimen to the right, its image appears to
   a. move to the right
   b. move to the left
   c. remain stationary
5. Which is the correct path of light in a compound microscope?
   a. lamp, objective, diaphragm, specimen, ocular
   b. lamp, diaphragm, specimen, objective, ocular
   c. diaphragm, lamp, specimen, ocular, objective
   d. lamp, diaphragm, specimen, ocular, objective
6. If your scope is not working properly, consult
   a. the lab instructor
   b. your lab partner
   c. the owner's manual
   d. the manufacturer
7. When carrying your microscope, use _?_ hands.
   a. one
   b. two

LAB EXERCISE 4

Cell Anatomy

The cell is often considered the basic unit of living organisms. Actually, cells are only one of several *levels of organization* in the human organism:

ATOMS
MOLECULES
ORGANELLES
CELLS
TISSUES
ORGANS
ORGAN SYSTEMS
ORGANISM

Thus, cells are parts of larger units (tissues and organs) and are composed of smaller units (organelles).

For now, we will concentrate on the structure and function of the cell and its organelles. We will study some of the other levels of organization in later units.

BEFORE YOU BEGIN

□ Read the appropriate chapter in your textbook.
□ Set your learning goals. When you finish this exercise, you should be able to:
  □ place the cell and its organelles within the scheme of organizational levels
  □ identify the major organelles on a model, chart, specimen, or micrograph
  □ describe primary function(s) of typical organelles
  □ discuss the anatomical relationship among various cell parts
□ Prepare your materials:
  □ cell model or chart
  □ compound light microscope
  □ clean slides
  □ coverslips
  □ paper wipes
  □ methylene blue stain
  □ colored pencils or pens
  □ prepared slides (instructor's option)
□ Read the directions and safety tips for this exercise *carefully* before starting any procedure.

Study TIPS

When studying the structure and function of the cell, it might be helpful to make an analogy between a cell and a factory. Factories have various departments that work together to manufacture a specific product(s). Cells have specialized departments (organelles) that also work together. For instance, the cell's nucleus can be compared to the factory headquarters; the endoplasmic reticulum to the warehouse; Golgi apparatus to the distribution center; mitochondria to the power plant; and so on. Try to develop other examples using additional cell organelles. Refer to the *A&P Guide*. The Internet has many cell tutorials. For example, www.cellsalive.com contains an array of interactive links that provide an excellent cell biology resource.

A. PARTS OF THE CELL

Cells are microscopic units composed of a bubble of fatty material filled with a water-based mixture of molecules and tiny particles. Parts of the cell are called **organelles** (meaning *"small organs"*). Begin your study of the cell by examining a *generalized* cell, such as that in the coloring exercise in **Figure 4-1**. A generalized cell is one with many cell features that are not all found in a single natural cell. Locate each of the listed organelles on a generalized cell model or chart.

□ 1 The outer boundary of the cell is the **plasma membrane.** It is composed of a double layer (or *bilayer*) of **phospholipid** molecules imbedded with other molecules. Each phospholipid molecule has a polar, hydrophilic ("water loving") *head* made up of phosphate and glycerol, and a nonpolar, hydrophobic ("water fearing") *tail* made up of two fatty acid chains. Imbedded in the membrane are **integral proteins,** which may have additional protein molecules called **peripheral proteins** attached to them on one side of the membrane or the other. **Figure 4-2** shows some of the types of molecules often associated with the plasma membrane. The plasma membrane has many functions, most involving transport and communication between the inside and outside of the cell.

> **Hint** ▶ Each membranous organelle described in the following is made of a lipid membrane similar to the cell membrane. Because they are so thin, cell membranes may seem invisible when observed with a light microscope. •

☐ **2** The double-walled **nucleus** is a large bubble containing the cell's genetic code. The code is in the form of **deoxyribonucleic acid (DNA)** strands called **chromatin.** Portions of chromatin accept stains readily, giving the nucleus a very dark appearance.

☐ **3** A **nucleolus** (literally, "tiny nucleus") is a small area within the nucleus for the synthesis of ribosomal **ribonucleic acid (RNA).** There may be more than one nucleolus (plural *nucleoli*) in a nucleus.

☐ **4** The **endoplasmic reticulum (ER)** is a network of membranous tubes and canals winding through the interior of the cell. A *rough ER* is speckled with tiny granules (ribosomes), and a *smooth ER* is not. The ER transports proteins synthesized by ribosomes and other molecules synthesized within its membrane. The ER also manufactures molecules that make up cellular membranes.

Coloring Exercises: Cell

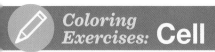

Use colored pens or pencils to shade in both the figure and the labels. Each red numeral in the figure corresponds to a matching red numeral following the appropriate label.

PLASMA MEMBRANE1
CENTRIOLE2
CENTROSOME3
CHROMATIN4
CYTOSOL5
GOLGI APPARATUS6
LYSOSOME7
MICROVILLI8

MITOCHONDRION9
NUCLEAR MEMBRANE10
NUCLEOLUS11
NUCLEAR PORE12
RIBOSOME13
ROUGH ER14
SMOOTH ER15
VESICLE16

FIGURE 4-1

Coloring Exercises: **Plasma Membrane**

Use colored pens or pencils to shade in both the figure and the labels. Each red numeral in the figure corresponds to a matching red numeral following the appropriate label.

CARBOHYDRATE₁
CARRIER PROTEIN₂
CELL MARKER₃
CHANNEL PROTEIN₄
CHOLESTEROL₅
ENZYME₆
INTEGRAL PROTEIN₇
PERIPHERAL PROTEIN₈
PHOSPHOLIPID,
   NONPOLAR TAIL₉
PHOSPHOLIPID,
   POLAR HEAD₁₀
RECEPTOR PROTEIN₁₁

FIGURE 4-2

5 The material within the plasma membrane is the **cytoplasm** (literally, *"cell stuff"*) and includes both the organelles and the liquid, or **cytosol,** surrounding the organelles.

6 **Ribosomes** are tiny bodies that serve as a site for protein synthesis. Some ribosomes are found on the outer surface of the ER, and some are found scattered elsewhere within the cell.

7 The **Golgi apparatus,** or *Golgi body,* appears as a stack of flattened sacs. The apparatus receives material from the ER, processes it, and then packages it in tiny *vesicles* (bubbles) for possible export from the cell.

8 **Mitochondria** (singular *mitochondrion*) are tiny bodies similar to bacteria that serve as sites for adenosine triphosphate (ATP) synthesis (energy conversion). Mitochondria have an outer membrane, forming a round or oblong capsule, and a folded inner membrane. The folds of the inner membrane are called **cristae.**

9 **Lysosomes** are vesicles containing digestive enzymes that digest foreign particles and worn cell parts.

10 **Microtubules** are very tiny, hollow beams that form part of the supporting cell skeleton, or *cytoskeleton.* They also form parts of other cell organelles (e.g., *flagella, cilia, centrioles,* and *spindle fibers*). Other components of the cytoskeleton include **microfilaments** and **intermediate filaments.**

11 The **centrosome,** or *microtubule organizing center,* is a dense area of cell fluid near the nucleus. The centrosome contains a pair of **centrioles,** cylinders formed by parallel microtubules. A network of microtubules called *spindle fibers* extends from the centrosome during cell division. Spindle fibers distribute DNA equally to the resulting daughter cells.

12 The cell may have any number of other assorted organelles. **Microvilli** are tiny, fingerlike projections of the cell that increase the membrane's surface area for more efficient absorption. **Cilia** are numerous short, hairlike organelles that propel material along a cell's surface. **Flagella** are single, long, hairlike organelles found in sperm cells to propel them through the female reproductive tract toward the egg. **Vesicles** are membranous bubbles that may be formed by the Golgi apparatus or by the pinching inward of the cell membrane to engulf external substances.

B. MICROSCOPIC CELL SPECIMEN

Prepare a stained wet-mount specimen of human cheek cells (see Lab Exercise 3 for instructions), or obtain another specimen provided by the instructor; try to identify as many cell parts as possible. Use high-power magnification (after first finding the specimen with low-power magnification). Sketch and label your observations in the Lab Report.

 Many organelles are very small and can only be seen when properly prepared and examined with a more powerful microscope.

C. INTERPRETING MICROGRAPHS

An **electron microscope** is an instrument that uses a beam of electrons, rather than a beam of light, to form the image of a tiny specimen. *Transmission* electron microscopes send an electron beam through the specimen, similar to the manner in which a light microscope sends a light beam through a specimen. However, the magnifying power and resolution are much greater in the electron microscope. **Resolution** is the ability to distinguish detail. *Scanning* electron microscopes, on the other hand, reflect an electron beam off the specimen. The shadows produced by a scanning electron beam lend a three-dimensional effect.

A **TEM** is a transmission electron micrograph (photograph taken with a transmission electron microscope). **Figure 4-3** shows TEM representations of major cell parts. Use them to help you identify all the cell parts in the labeling exercises in **Figure 4-4,** which shows artists' renderings of TEM images. **Figure 4-5** shows actual TEMs of human cells. This will be a worthwhile challenge to illustrate the difficulty of studying cell structure.

FIGURE 4-3 Transmission electron micrographs (TEMs) of major organelles. **A,** Rough and smooth endoplasmic reticulum (portions of several mitochondria are also visible). **B,** Nucleus with several nucleoli. **C,** Golgi apparatus. **D,** Centrosome with both centrioles visible. **E,** Mitochondrion with cristae visible.

1
2
3
4
5

6
7
8
9

Collagen
fibers

10
11
12

13
14
15
16
17
18

19
20
21

22
23
24
25

26

FIGURE 4-4 Try to identify the cell organelles labeled in these artist's renderings of TEMs; list them on the lines provided and also on the blanks in the Lab Report at the end of this exercise.

FIGURE 4-5 Try to identify the cell organelles labeled in these actual TEMs of human cells; list them on the lines provided and also on the blanks in the Lab Report at the end of this exercise.

Continued

9

10

11

12

13

14

FIGURE 4-5, cont'd

Name: _____ Date: _____ Section: _____

Cell Anatomy

Checklist for Cell Model

- ❏ plasma membrane
- ❏ cytosol
- ❏ nucleus
  - ❏ chromatin
- ❏ nucleolus
- ❏ endoplasmic reticulum
  - ❏ rough ER
  - ❏ smooth ER
- ❏ ribosomes
  - ❏ free
  - ❏ associated with ER
- ❏ Golgi apparatus
  - ❏ secretory vesicles
- ❏ mitochondria
- ❏ lysosomes
- ❏ microtubules
- ❏ centrosome
  - ❏ centrioles
- ❏ microvilli
- ❏ cilia
- ❏ flagella
- ❏ _____
- ❏ _____
- ❏ _____

Specimen: _____
Total Magnification: _____

Specimen: _____
Total Magnification: _____

Specimen: _____
Total Magnification: _____

Figure 4-4 (from p. 37)

1. _____
2. _____
3. _____
4. _____
5. _____
6. _____
7. _____
8. _____
9. _____
10. _____
11. _____
12. _____
13. _____
14. _____
15. _____
16. _____
17. _____
18. _____
19. _____
20. _____
21. _____
22. _____
23. _____
24. _____
25. _____
26. _____

Figure 4-5 (from pp. 38-39)

1. _____
2. _____
3. _____
4. _____
5. _____
6. _____
7. _____
8. _____
9. _____
10. _____
11. _____
12. _____
13. _____
14. _____

Matching

1. _____   6. _____
2. _____   7. _____
3. _____   8. _____
4. _____   9. _____
5. _____   10. _____

Matching (may be used more than once or not at all)

 a. plasma membrane
 b. centriole
 c. endoplasmic reticulum
 d. Golgi apparatus
 e. lysosome
 f. mitochondrion
 g. nucleolus
 h. nucleus
 i. ribosome

1. A double-walled structure containing the cell's genetic code
2. A network of membranous tubes and canals that transports proteins
3. A stack of flattened sacs that process and package proteins
4. Site of manufacture of ribosomal RNA
5. A cylinder formed by parallel microtubules
6. An organelle that serves as the site of protein synthesis
7. A bubble containing digestive enzymes
8. May be *rough* (with ribosomes) or *smooth* (ribosome-free)
9. Allows communication between the internal and external cell environment
10. Forms secretory vesicles

Fill-in Table (write out the names of the organelles listed, *a* to *i*, in the section above in the appropriate column of the table)

MEMBRANOUS	NONMEMBRANOUS

5

Transport Through Cell Membranes

Cells use both passive and active processes to transport substances across their membranes. **Passive transport processes** are those that require no metabolic energy from the cell but rely solely on the physical properties of the substances themselves. **Active transport processes** require energy expenditure by the cell to move substances whose physical properties prevent their independent motion. In this exercise, we observe large-scale examples of passive transport processes.

BEFORE YOU BEGIN

- ❑ Read the appropriate chapter in your textbook.
- ❑ Set your learning goals. When you finish this exercise, you should be able to:
  - ❑ discuss the nature of diffusion and osmosis
  - ❑ use the terms *hypertonic, hypotonic,* and *isotonic* to compare solutions
  - ❑ compare and contrast diffusion, osmosis, and filtration
- ❑ Prepare your materials:
  - ❑ India ink (dropper bottle)
  - ❑ microscope
  - ❑ microscope slides and coverslips
  - ❑ potassium permanganate crystals
  - ❑ petri dishes
  - ❑ boiling water (100° C) and ice water (0° C)
  - ❑ forceps
  - ❑ dialysis tubing (8-10 cm, presoaked)
  - ❑ string (or tubing clamps)
  - ❑ sucrose solutions (15% and 40%)
  - ❑ syringe (or pipette) to fill dialysis bags
  - ❑ laboratory balance
  - ❑ jar or beaker (75-200 ml)
  - ❑ distilled water
  - ❑ filter paper (circular, large pore)
  - ❑ glass funnel
  - ❑ flask (to hold funnel and filtrate)
  - ❑ copper sulfate (saturated solution)
  - ❑ boiled starch solution (10%)
  - ❑ charcoal (powdered)
  - ❑ Lugol's reagent
- ❑ Read the directions and safety tips for this exercise.

A. PHYSICAL BASIS OF PASSIVE TRANSPORT

Naturally occurring **brownian motion** drives passive transport processes. Discovered by Scottish scientist Robert Brown, brownian motion is the constant movement of all particles of matter.

- ❑ 1 Prepare a wet-mount slide with a drop of India ink.
- ❑ 2 Observe the slide under high-power magnification. You should be able to see the dye particles moving short, irregular distances. This is brownian motion.

  Because small particles of matter are always bouncing around, brownian motion causes matter to spread (**diffuse**) to areas where there is more room to bounce around. That is, particles tend to move toward an area of lower particle concentration. You can observe this movement by following steps 3 and 4.
- ❑ 3 Using forceps, place a small crystal of potassium permanganate in the center of a petri dish of calm, hot water (**Figure 5-1**). Place a second crystal of the same size in a dish of calm, cold water. Be careful not to disturb the dishes by touching them or causing them to shake.
- ❑ 4 Observe the two dishes over a period of 30 minutes, carefully noting any changes in the crystals. Answer the questions in the Lab Report.

B. DIFFUSION AND OSMOSIS

Diffusion can be defined as the net movement of particles from an area of high concentration to an area of low concentration. Some particles move down such a *concentration gradient* when they are allowed to cross a cell membrane.

If the particles transported are water molecules, and there is at least one impermeant solute present (that is, a solute that cannot cross the membrane freely), we see a transport process called **osmosis.** Osmosis is similar to diffusion in many ways but is driven by a force called *osmotic pressure.* In this activity, you will observe the osmosis of water across a nonliving membrane called *dialysis tubing.* Dialysis tubing, like the cell membrane, is *semipermeable* (allowing only certain substances to pass through its pores). The bag that you construct from a piece of dialysis tubing serves as a model of the cell.

One of the three model cells you construct will be immersed in an **isotonic** solution. *Isotonic* is a comparative term that refers to a solution that has the same *potential osmotic pressure* as the cell solution. In other words, there will be no osmosis into or out of the cell. With the cell model, the solution outside is isotonic to the solution inside (**Figure 5-2, A**).

Another cell model will be immersed in a **hypotonic** solution. A hypotonic solution is one with a lower potential osmotic pressure (that is, a higher water concentration). Thus, the outside solution is hypotonic to the solution inside the cell model. Another cell model will be immersed in a **hypertonic** solution, a solution with a higher potential osmotic pressure (or lower water concentration). When the osmotic pressure of two solutions on either side of

White paper (under the dish)

FIGURE 5-1 Place the potassium permanganate crystal slowly, taking care not to disturb the water.

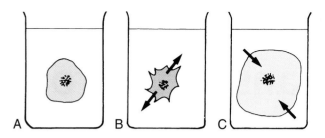

FIGURE 5-2 A, A cell in isotonic solution. **B,** A cell in hypertonic solution. **C,** A cell in hypotonic solution. The arrows show direction of net osmosis.

a membrane is known, the net direction of osmosis can be predicted.

As you set up each of the three situations described in the following, predict the direction of net osmosis.

Intracellular

Extracellular

FIGURE 5-3 A, Folding the end of the dialysis tube before tying it prevents leaking. **B,** Your model cell contains a sucrose solution that represents intracellular fluid. The bath solution represents extracellular fluid.

> **Hint**   These hints may help you:
> - Either presoak the dialysis tubing before using it, or hold it under water and rub the end of the tube between your fingers until it opens.
> - Set up the jars described in step 4 *before* beginning this activity.
> - Because this activity calls for an extended waiting period, you may want to do the other activities of this exercise while you wait.

Study TIPS

To understand the potential osmotic pressure of a solution, remember that the terms *isotonic, hypertonic,* and *hypotonic* refer to the osmotic pressure, which is related to the solute concentration. *Iso-* means the same thing. Both the intracellular and extracellular solute and water concentrations would be the same. *Hyper-* means excessive. If a cell was placed in a hypertonic solution, it would be in an extracellular environment, which has a higher concentration of solute and a lower concentration of water. *Hypo-* means "under." If the cell was placed in a hypotonic solution, it would be in an extracellular environment, which has a lower solute concentration and a higher concentration of water. Refer to the *A&P Survival Guide*.

☐ Obtain three 8- to 10-cm pieces of dialysis tubing. Tie one end shut with string, forming a watertight bag. Leave about 10 cm of string dangling freely.

☐ With a syringe, carefully fill each of three bags with 15% sucrose solution. Try to avoid spilling any solution on the outside of the bag. Tie off the open end of each tube with another piece of string.

☐ Quickly measure the mass of each tube on a laboratory balance.

☐ Place bag 1 in a jar or beaker half-filled with distilled water. Place bag 2 in a jar half-filled with 15% sucrose solution. Place bag 3 in a jar half-filled with 40% sucrose solution. Leave a piece of string dangling out of the jar, as you would with the string on a tea bag **(Figure 5-3)**.

☐ After 45 to 60 minutes, remove the tubes from the jars, drying and weighing each as you do so. Record and interpret your result in Lab Report 5.

C. FILTRATION

The movement of particles across a membrane from an area of high pressure to an area of low pressure (down a hydrostatic pressure gradient) is called **filtration.** In this experiment, gravity creates the pressure needed to push some particles across a paper membrane

In the human body, forces such as blood pressure push particles through living membranes.

☐ 1 Place a cone made of filter paper inside a glass funnel.
☐ 2 Position the funnel over an empty flask, as shown in **Figure 5-4**.

> **Hint** To make the cone, fold a circle of paper in half, then in half again. You should now have a triangle four layers thick. Pull one of the layers away from the rest. You now have a paper cone. Place it in the funnel and wet it with distilled water so that it sticks to the side of the funnel. •

☐ 3 Mix together 3 ml of copper sulfate solution, 4 ml of boiled starch solution, a pinch of charcoal powder, and 5 to 8 ml of distilled water. Note the physical characteristics of each as you mix them.
☐ 4 Pour the mixture into the funnel.
☐ 5 Observe the mixture being filtered by the paper. Does the process become progressively faster, progressively slower, or remain steady? Record and explain your results in Lab Report 5.
☐ 6 Examine the *filtrate* (filtered material). Test for the presence of each component of the original mixture:

Funnel
Paper filter
Flask

FIGURE 5-4 Set up your filtration apparatus as shown.

a *Charcoal*—Observe visually
b *Copper sulfate*—Observe visually
c *Starch*—Add a few drops of Lugol's reagent (a color change to black means that starch is present)

What substances were not allowed through the filter? Record and explain your results in Lab Report 5.

clinical application: Solution Tonicity—Cellular Effects

Results similar to those in your osmosis experiment occur when red blood cells come into contact with various solutions that are injected into the blood supply, as in intravenous (IV) therapy. When blood cells are bathed in a solution that is isotonic to them, they remain unchanged. If a hypotonic solution is introduced, the cells experience an inflow of water and usually burst. Bursting of red blood cells caused by osmosis is called **hemolysis.** If hypertonic solution is introduced, the cells lose water and shrivel. Shriveling that results from osmotic loss of water is called **crenation.** Therefore, the concentration of injected materials is critical to the survival of the patient.

| Crenated | Normal | Swollen | Lysed |
| Hypertonic | Isotonic | Hypotonic | Hypotonic |

Increasing solute concentration in extracellular fluid

FIGURE 5-5 The effects on red blood cells when changing the tonicity of the extracellular fluid (plasma).

Predict the expected results in these situations:

☐ **1** Randy is a nursing student. He has been asked to intravenously inject his patient with 10 ml of an isotonic preparation. Mistakenly, he injects his patient with 10 ml of pure water. What is likely to happen to the red blood cells near the site of the injection?

☐ **2** Jennifer is Randy's patient. She is carefully watching him fill an IV bottle with a mixture specially ordered by the physician. She notices that he accidentally fills the bottle with concentrated (10%) salt solution instead of the mixture from the pharmacy. Why should she refuse to allow Randy to attach the IV bottle to her system?

☐ **3** Randy is now assigned to the surgical unit. He is given a piece of living tissue and asked to put it in fluid before taking the sample to the pathology lab. What essential characteristic must such fluid have so that it will not damage any cells in the tissue?

Name: _____   Date: _____   Section: _____

Transport Through Cell Membranes

. Describe the movement of the India ink particles. Was it uniform or random? Were the particles moving great distances?

OBSERVATION	ELAPSED TIME	EXTENT OF DIFFUSION IN COLD WATER	EXTENT OF DIFFUSION IN HOT WATER
1	*0 minutes*	*No diffusion of dye particles*	*No diffusion of dye particles*
2			
3			
4	*30 minutes*		
Results			

. Using potassium permanganate as an example, explain in your own words how brownian motion relates to diffusion.

. Based on your results in the potassium permanganate experiment, would you state that increased temperature increases or decreases brownian motion?

BAG	PREDICTED RESULT	INITIAL MASS	FINAL MASS	GAIN OR LOSS OF MASS	EXPLANATION OF RESULTS
1					
2					
3					

. Did the filtration rate of your mixture become progressively faster or slower, or was it steady? Explain.

SUBSTANCE	TEST RESULT (PRESENT OR ABSENT)	EXPLANATION OF RESULT
Charcoal		
Copper sulfate		
Starch		

Matching

1. _____
2. _____
3. _____
4. _____
5. _____
6. _____
7. _____
8. _____
9. _____
10. _____

Identify

1. _____
2. _____
3. _____
4. _____
5. _____

Matching (may be used more than once or not at all)

a. brownian motion
b. diffusion
c. filtration
d. hydrostatic pressure
e. hypertonic
f. hypotonic
g. isotonic
h. osmosis
i. semipermeable

1. The tendency of matter to spread to areas of lower concentration.
2. Movement through a membrane driven by a hydrostatic pressure gradient.
3. Term that specifically describes the diffusion of water across a membrane.
4. Term that describes a membrane that allows only some types of particles to pass through it.
5. The natural vibration of particles; it drives diffusion.
6. In the kidney, blood pressure forces some water and solute particles from a blood vessel and into a kidney tubule. What is this type of transport called?
7. A cell is bathed in solution X. The cell quickly shrivels. What term describes solution X (when compared with the cell's fluid)?
8. Solution Q has a higher water content than solution Z. Therefore, solution Q is _?_ to solution Z.
9. A saline (salt) solution is to be injected into a patient. The salt/water ratio should be adjusted so that the saline solution is _?_ to the patient's cells.
10. Particles of substance Y move into a cell because there are fewer particles inside the cell than outside. This is an example of _?_.

Identify (state whether each item is an example of *diffusion, osmosis, filtration,* or *active transport*)

1. Movement of water from an area of high concentration to an area of low concentration
2. Dye particles spread evenly through water
3. Starch particles pass through a paper membrane
4. A cell uses energy to "pump" sugar molecules from its external environment
5. Water in cell moves out into a concentrated salt solution bathing the cell.

The Cell's Life Cycle

Cells in many parts of the human body divide to produce more cells of the same type. The hereditary information (DNA) contained within the nucleus of a resting *parent* cell must first be **replicated** (copied) and then evenly distributed between the two daughter cells that result from division. The process of distributing genetic material in the parent cell and its subsequent division into offspring cells is termed **mitosis**. Mitosis was named in the late nineteenth century by Walther Flemming, who noticed threadlike structures in cells during cell division (*mitos-* means "threads," and *-osis* means "condition of").

The pinching in of the plasma membrane, and eventual split of the membrane and its contents into two *daughter cells*, is termed **cytokinesis**. Cytokinesis occurs about the same time (or just after) the last phases of mitosis.

Life cycles are circular patterns of organisms' life histories. For example, the life cycle of humans would list conception, development, adulthood, and reproduction, and then again list conception and so on for the offspring. Likewise, individual body cells are formed, they reproduce, and their daughter cells continue the cycle of life. In this exercise, we explore the major events of the human cell's life cycle.

BEFORE YOU BEGIN

☐ Read the appropriate chapter in your textbook.
☐ Set your learning goals. When you finish this exercise, you should be able to:
  ☐ list the major phases of a cell's life cycle
  ☐ describe the principal events of mitosis
  ☐ identify cell parts involved in mitosis
  ☐ explain the importance of mitosis
  ☐ define the term *cytokinesis*
☐ Prepare your materials:
  ☐ chart or model: animal mitosis series
  ☐ colored pencils or pens
  ☐ microscope
  ☐ prepared microslide: whitefish blastula
☐ Read the directions and safety tips for this exercise *carefully* before starting any procedure.

Study TIPS

An effective way to identify the phases of mitosis is to have your lab partner arrange mitosis models or slides randomly and quiz you on the respective phases. During this exercise, concentrate on the appearance of the chromosomes/chromatids. Don't forget to utilize all the resources available to you (textbook, lab manual, prepared mitosis slides, etc.).

A. INTRODUCTION TO THE CELL LIFE CYCLE

The process of mitosis can be described step by step to make it a little easier to picture. We will divide the whole life cycle into five phases: **interphase, prophase, metaphase, anaphase,** and **telophase**.

Note the major events of each life cycle phase listed in **Figure 6-1**. Try to identify the physical representation of those events in a chart or model of cells at various life cycle stages.

☐ 1 **Interphase** is not a phase of mitosis but is the period between cell divisions. It is not an inactive time, however, because the chromatin replicates during interphase (forming two sister **chromatids** joined at a **centromere**). In anticipation of division, additional cell fluid and organelles are formed during interphase. As Figure 6-1 shows, an initial growth phase (G_1) is followed by the DNA replication or synthesis (S) phase, which is in turn followed by a second growth (G_2) phase.

☐ 2 **Prophase** is the first phase of mitosis. During prophase, the nuclear membrane disappears, freeing the chromatin (which first shortens into tiny bodies called **chromosomes**). Also, centriole pairs move to opposite poles of the cell as **spindle fibers** begin to project from them. The spindle fibers extend toward the equator of the cell and may overlap with spindle fibers projecting from the opposite centriole pair. A spindle fiber may also attach to one side of a chromosome's centromere.

> **Hint** ▶ The cell life cycle is a continuous process. The cell does not suddenly jump from one phase to another but gradually changes. Therefore, cell models represent a snapshot of each phase at a point where it is most distinct from the phases before and after it. •

☐ 3 **Metaphase** is the period during which the chromosomes (each a pair of replicate chromatids joined at a centromere) line up along the cell's equator (imaginary center plane). Each chromosome now has a pair of spindle fibers attached to it, one from each centriole pair.

☐ 4 **Anaphase** is the phase during which the chromatids split at the centromere, each moving toward an opposite pole along the path of a spindle fiber. At the end of anaphase, each pole of the cell has a full group of 46 single chromosomes.

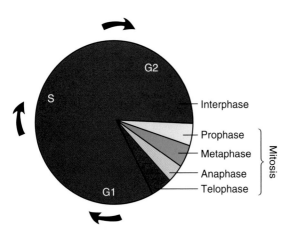

FIGURE 6-1 Cell life cycle and its major phases.

The chromosomes on one side of the cell are replicates of the set of chromosomes on the other side.

☐ **5** **Telophase** is the time during which each side of the cell changes everything to the way it should be during interphase:

☐ a nuclear membrane forms around each group of chromosomes

☐ the chromosomes uncoil to form long chromatin strands

☐ remnants of the spindle fibers disintegrate

☐ **6** During anaphase of mitosis, the separate (but concurrent) process of *cytokinesis* begins. By the end of anaphase, cleavage, or pinching in, of the parent cell is evident. By the end of telophase, complete splitting of the parent cell into two similar daughter cells is complete. Each daughter cell has a nucleus and roughly half of the cytoplasm and organelles of the parent cell.

☐ **7** Review the major events of the cell life cycle by completing the coloring exercise *Cell Life Cycle* (**Figure 6-2**).

The length of time between divisions and the time required for division to take place vary considerably from cell to cell. Even the relative length of different phases varies among individual cells. Cell division can range from 20 minutes to several hours.

> **!** **safety first**
>
> Do not forget to check the microscope's power cord for frays and for proper placement. Take care that you don't crack a slide or lens by zooming in with coarse focus without looking from the side. Accidents do not happen when you are careful. •

B. MICROSCOPIC OBSERVATIONS

In this activity, you will observe cells of the *whitefish blastula* in a prepared slide as in **Figures 6-3** and **6-4**. The blastula is a developmental stage in the growth of many animals. The original cell formed by the joining of the egg and sperm undergoes mitosis many times, at one stage forming a ball of cells called a *blastula*. The cells of the blastula are still undergoing rapid cell division, making it a specimen likely to have many cells at various stages of the cell life cycle.

☐ Obtain a prepared microscope slide (microslide) of whitefish blastula cross sections (c.s.).

☐ Locate a group of cells by using low-power magnification. There are usually several different cell groups from which to choose on each slide.

☐ Switch to high power and try to locate individual cells in each of the five phases of the cell life cycle. You may need to occasionally switch slides to find all the phases.

> **📌** *landmark characteristics*
>
> Many prepared whitefish blastula specimens are stained so that the cytoplasm appears pinkish to brown-red (see Figure 6-3). The DNA (chromatin, chromosomes) is stained black. Therefore, look for fine, black formations when looking for the major events of mitosis. The plasma membranes and centrioles are so small that they will not appear distinctly in your specimen.
>
> In a single microscopic field you will see many cells, all at different points in the cell life cycle. There is no pattern to the way the cells in different phases are arranged (they are not laid out in order of mitotic phases, for instance). If you are fortunate, you may find at least one example of each phase in a single field. •

Coloring Exercises: Cell Life Cycle

Use colored pens or pencils to shade in both the figure and the labels. Each red numeral in the figure corresponds to a matching red numeral following the appropriate label.

MITOSIS₁

CYTOKINESIS₂

INTERPHASE₃

PROPHASE₄

METAPHASE₅

ANAPHASE₆

TELOPHASE₇

CELL MEMBRANE₈

NUCLEAR MEMBRANE₉

NUCLEOLUS₁₀

CENTRIOLES₁₁

CHROMATIN/CHROMOSOME₁₂

CENTROMERE₁₃

FIGURE 6-2

FIGURE 6-3 The cell life cycle. **A,** Interphase. **B,** Prophase. **C,** Metaphase. **D,** Anaphase. **E,** Telophase.

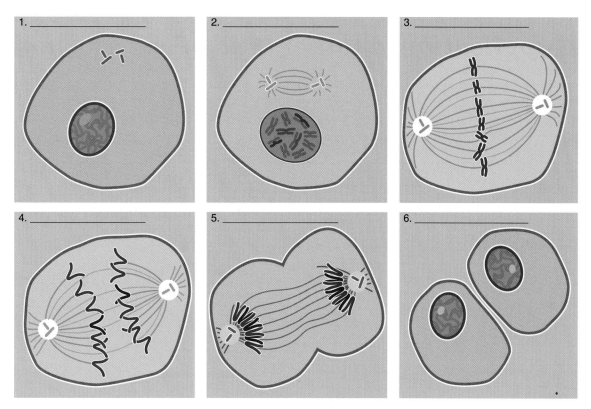

1. _____
2. _____
3. _____
4. _____
5. _____
6. _____

FIGURE 6-4 Examples of whitefish cells. Label each with the name of the appropriate phase on the lines provided and on the blanks in the Lab Report at the end of this exercise.

clinical application: *another kind of cell division*

Meiosis is a process distinct from mitosis. Meiosis is associated with a type of cell division that occurs during the formation of reproductive cells (*sperm* and *eggs*). Mitosis occurs in the division of all other cell types.

Diploid parent cell
(46 chromosomes)

Mitosis

Primary sex cells
(DNA replicated
before division)

Meiosis I

Secondary sex cells
(DNA not replicated
before division)

Meiosis II

Haploid gametes
(23 chromosomes)

FIGURE 6-5 Meiosis. Meiotic cell division takes place in two steps: meiosis I and meiosis II. Meiosis is called *reduction division* because the number of chromosomes is reduced by half (from the diploid number to the haploid number).

Meiosis results in daughter cells that have only half the number of chromosomes that other cells, including the parent cells, have. That is, during meiosis, a parent cell with 46 chromosomes (the diploid number) produces daughter cells that have 23 chromosomes each (the haploid number). This must occur so that when the sperm and egg unite during conception, the newly formed cell has 46 chromosomes (23 from the sperm plus 23 from the egg). Thus, the offspring has equal amounts of hereditary information from each parent.

Theoretically, what would happen if meiosis did not occur and sperm and egg cells could only form using mitosis?

What would happen if *all* your body cells divided using meiosis instead of mitosis?

Name: _____ Date: _____ Section: _____

LAB REPORT 6
The Cell's Life Cycle

Sketch your observations of particularly clear examples of mitotic phases in whitefish cells.

Specimen: *whitefish, phase* _____
Total Magnification: _____

Specimen: *whitefish, phase* _____
Total Magnification: _____

Specimen: *whitefish, phase* _____
Total Magnification: _____

Specimen: *whitefish, phase* _____
Total Magnification: _____

Specimen: *whitefish, phase* _____
Total Magnification: _____

Specimen: *whitefish, phase* _____
Total Magnification: _____

Figure 6-4 (from p. 53)

1. _____
2. _____
3. _____
4. _____
5. _____

Fill-in

1. _____
2. _____
3. _____
4. _____
5. _____
6. _____
7. _____
8. _____
9. _____
10. _____

Multiple Choice

1. _____
2. _____
3. _____
4. _____
5. _____

Fill-in (write the name of the mitotic phase identified in each item)

1. The centrioles move toward opposite poles during _?_.
2. During _?_ the nuclear membrane disintegrates _?_.
3. The nuclear membrane reappears during _?_.
4. The last phase of mitosis is _?_.
5. During _?_ the chromosomes align at the cell's equator.
6. Cytokinesis usually begins during _?_ of mitosis.
7. The first phase of mitosis is _?_.
8. During _?_ the chromatids separate and move toward opposite poles.
9. Spindle fibers appear during _?_.
10. During __?__ the chromosomes uncoil and form long chromatin strands.

Multiple Choice (only one choice is correct)

1. The function of mitosis is
   a. to distribute the cell's DNA equally between the daughter cells
   b. to divide the cytoplasm equally between the daughter cells
   c. to distribute the parent cell's organelles evenly
   d. all of the above
   e. none of the above
2. The chromosomes of daughter cells formed during mitosis
   a. are double the number of those in the parent cell
   b. are identical to the chromosomes of the other daughter
   c. are half the number of those in the parent cell
   d. b and c are correct
   e. all are correct
3. Which of these cells is likely to have been formed using mitosis?
   a. skin cell
   b. sperm cell
   c. egg cell
   d. heart muscle cell
   e. a and d are correct
4. A certain stain colors DNA violet. When stained, which of these should appear violet?
   a. chromatin
   b. chromosomes
   c. chromatids
   d. a and b are correct
   e. all of the above
5. Two DNA molecules, joined at a centromere, have coiled to form tiny bodies. This connected pair of DNA molecules should properly be called a
   a. centromere
   b. centriole
   c. chromosome
   d. chromatid
   e. chromatin strand

LAB EXERCISE 7

Epithelial Tissue

As we continue our study of the human body, we progress from the cellular level of organization to the tissue level. Tissues are masses of similar cells (and their extracellular *matrix*) that combine with other tissues to form *membranes* or *organs*. The systematic study of tissue types is called **histology**. There are four basic tissue types in the human:

Epithelial tissue
Connective tissue
Muscle tissue
Nerve tissue

Each of these categories includes several subcategories, based on differences in structure and function. We will consider some of the major subcategories in this and the next several exercises. We will begin our exploration with a brief look at epithelial tissue types. We will look at connective tissue in exercise 8 and muscle and nerve tissue in exercise 9.

BEFORE YOU BEGIN

- ☐ Read the appropriate chapter in your textbook.
- ☐ Set your learning goals. When you finish this exercise, you should be able to:
  - ☐ define the term *epithelium*
  - ☐ classify epithelial tissue types
  - ☐ identify and give examples of the major types of epithelia in figures and specimens
- ☐ Prepare your materials:
  - ☐ unlabeled photos of epithelial types (optional)
  - ☐ microscope
  - ☐ prepared microslides:
    - ☐ simple squamous (surface)
    - ☐ stratified squamous (nonkeratinized) c.s.
    - ☐ stratified squamous (keratinized) c.s.
    - ☐ simple cuboidal c.s.
    - ☐ simple columnar c.s.
    - ☐ pseudostratified (ciliated) c.s.
    - ☐ transitional c.s.
- ☐ Read the directions and safety tips for this exercise *carefully* before starting any procedure.

Study TIPS

As you observe the prepared sectional slides of epithelial tissue, it is important that you first identify the "exposed" space. Since membranous epithelium covers the body or lines a cavity, there is always an exposed space. After you have identified the exposed space, classify the shape (squamous, cuboidal, or columnar) of the cells. Then determine the number of layers (simple or stratified).

The use of flash cards or review cards is an excellent strategy to learn the various types of epithelial tissue. Obtain photos or illustrations of the different types of epithelial tissue. Place the photo or illustration on one side of an index card. On the opposite side of the card, put the name of the tissue. You can also add additional information such as unique characteristics or location in the body.

A. HOW TO CLASSIFY EPITHELIAL TISSUES (FIGURE 7-1)

Epithelial tissue can have either of two basic roles: covering/lining or glandular. The first kind, covering/lining epithelium, is found in sheets that cover body structures (e.g., the outer layer of the skin) or line body spaces (e.g., the lining of the stomach). A key characteristic of covering/lining epithelium is that it always has one side exposed, or free to face outward (covering) or inward (lining). Because the cells form a continuous sheet, they are held together very tightly and have very little matrix (extracellular material). The nonfree face of the epithelial sheet is attached to underlying connective tissue by the **basement membrane**. The basement membrane is a thin, gluelike layer that holds the epithelium in place while remaining highly permeable to water and other substances. This is important because epithelia do not have their own blood supply. Water and other important substances must diffuse between the epithelial cells and the underlying tissue through the basement membrane.

The second kind of epithelium is the type that forms glands. Glandular epithelium forms the functional portions of **exocrine** glands (glands that secrete substances into ducts that empty onto epithelial surfaces). It also forms **endocrine** glands (glands that secrete substances that diffuse into the bloodstream).

Epithelial tissue that forms membranes is usually categorized by its structure **(Figure 7-2)**. The most common scheme classifies types by identifying the number of cell layers and the shape of the cells in the outer layer. We will practice classifying membranous epithelia by using photomicrographs or drawings provided by your instructor, or the samples in **Figure 7-3**.

☐ 1 Randomly choose a sample from those provided.

☐ 2 The first step in classifying an epithelial tissue is determining how many layers of cells compose the sheet. The sample falls into one of three categories based on number of layers:

☐ **Simple**—This category includes all tissues that have exactly one layer of cells.

☐ **Stratified**—This group includes epithelia with more than one layer (or *stratum*) of cells.

☐ **Pseudostratified**—The name of this category means "false stratified." This term is based on the fact that pseudostratified epithelium looks as if it's stratified but is really only one layer deep. This illusion is caused by the way the cells seem to be pushed together, with some nuclei pushed into the upper portion of the cell and nuclei of other cells located in the bottom part. The nuclei then seem to form an upper and lower row, giving the illusion of two rows of cells. Remember, cell membranes are often too thin for you to be able to see the boundary between epithelial cells.

Coloring Exercises: Epithelial Cell Types

Use colored pens to shade in both the figure and the labels.

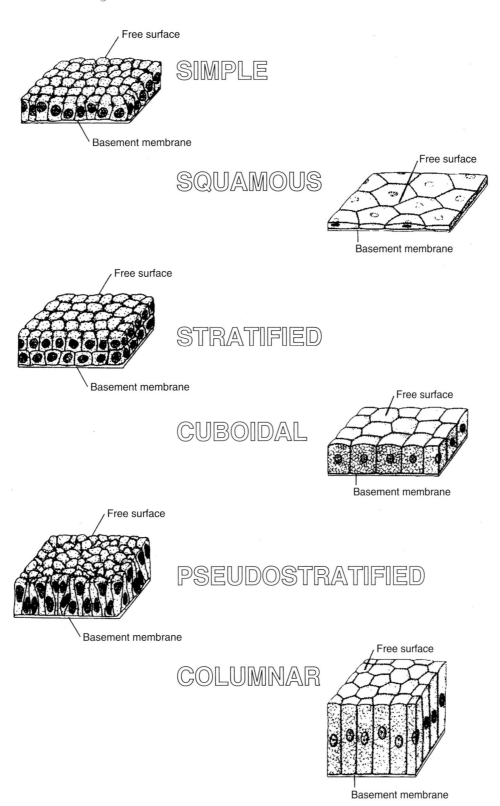

Free surface

SIMPLE

Basement membrane

SQUAMOUS

Free surface

Basement membrane

Free surface

STRATIFIED

Basement membrane

CUBOIDAL

Free surface

Basement membrane

Free surface

PSEUDOSTRATIFIED

Basement membrane

COLUMNAR

Free surface

Basement membrane

FIGURE 7-1 The *figures on the left* show how epithelia are classified according to number of layers. The *figures on the right* show how epithelia are classified according to shape.

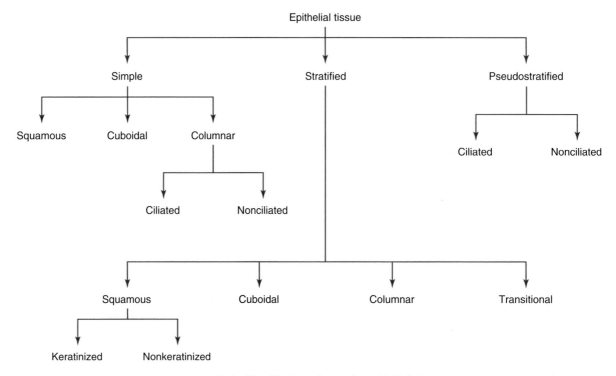

FIGURE 7-2 Classification scheme for epithelial tissues.

☐ **3** If you have determined that your sample is simple or stratified, skip to step 4. If your sample is pseudostratified, you must determine whether it is **ciliated** or **nonciliated**. Cilia are short, hairlike projections from each cell's free surface that propel material along the epithelial surface. You have now completely classified your sample and can try it again with a new sample.

☐ **4** Look at the layer of cells along the sample's free surface. Determine which shape these cells have:
   ☐ **Squamous**—Shaped like fish scales, these cells are much wider than they are tall when viewed in a cross section. Nuclei may be absent in cross sections.
   ☐ **Cuboidal**—As their name implies, these cells are roughly cube-shaped—about as tall as they are wide. Do not expect squared corners, as in a cube. Although they sometimes appear that way in a cross section, they more often resemble rounded squares or even circles.
   ☐ **Columnar**—These column-like (rectangular) cells are taller than they are wide when viewed in a cross section.
   ☐ **Transitional**—The term *transitional* refers to the fact that these cells change shape as the need arises, being stretched or compressed into any of the three shapes already listed. Transitional cells are usually found as a hodgepodge of different cell shapes in membranes subject to a great degree of stretching and recoil. Transitional epithelia are always stratified.
   ☐ If your sample is simple squamous, simple or stratified cuboidal, or stratified columnar, you are finished with this sample and can try another one. If you have simple columnar, move to step 5. If you have stratified squamous, skip to step 6.

☐ **5** Determine whether the sample is ciliated or nonciliated. See step 3 for clarification. You are now finished classifying this sample and can try another sample.

☐ **6** Determine whether your stratified squamous tissue is **keratinized** or **nonkeratinized**. In some stratified squamous tissues, the upper layers of cells are dead (evidenced by the lack of nuclei) and filled with a tough, waterproof material called *keratin*. If your sample has a thick sheet of material with no visible nuclei along its free surface, it is probably keratinized. Nonkeratinized samples have nucleated squamous cells along the free edge.

☐ **7** Once you have determined the specific tissue type of each specimen, refer to **Table 7-1** to discover its typical locations and functions.

B. MICROSCOPIC SPECIMENS

In this activity, we will examine prepared slides of human epithelial tissues. Before beginning, review the microscopy techniques outlined in Lab Exercise 3.

> *safety first*
> Avoid the hazards associated with frayed power cords and broken glass slides. Do not reach for anything while looking into the ocular, or you may knock over something (or someone). Remember to make sure the intensity dial is on its lowest setting before plugging in the microscope. •

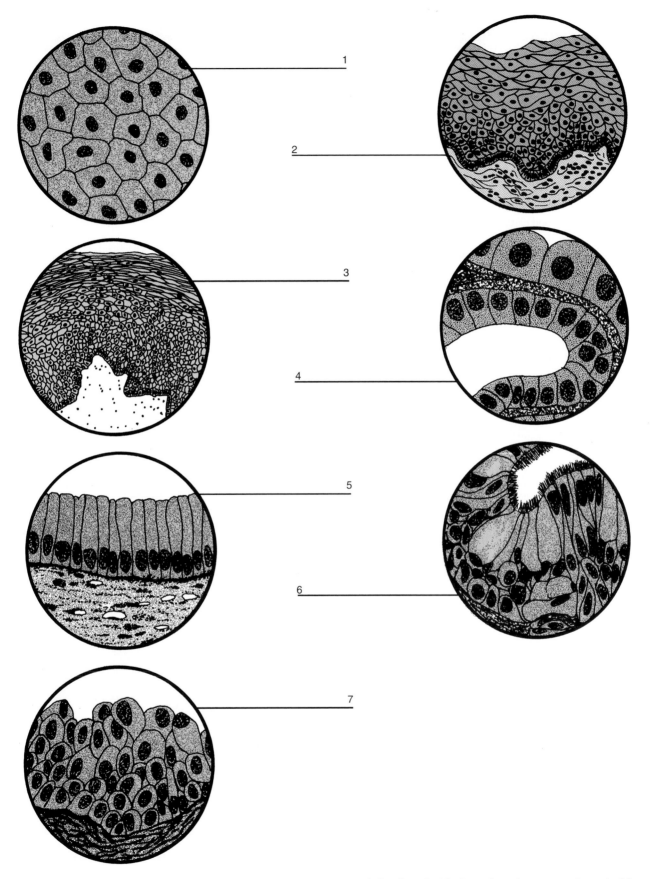

FIGURE 7-3 Try to identify each of the tissue types represented on the lines provided and on the blanks in the Lab Report at the end of this exercise.

T A B L E   7 - 1   **Examples of Major Membranous Epithelial Tissues**

TISSUE	LOCATION	FUNCTION
Simple squamous	Alveoli of lungs Lining of blood and lymphatic vessels (called **endothelium**; classed as connective tissue by some histologists) Surface layer of pleura, pericardium, peritoneum (called **mesothelium**; classed as connective tissue by some histologists)	Absorption by diffusion of respiratory gases between alveolar air and blood Absorption by diffusion, filtration, osmosis Absorption by diffusion and osmosis; also secretion
Stratified squamous Nonkeratinized Keratinized	Surface of mucous membrane lining mouth, esophagus, and vagina Surface of skin (epidermis)	Protection Protection
Simple cuboidal	In many types of glands and their ducts; also found in ducts and tubules of other organs, such as the kidney	Secretion; absorption
Pseudostratified	Surface of mucous membrane lining trachea, large bronchi, nasal mucosa, and parts of male reproductive tract (epididymis and vas deferens); lines large ducts of some glands (e.g., parotid)	Protection
Simple columnar	Surface layer of mucous lining of stomach, intestines, and part of respiratory tract	Protection; secretion; absorption; moving of mucus (by ciliated columnar epithelium)
Transitional	Surface of mucous membrane lining urinary bladder and ureters	Permits stretching

For each of the epithelial tissues listed, examine at least one example in a prepared slide. Practice looking for the key characteristics by which each type can be classified. Sketch some representative examples in Lab Report 7.

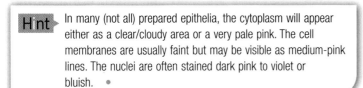

Hint In many (not all) prepared epithelia, the cytoplasm will appear either as a clear/cloudy area or a very pale pink. The cell membranes are usually faint but may be visible as medium-pink lines. The nuclei are often stained dark pink to violet or bluish. •

☐ **1 Simple squamous epithelium**—As the name implies, simple squamous epithelium is a single layer of flattened cells. This type of epithelium forms the very thin lining found in the blood vessels, in the alveoli (air sacs) of the lungs, and in other areas where thin membranes are required. Because it is so thin, simple squamous is well adapted for diffusion or filtration of water, gases, and other substances.

📌 landmark characteristics

Viewed from the side, as in a cross section, simple squamous epithelium looks like a thin line of cells—often with distinguishable nuclei (**Figure 7-4, A**). Viewed as a sheet from above, simple squamous epithelium looks like a two-dimensional layout of polygonal or rounded "tiles," each with a central nucleus (Figure 7-4, B). •

Simple squamous epithelial cell   Basement membrane   Nucleus   Free surface

A

B

Squamous epithelial cell   Nucleus

FIGURE 7-4 Simple squamous epithelium.

2 Stratified squamous epithelium—This tissue type is composed of multiple layers of cells: columnar cells along the basement membrane, topped by cuboidal cells, then by squamous cells. Cells divide in the columnar layer and are pushed upward, where they are distorted into cuboidal, then squamous, cells. The cells on the surface slough off but are continually replaced by cells moving up from the bottom layer. Because of its thickness and its constant renewal, it is well adapted for protection. For example, stratified squamous epithelium is found in the outer part of the skin and the mucous linings of the mouth, vagina, and esophagus.

FIGURE 7-5 Stratified squamous (nonkeratinized) epithelium.

landmark characteristics

- *Nonkeratinized stratified squamous epithelium* **(Figure 7-5)** typically has a dense concentration of nuclei (of columnar and cuboidal cells) near the basement membrane, becoming less dense toward the free surface. Most of the squamous cells near the free surface should have identifiable nuclei.
- *Keratinized stratified squamous* samples will be from the epidermis (outer layer) of the skin. They will look similar to nonkeratinized specimens, except that they have distinct additional layers overlying the top layers of squamous cells **(Figure 7-6)**. This layer has no distinguishable nuclei.

FIGURE 7-6 Stratified squamous (keratinized) epithelium.

3 Simple cuboidal epithelium—Composed of a single layer of almost cubic cells, this type is found in secreting organs such as glands. Simple cuboidal epithelium also forms the kidney tubules, where it is specialized for water reabsorption and ion movement **(Figure 7-7)**.

landmark characteristics

The cuboid shape of cells is easily seen in cross sections of kidney tubules (see Figure 7-7). Because the sample is formed by many tubules cut at an angle, you will see many circles and loops made of simple cuboidal epithelium. Similar specimens are seen in thyroid tissue or other glands and glandular ducts. •

large, cuplike vesicle that may open onto the free surface. The cup has no wine but rather **mucus**, which the goblet cells produce and secrete in great quantity. Mucus has many functions, including the lubrication and protection of the epithelial lining.

4 Simple columnar epithelium—Forming linings specialized for absorption and secretion, simple columnar epithelium is found in many parts of the body **(Figure 7-8)**. For example, this type of epithelium lines portions of the reproductive tract, digestive tract, excretory ducts, and respiratory tract. A special cell that is often interspersed among the other columnar cells is the **goblet cell**. The goblet cell resembles its namesake, the wine goblet, in that it has a

landmark characteristics

Simple columnar sheets often line cavities with deeply folded or grooved walls. The specimen, then, will appear to zigzag when viewed in a cross section. One surface of the sheet is always free, however, even though the free surfaces may fold back and touch one another. A goblet cell is easily recognizable by the very large bubble (vesicle) in the center or near the top (see Figure 7-8). Because the vesicle contains clear, unstained mucus, it will appear more lightly colored than the surrounding material. •

☐ 5 **Ciliated pseudostratified epithelium**—This type of epithelium is a single layer of columnar cells that all attach to the basement membrane. However, some cells are short and do not quite reach the free surface **(Figure 7-9)**. Nuclei of short cells are nearer the basement membrane than the nuclei of tall cells, so there appear to be two rows of cells. Like simple columnar epithelium, pseudostratified epithelium is found in both ciliated and nonciliated forms. It is found in many of the same general areas of the body as simple columnar epithelium (e.g., the upper throat, upper respiratory tract, and parts of the male urinary and reproductive tracts).

landmark characteristics

On initial examination, pseudostratified epithelium resembles simple columnar epithelium (see Figure 7-9); however, the telltale double row of nuclei gives it away. As in simple columnar epithelium, goblet cells may be present. Cilia look like distinct, tiny hairs along the free surface. Some specimens may have some areas of matted cilia or even "bald" spots. Under low magnification, the cilia look like "fuzz" on the free edge.   •

Hint   The terms *mucous* and *mucus* are often confused. Mucus is a noun, naming a glycoprotein-water solution. Mucous is an adjective describing something covered with mucus. Thus, mucous membranes are covered with mucus.   •

FIGURE 7-7 Simple cuboidal epithelium.

FIGURE 7-8 Simple columnar epithelium.

FIGURE 7-9 Pseudostratified ciliated epithelium.

❏ 6 **Transitional epithelium**—Transitional tissue is adapted for stretching, so it is found in areas subject to a great deal of elastic stress. You will most likely see specimens from the lining of the urinary bladder, which must stretch a great deal from time to time throughout the day **(Figure 7-10)**.

Connective tissue   Basement membrane

FIGURE 7-10 Transitional epithelium.

landmark characteristics

Transitional epithelium resembles nonkeratinized stratified squamous epithelium at first glance. Transitional epithelium, however, often has rounded cuboidal cells in the top layer (rather than only squamous cells). Depending on the individual specimen, you may see a great variety of shapes scattered throughout the tissue. Some of them may have a sort of distorted teardrop or umbrella shape. This gives transitional tissue a rather unorganized appearance, compared with the other epithelial types. Occasionally, transitional cells have two nuclei—an unusual characteristic that can help you distinguish transitional from other epithelial types that have just one nucleus per cell (see Figure 7-10). •

Study TIPS

To understand the shape of epithelial cells, you can use a soda can analogy. Imagine a soda can that has been completely smashed. This would represent a squamous-shaped cell. A soda can that has only been smashed halfway would represent a cuboidal-shaped cell. A soda can that has not been smashed would represent a columnar-shaped cell. Finally, soda cans arranged in all of these shapes would represent stratified transitional epilthelium.

clinical application: *using epithelial tissue*

Researchers are always looking for new ways to deliver therapeutic drugs to the bloodstream for distribution throughout the body. Currently, biomedical research teams are using epithelial tissue cultures to investigate a relatively new approach to drug introduction. For some time, science has known that certain compounds are easily absorbed by epithelial membranes and picked up by the blood. For example, patches of material containing drugs that inhibit motion sickness have been used by tourists on ocean cruises. Patients with heart disease or burns often receive therapy by means of similar patches. Today, however, researchers are looking for wider and more varied uses of epithelial absorption as a drug delivery method.

Based on what you know of the different epithelial tissue types, which are the best candidates for this type of therapy? Explain your choices.

How could a clinician actually apply epithelial absorption techniques? Try to think of strategies other than the skin-patch approach.

Explain some of the harmful side effects of smoking tobacco, cocaine, and marijuana in terms of epithelial absorption.

Study TIPS

Use Table 7-1 to develop a concept map much like the one in Figure 7-2; however, include locations in the body where you would find each type of epithelial tissue. You can refer to your text or the *A&P Survival Guide* for tables that describe the different epithelial tissues.

Name: _____ Date: _____ Section: _____

LAB REPORT 7
Epithelial Tissue

Activity A:

TRIAL NUMBER	IDENTIFYING CODE*	TISSUE TYPE	NOTES
1			
2			
3			
4			
5			
6			
7			

The IDENTIFYING CODE is the code number (letter) assigned to your sample by the instructor. If you are using figures from this or another book, put the plate and/or figure number in this column.

Specimen: *simple squamous epithelium (surface view)*
Total Magnification: _____

Specimen: *stratified squamous epithelium (nonkeratinized)*
Total Magnification: _____

Specimen: *stratified squamous epithelium (keratinized)*
Total Magnification: _____

Specimen: *simple cuboidal epithelium*
Total Magnification: _____

Specimen: *simple columnar epithelium*
Total Magnification: _____

Specimen: *ciliated pseudostratified epithelium*
Total Magnification: _____

Specimen: *transitional epithelium*
Total Magnification: _____

Specimen: _____
Total Magnification: _____

Figure 7-3 (from p. 61)

1. _____

2. _____

3. _____

4. _____

5. _____

6. _____

7. _____

Identify

1. _____

2. _____

3. _____

4. _____

5. _____

6. _____

7. _____

8. _____

Identify (identify the term associated with each description)

1. A type of cell found in simple columnar and pseudostratified tissue that secretes mucus
2. One of two kinds of glands, it secretes substances onto epithelial surfaces
3. A cellular organelle, it is a projection that moves substances along the surface of a cell
4. A type of epithelial tissue especially well adapted to excessive stretching
5. Mucous membranes secrete this water-based protein solution
6. A tough, waterproof material found in the upper layers of some examples of stratified squamous epithelium
7. The type of epithelial tissue likely to be found forming glands
8. The type of epithelial tissue likely to be found on the palm of the hand

Connective Tissue

Some tissues are called **connective tissues** because they act as connections among various other tissues. **Bone, cartilage,** and **fibrous connective tissues** actually hold parts together or support them in some way. **Blood** tissue connects other tissues in the sense of transporting materials between them.

An additional function of some connective tissues is storage. For example, bone tissue is an important storage site for calcium and phosphorus—minerals that are vital to proper function in many parts of the body.

In this exercise, we learn to identify some of the more common connective tissue types found in the human body.

BEFORE YOU BEGIN

☐ Read the appropriate chapter in your textbook.
☐ Set your learning goals. When you finish this exercise, you should be able to:
  ☐ describe the general pattern of structure in connective tissues
  ☐ classify major connective tissue types
  ☐ identify examples of connective tissue types in figures and specimens
☐ Prepare your materials:
  ☐ microscope
  ☐ prepared microslides:
    ☐ dense fibrous (regular) connective tissue
    ☐ dense fibrous (irregular) connective tissue
    ☐ loose fibrous (areolar) connective tissue
    ☐ adipose tissue
    ☐ reticular tissue
    ☐ hyaline cartilage
    ☐ fibrocartilage
    ☐ elastic cartilage
    ☐ compact bone
    ☐ cancellous bone
    ☐ blood smear
    ☐ fresh animal connective tissue samples (as available)
☐ Read the directions and safety tips for this exercise *carefully* before starting any procedure.

Study TIPS

The use of flash cards or review cards is an excellent strategy to learn the various types of connective tissue. Obtain photos or illustrations of the different types of connective tissue. Place the photo or illustration on one side of an index card. On the opposite side of the card, put the name of the tissue. You can also add additional information such as unique characteristics or location in the body.

A. CLASSIFYING CONNECTIVE TISSUES

A structural feature common to all connective tissues is the dominance of the tissue matrix, or extracellular material. Recall that epithelial tissues have almost no extracellular material separating individual cells. Connective tissue cells are often widely separated by one of three basic types of matrix:

☐ 1 **Protein matrix** is extracellular material composed of many substances but with a dominance of protein fibers. **Collagen** is a common protein, forming bundles of tough, flexible fibers. Because they have a whitish color, collagen fibers are often called *white fibers*. **Elastin,** a stretchy, fibrous protein, forms thick, single fibers in connective tissue matrices. Elastin fibers are sometimes called *yellow fibers*. Identify these categories of protein-matrix connective tissues in **Figure 8-1**:
  ☐ **Fibrous**—Fibrous tissues are categorized as either **dense fibrous** or **loose fibrous**, depending on the density of protein fibers in the matrix. Dense fibrous tissue can either be **regular dense fibrous** (having regular parallel bundles of fibers) or **irregular dense fibrous** (having an irregular hodgepodge of fibers). Loose fibrous tissue is also called **loose, ordinary areolar tissue.**
  ☐ **Adipose**—Adipose tissue is often simply called *fat tissue* because its primary function is the storage of fat (for later use or for body support). Adipose tissue is actually a modified form of areolar tissue, with fat storage cells having been filled with stored lipids and expanded into the extracellular spaces **(Figure 8-2)**.

☐ 2 **Protein/ground substance matrix** is extracellular material that has some protein fibers in it but also a great deal of nonfibrous protein and other substances. Identify these categories of protein/ground substance tissues in Figure 8-1:
  ☐ **Cartilage**—The matrix of cartilage is a combination of fibers and ground substance that gives it a rubbery quality. **Hyaline cartilage** has a moderate amount of collagen fiber in its matrix. **Fibrocartilage,** as its name implies, has a large amount of collagen fiber in its matrix. **Elastic cartilage** is distinguished by the presence of elastin fibers, giving it a stretchy quality.
  ☐ **Bone**—There are two broad categories of bone: **compact bone** and **cancellous (spongy) bone.** Both have a matrix of collagen fibers encrusted with mineral crystals that give it a solid consistency. Compact bone forms rather large, dense pieces of bone matrix. Cancellous bone

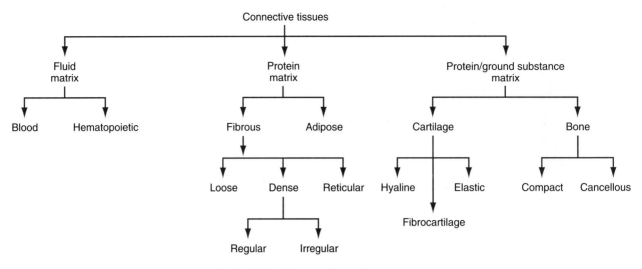

Connective tissues

Fluid matrix → Blood, Hematopoietic

Protein matrix → Fibrous → Loose, Dense → Regular, Irregular; Reticular; Adipose

Protein/ground substance matrix → Cartilage → Hyaline, Fibrocartilage, Elastic; Bone → Compact, Cancellous

FIGURE 8-1 A classification scheme for connective tissues.

forms thin, narrow beams of hard bone matrix in which **red bone marrow** can be supported **(Figure 8-3)**.

☐ **3 Fluid matrix** is composed of a water-based solution with a fluid consistency. **Blood** is the major type of fluid matrix connective tissue. Blood cells are suspended within the fluid *plasma* and can slide past one another freely. Another type of fluid matrix tissue is **hematopoietic tissue**, which produces blood cells. Hematopoietic tissue is also called **myeloid tissue**, or simply *red bone marrow*. Identify fluid matrix tissue in the general scheme presented in Figure 8-1.

> **Hint** ► Many cells found in connective tissues are named according to their action. Cells that produce matrix often have the suffix *-blast* ("make"). Cells that destroy matrix during remodeling have the suffix *-clast* ("break"). Cells that are in a relatively inactive mode have a *-cyte* ("cell") suffix. The first part of the name tells the specific kind of matrix involved: *fibro-* ("fiber"), *chondro-* ("cartilage"), or *osteo-* ("bone"). Thus, *fibroblasts* make fibers, *chondroblasts* manufacture cartilage matrix, and *osteoblasts* lay down bone matrix. •

Histologists classify tissues for convenience in naming them and for better identification of their nature. However, different histologists use slightly different schemes, depending on the context in which they are working. The histology schemes used in this manual are fairly universal.

Table 8-1 summarizes the locations and functions of some of the major types of connective tissue.

Study TIPS

When classifying connective tissues, pay close attention to the matrix. Identify whether the matrix is protein (fibrous), protein (ground substance), or fluid. Use available resources (textbook, lab manual, atlas, or Internet sources) to familiarize yourself with the difference among these matrices. Develop a concept map similar to the one in Figure 8-1. However, use Table 8-1 and include the locations of these tissues in the body. If time allows during your lab or during an open lab, meet with a lab partner and set up randomly prepared connective tissue slides and quiz one another on its type and location.

B. MICROSCOPIC SPECIMENS

safety first

Avoid electrical hazards while using the microscope. Be sure to exercise care in dealing with broken glass slides. Do not reach for slides or other objects while you are looking into the ocular, or you may knock over something (or someone). •

This activity asks you to observe representative connective tissue types in prepared specimens. For each type listed in the following steps, locate an example in a slide and sketch it in Lab Report 8.

☐ **1 Loose, ordinary fibrous (areolar) connective tissue (Figure 8-4)**—Areolar (meaning "spacious") tissue forms loose bonds between other tissues. For example, under the skin it allows the skin to be slid around, over, or pulled from the underlying muscle to some degree. Both collagen and elastin fibers are found in this tissue but are widely spaced

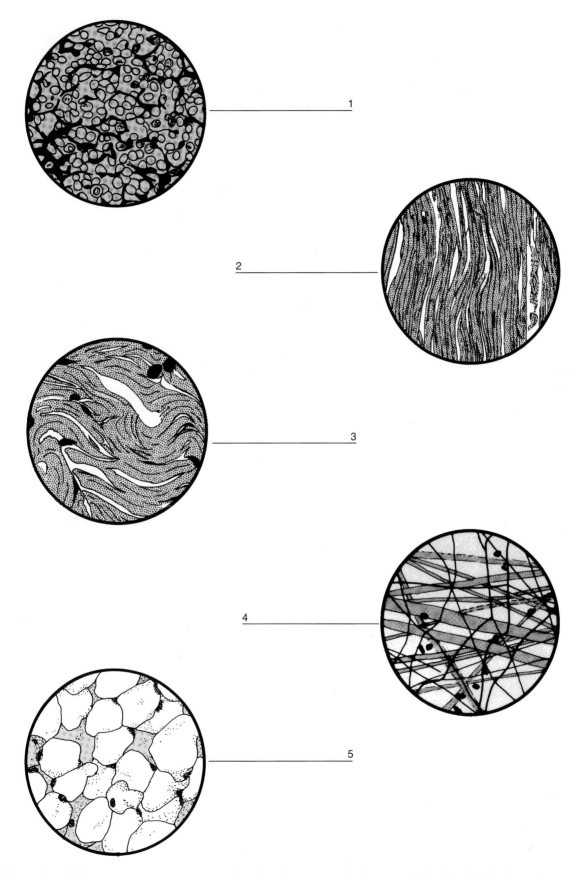

FIGURE 8-2 Try to identify the connective tissues represented in these drawings on the lines provided and on the blanks in the Lab Report at the end of this exercise.

FIGURE 8-3 Try to identify the connective tissues represented in these drawings on the lines provided and on the blanks in the Lab Report at the end of this exercise.

TABLE 8-1   **Examples of Major Connective Tissues**

TISSUE	LOCATION	FUNCTION
Fibrous		
Loose, ordinary (areolar)	Between other tissues Superficial fascia	Connection Connection
Adipose (fat)	Under skin Padding at various points	Protection Insulation Support Reserve food
Reticular	Inner framework of spleen, lymph nodes, bone marrow	Support Filtration
Dense Fibrous		
Regular	Tendons Ligaments Aponeuroses	Flexible but strong connection
Irregular	Deep fascia Dermis Scars Capsule of kidney, etc.	Connection Support
Bone		
Compact	Skeleton	Support Protection Calcium reservoir
Cancellous	Skeleton	Support of bone marrow
Cartilage		
Hyaline	Part of nasal septum Covering articular surfaces of bones Larynx Rings in trachea and bronchi	Firm but flexible support
Fibrocartilage	Disks between vertebrae Symphysis pubis	
Elastic	External ear Auditory (eustachian) tube	
Fluid		
Blood	In blood vessels	Transportation Protection
Hematopoietic	Skeleton (in cavities of cancellous bone)	Blood tissue production

Blood vessels, as well as nerves, course through it. A variety of cell types may be found here (e.g., fibrocytes, adipose cells, and white blood cells).

📌 *landmark characteristics*

Areolar tissue's widely spaced fibers and variety of cell types make it easy tissue to identify. The elastin fibers appear as dark, thick, jagged strands. Collagen fibers form bundles that often appear as hazy pink or light purple crisscrossing lines (see Figure 8-4). •

☐ **2 Adipose tissue**—Adipose cells in common white fat are specialized to store lipids in large vesicles. The vesicle can be so large that it pushes the nucleus and other organelles up to the cell membrane, which enlarges to accommodate the large cell volume **(Figure 8-5)**. Some histologists classify adipose tissue as a subcategory of areolar tissue. If the adipose cells in areolar tissue enlarge (because of increased storage of fat), they crowd the fibers and other cells, eventually forming adipose tissue. Thus, adipose tissue has very little matrix compared with other connective tissue types.

Adipose tissue is found wherever areolar tissue is found, but it is most often seen around the heart and kidney and under the skin. It not only stores lipids for later use, but it also serves as support (as in the breasts), as insulation (under the skin), and as a cushion (you are sitting on it).

📌 *landmark characteristics*

Unlike other connective tissue cells, adipose cells are very close to one another. The large fat globule inside each cell pushes the cytoplasm and organelles into a thin, dark ring around the inside of the cell membrane. The nucleus often appears as a bulge in the ring. The most obvious characteristic of this tissue is the presence of large fat vesicles, which generally look clear, yellowish, or light pink. The overall appearance is that of a host of large bubbles (see Figure 8-5). •

☐ **3 Reticular tissue**—Reticular tissue is named for a word that means "network," referring to this tissue's characteristic three-dimensional web of fine reticular fibers **(Figure 8-6)**. The fine fibers that characterize this tissue are made of a special type of collagen. Reticular cells are found overlying the fine fibers that form the reticular meshwork. Branches of the cytoplasm of reticular cells follow the branching reticular fibers. Reticular fiber tissue forms the framework of the spleen, lymph nodes, and bone marrow cavities. It functions as part of the body's defensive system.

Elastic fibers

Bundles of collagenous fibers

FIGURE 8-4 Loose, ordinary (areolar) connective tissue.

Nuclei of adipocyte   Fat (lipid) storage area

Plasma membrane

FIGURE 8-5 Adipose tissue.

Blood cells   Reticular fibers

FIGURE 8-6 Reticular tissue.

☐ **4 Dense fibrous connective tissue**—As its name indicates, this tissue is a dense arrangement of fibers **(Figure 8-7)**. They may be collagen fibers or elastic fibers. Their arrangement may be regular (roughly parallel) or irregular (swirling or random). Interspersed among the fibers of a mature tissue are **fibrocytes**. Irregular dense fibrous tissue forms the lower layer of the skin (dermis), much of the body's fascia, and the capsules of many organs **(Figure 8-8)**. Regular dense fibrous tissue is used for structures that require a better-engineered connection between parts that are pulled with great force. For example, this tissue forms *tendons* (connecting muscle to bone) and *ligaments* (connecting bone to bone).

Collagen fibers   Fibroblast

FIGURE 8-7 Dense fibrous (regular) connective tissue.

Collagen fibers   Fibroblast

FIGURE 8-8 Dense fibrous (irregular) connective tissue.

☐ **5 Hyaline cartilage**—All cartilage is distinctive in the consistency of its semisolid rubbery matrix of protein fibers mixed with other substances. **Chondrocytes** are scattered throughout the matrix in little pockets called **lacunae** (meaning "lakes," **Figure 8-9**). Hyaline cartilage has a moderate amount of collagen, giving it a great deal of toughness along with its cushiony quality. This cartilage type forms the bulk of the fetal skeleton (before it is replaced by bone) and continues to be the most abundant type of cartilage throughout life. It forms the thin, rubbery layer over the ends of long bones and is found in parts of the larynx, nose, and trachea. Specimens of cartilage may exhibit a fibrous **perichondrium** surrounding the cartilage tissue.

Cartilaginous matrix   Perichondrium

Chondrocyte in lacuna

FIGURE 8-9 Hyaline cartilage.

☐ **6 Fibrocartilage**—The name of this tissue indicates its high concentration of collagen fibers. These fibers give the tissue a distinctive fibrous appearance **(Figure 8-10)**. Fibrocartilage has a more rigid, less rubbery consistency than other cartilage types. Fibrocartilage forms the disks between vertebrae and may be found at other semimovable joints.

☐ **7 Elastic cartilage**—As its name implies, elastic cartilage has a large proportion of elastin fibers in its matrix **(Figure 8-11)**. Elastic cartilage is found in structures in which springiness is desirable in the support material. For example, the elasticity of the pinna (ear flap) is provided by elastic cartilage.

☐ **8 Compact bone**—Compact bone is formed by solid, cylindrical units called **osteons** packed tightly together. The osteon, or *haversian system*, consists of multiple concentric layers of hard bone matrix, with cells sandwiched between each layer **(Figure 8-12)**. Each layer is a **lamella** (plural, *lamellae*). **Osteocytes** are literally trapped within lacunae between the lamellae. The osteocytes were once active **osteoblasts** but have trapped themselves in the solid matrix they formed. The lamellae are centered around the **central (haversian) canal's** blood vessels. The cells transport materials to and from the canal by way of tiny **canaliculi** ("small canals") that connect the osteocytes to one another and to the canal.

Collagen fiber matrix

Cells in lacuna

FIGURE 8-10 Fibrocartilage.

Elastin fibers

FIGURE 8-11 Elastic cartilage.

☐ **9 Cancellous bone and hematopoietic tissue**—Cancellou bone is easily identified by its open, lattice-like structure Thin plates of bone matrix, with a scattering of osteocyte trapped within lacunae, form structural beams that have great strength despite the open spaces. These beams of hard bone are called **trabeculae**. Because cancellous bone ha open spaces, it is sometimes called *spongy bone*. This name can be misleading because one might think spongy bone is as soft as a bath sponge. It is not soft at all because it has hard trabeculae. The spaces are filled with *hematopoietic* or *myeloid tissue*, a special type of blood tissue that produces new blood cells **(Figure 8-13)**. Hematopoietic tissue is also called *red bone marrow*.

📌 landmark characteristics

Cancellous bone is distinguished by its rather disorganized array of trabecular beams of bone surrounded by myeloid tissue. The bone pieces may look like slivers of compact bone, with lamellae that often do not form complete circles. The myeloid tissue is a scattering of blood cells, which appear as tiny, dark circles. Myeloid (hematopoietic) tissue may also have a netlike formation of very thin collagen fibers called *reticular fibers*. In some preparations, the bone tissue is pink and the myeloid cells are dark red (see Figure 8-13). ●

☐ **10 Blood**—Blood tissue is a fluid matrix connective tissue characterized by a variety of cell types **(Figure 8-14)**. Tiny **red blood cells (RBCs)**, tinier fragments called **platelets**, and larger **white blood cells (WBCs)** may all be seen in a blood smear preparation. Of course, blood is found within the circulation vessels and has many functions. Blood transports and exchanges materials, serves in immune protection of the body, and helps regulate body temperature, among other functions. We will study blood in more detail in Lab Exercise 34.

📌 landmark characteristics

A prepared blood smear is a drop of blood smeared on a slide and stained. The RBCs are the more numerous, smaller cells stained pink to orange-red. RBCs have no nuclei. The WBCs are much larger, with distinct, often distorted nuclei. Lab Exercise 34 has more complete details (see Figure 8-14). ●

C. GROSS TISSUE SAMPLES

Gross (large) examples of connective tissues often give one a more complete mental image of connective tissue types. If gross specimens are available, explore the texture, consistency, and other physical characteristics of the connective tissue listed.

❗ safety first

Any animal tissue at room temperature can harbor growing colonies of microorganisms. As a safety precaution, treat the samples as if they are contaminated with harmful microbes. Use gloves or dissection tools when handling the samples and disinfect any surfaces that they touch. ●

FIGURE 8-12 Compact bone.

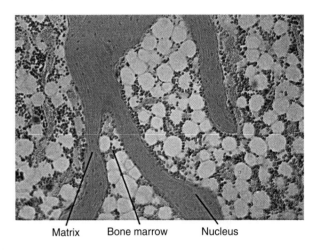

FIGURE 8-13 Cancellous bone and hematopoietic tissue.

FIGURE 8-14 Blood tissue.

Fill in **Table 8-2** with the physical characteristics of different types of tissue **(Figure 8-15)**.

TABLE 8-2   **Tissue Characteristics**

TYPE	PHYSICAL CHARACTERISTICS
Dense fibrous (regular)	
Dense fibrous (irregular)	
Loose fibrous (areolar)	
Adipose	
Hyaline cartilage	
Fibrocartilage	
Elastic cartilage	
Compact bone	
Cancellous bone	

Coloring Exercises: Connective Tissues

Use colored pens or pencils to shade in both the figure and the labels. Each red numeral in the figure corresponds to a matching red numeral following the appropriate label.

LOOSE, ORDINARY
  (AREOLAR)1
RETICULAR3
HYALINE CARTILAGE5
ELASTIC CARTILAGE7

ADIPOSE2
DENSE FIBROUS
  (REGULAR)4
FIBROCARTILAGE6
COMPACT BONE8

FIGURE 8-15 Types of connective tissues.

Name: _____   Date: _____   Section: _____

Connective Tissue

Specimen: *dense fibrous (regular) connective tissue*
Total Magnification: _____

Specimen: *dense fibrous (irregular) connective tissue*
Total Magnification: _____

Specimen: *loose fibrous (areolar) tissue*
Total Magnification: _____

Specimen: *adipose tissue*
Total Magnification: _____

Specimen: *reticular tissue*
Total Magnification: _____

Specimen: *hyaline cartilage*
Total Magnification: _____

Specimen: *fibrocartilage*
Total Magnification: _____

Specimen: *elastic cartilage*
Total Magnification: _____

Specimen: *compact bone*
Total Magnification: _____

Specimen: *cancellous bone*
Total Magnification: _____

Specimen: *blood smear*
Total Magnification: _____

Name: _____ Date: _____ Section: _____

Figure 8-2 (from p. 71)

1. _____
2. _____
3. _____
4. _____
5. _____

Figure 8-3 (from p. 72)

1. _____
2. _____
3. _____
4. _____
5. _____
6. _____

Matching

1. _____
2. _____
3. _____
4. _____
5. _____
6. _____
7. _____
8. _____
9. _____
10. _____

Matching (may be used more than once)

 a. dense fibrous connective tissue
 b. adipose
 c. hyaline cartilage
 d. fibrocartilage
 e. elastic cartilage
 f. compact bone
 g. cancellous bone

1. Cartilage type with a great deal of collagen in the matrix
2. Tissue type that is actually modified areolar tissue
3. Tissue type that stores lipid molecules
4. Tissue type composed of haversian systems
5. The most common type of cartilage
6. Strong tissue that forms tendons and ligaments
7. Tissue type associated with red bone marrow
8. Tissue type found in the external ear
9. Connective tissue that forms the disks between vertebrae
10. Tissue type that forms hard mineral trabeculae

9
Muscle and Nerve Tissue

Our exploration of the four basic human tissue types concludes with this study of muscle and nerve tissue. Detailed study of these tissue types is more appropriate for a later part of this course, but it is essential to achieve a basic understanding of these tissues now.

BEFORE YOU BEGIN

- ☐ Read the appropriate chapter in your textbook.
- ☐ Set your learning goals. When you finish this exercise, you should be able to:
  - ☐ distinguish the three basic types of muscle tissue
  - ☐ identify the primary components of nerve tissue
  - ☐ recognize muscle and nerve tissue types in figures and specimens
- ☐ Prepare your materials:
  - ☐ microscope
  - ☐ prepared microslides:
    - ☐ skeletal muscle l.s.
    - ☐ cardiac muscle l.s.
    - ☐ smooth muscle l.s.
    - ☐ spinal cord smear
- ☐ Read the directions and safety tips for this exercise *carefully* before starting any procedure.

A. MUSCLE TISSUE

All three muscle tissue types contain cells with the ability to contract. Contraction in muscle tissue allows a muscle organ to pull with great force. Such pulling can move the skeleton or squeeze the contents of a hollow organ. In addition to this common function, all muscle tissues are composed of long, cylindrical cells called **muscle fibers**. Muscle fibers are living cells, unlike connective tissue fibers, which are nonliving protein fibers. Locations and functions of the major types of muscle tissue (as well as nervous tissue) are summarized in **Table 9-1**.

safety first
Observe the usual precautions when using the microscope and slides. •

☐ **1 Skeletal muscle** gets its name because it forms muscular organs that attach to the skeleton and move its parts. This tissue is also called *striated muscle and voluntary muscle* because it has striations (stripes) and is primarily controlled by the conscious mind and the voluntary motor nerves. Skeletal muscle cells are large, fiberlike cells with fine cross stripes and many nuclei per cell **(Figure 9-1)**. Skeletal muscle fibers and bundles of muscle fibers often have a coating of fibrous connective tissue.

landmark characteristics
Skeletal muscle preparations include very large cells with the characteristic striped pattern. The striping is very fine, so good focusing technique is critical with this specimen. The muscle fibers are generally parallel to one another in a longitudinal section, with the stripes at right angles across each fiber. Unlike the other types of muscle, skeletal muscle fibers have many nuclei per cell. The nuclei are often up against the cell membrane. Some fibrous connective tissue may be seen between the muscle cells (see Figure 9-1). •

Skeletal muscle   Nucleus   Striations
fiber

FIGURE 9-1 Skeletal muscle.

T A B L E   9 - 1   **Examples of Major Muscle and Nerve Tissues**

TISSUE	LOCATION	FUNCTION
Muscle		
Skeletal (striated voluntary)	Muscles that attach to bones	Movement of bones
	Extrinsic eyeball muscles	Eye movements
	Upper third of esophagus	First part of swallowing
Smooth (nonstriated, involuntary, or visceral)	In walls of tubular viscera of digestive, respiratory, and genitourinary tracts	Movement of substances along respective tracts
	In walls of blood vessels and large lymphatic vessels	Change diameter of blood vessels, thereby aiding in regulation of blood pressure
	In ducts of glands	Movement of substances along ducts
	Intrinsic eye muscles (iris and ciliary body)	Change diameter of pupils and shape of lens
	Arrector muscles of hairs	Erection of hairs (goose pimples)
Cardiac (striated involuntary)	Wall of heart	Contraction of heart
Nervous	Brain	Excitability
	Spinal cord	Conduction
	Nerves	

☐ 2 **Cardiac muscle** is also known as *striated involuntary muscle.* This tissue also has striations, though less distinct than in skeletal muscle **(Figure 9-2)**. Cardiac muscle is involuntary in the sense that its contraction is not under the control of the voluntary motor nerves. Cardiac muscle is found only in the walls of the heart. Because it must encircle and compress the heart chambers with great strength to pump blood, cardiac muscle requires some features not found in other muscle types. For example, the individual fibers are branched, allowing the fibers to mesh with other cells at different layers. Also, cardiac muscle fibers are fused end-to-end by **intercalated disks**. This branching and fusing gives a group of cells the ability to functionally imitate a giant cell encircling one or more chambers of the heart.

Nucleus

Intercalated disks

FIGURE 9-2 Cardiac muscle.

landmark characteristics

Cardiac muscle striations are less distinct than those in skeletal muscle. Cardiac fibers have single nuclei, usually have branches, and do not taper at their ends. Many fibers attach end-to-end via intercalated disks, which appear as fine, dark (sometimes purple) lines at a right angle to a seemingly continuous fiber (see Figure 9-2). •

☐ 3 **Smooth muscle** gets its name because it has no distinct striations. Like cardiac muscle, it also is an involuntary muscle type. Smooth muscle is found in the walls of hollow organs, such as digestive organs and blood vessels. This tissue type is composed of long, threadlike cells, each with a single nucleus. The cells are generally parallel with one another and with the edge of the wall in which they are embedded **(Figure 9-3)**.

Smooth muscle cell

Nuclei

FIGURE 9-3 Smooth muscle.

landmark characteristics

Unlike other muscle cells, smooth muscle fibers are unstriated and have single nuclei. In some preparations the cells are pink and the nuclei purple or black. At first glance, you may confuse smooth muscle tissue with dense fibrous (regular) connective tissue. Smooth muscle is not wavy, like dense fibrous tissue sometimes is, and has a more even distribution of nuclei than dense fibrous tissue (see Figure 9-3). •

B. NERVE TISSUE

Nerve tissue composes organs of the nervous system: the brain, spinal cord, and nerves. Two basic types of cells are found in this tissue: **neurons** (impulse-conducting cells) and **glia** (support cells). Neurons are large cells with nucleated *bodies* and projections called *axons* and *dendrites* **(Figure 9-4)**. There are many types of glia, or *neuroglia*, as they are sometimes called, but they are generally smaller than neurons, which they outnumber by several times. Glia surround and support neurons physically or biochemically.

FIGURE 9-4 Nerve tissue.

landmark characteristics

In a smear of spinal cord tissue, the neurons and glia are scattered randomly on the slide. The neurons are extremely large, each with a body having a single nucleus. Neuron projections crisscross throughout. Glia appear as tiny, dark dots (see Figure 9-4). •

Study TIPS

Refer to the Landmark Characteristic boxes and familiarize yourself with the unique characteristics that define each type of muscle tissue. The use of flash cards or review cards is an excellent strategy to learn the various types of muscle and nerve tissue. Obtain photos or illustrations of the different types of muscle and nerve tissue. Place the photo or illustration on one side of an index card. On the opposite side of the card, put the name of the tissue. You can also add additional information such as unique characteristics or location in the body.

Coloring Exercises: **Muscle and Nerve Tissues**

Use colored pens or pencils to shade in both the figure and the labels. Each red numeral in the figure corresponds to a matching red numeral following the appropriate label.

SKELETAL MUSCLE₁
SMOOTH MUSCLE₂

CARDIAC MUSCLE₃
NERVE TISSUE₄

FIGURE 9-5 Muscle and nerve tissue drawings.

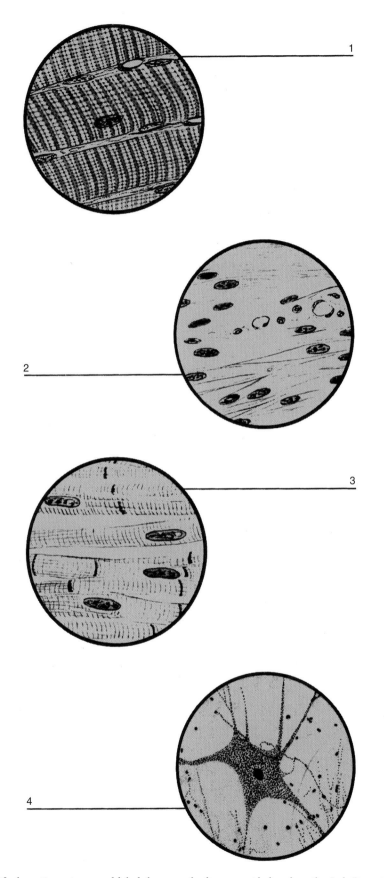

FIGURE 9-6 Try to identify these tissue types and label them on the lines provided and on the Lab Report at the end of this exercise.

Name: _____   Date: _____   Section: _____

LAB REPORT 9
Muscle and Nerve Tissue

Specimen: *skeletal muscle*
Total Magnification: _____

Specimen: *cardiac muscle*
Total Magnification: _____

Specimen: *smooth muscle*
Total Magnification: _____

Specimen: *spinal cord smear*
Total Magnification: _____

Figure 9-6 (from p. 89)

1. _____

2. _____

3. _____

4. _____

Multiple Choice

1. _____

2. _____

3. _____

4. _____

5. _____

6. _____

7. _____

8. _____

Multiple Choice (only one response is correct)

1. A voluntary type of muscle tissue is
   a. skeletal
   b. cardiac
   c. smooth
   d. a and b are correct
   e. a and c are correct
2. An involuntary muscle tissue is
   a. skeletal
   b. cardiac
   c. smooth
   d. b and c are correct
   e. a and c are correct
3. Which of these muscle tissues is striated?
   a. skeletal
   b. cardiac
   c. smooth
   d. a and b are correct
   e. all are correct
4. Which of these is most likely to be found in the wall of the urinary tract?
   a. skeletal
   b. cardiac
   c. smooth
5. Cardiac muscle fibers are connected end-to-end by means of
   a. Velcro
   b. intercalated disks
   c. striations
   d. branching
6. Which of these cells is likely to have multiple nuclei?
   a. skeletal muscle
   b. cardiac muscle
   c. smooth muscle
   d. neuron
   e. a and c are correct
   f. a, c, and d are correct
7. Nerve tissue contains cells called
   a. fibers
   b. neurons
   c. glia
   d. striated cells
   e. b and c are correct
8. Nerve tissue forms the bulk of the
   a. brain
   b. heart
   c. digestive tract
   d. vertebrae
   e. a and d are correct

LAB EXERCISE 10

The Skin

The **skin** is the primary organ of the integumentary system and is the largest organ of the body. Forming the outer protective covering of the body, the skin is a continuous sheet of **cutaneous membrane**.

BEFORE YOU BEGIN

☐ Read the appropriate chapter in your textbook.
☐ Set your learning goals. When you finish this exercise, you should be able to:
   ☐ describe the major structures of the skin and identify their functions
   ☐ identify important skin structures in a diagram, model, and prepared specimen
   ☐ compare and contrast features of thick skin and thin skin
   ☐ describe the gross structure of skin in a preserved mammalian specimen
☐ Prepare your materials:
   ☐ model or chart of a skin cross section
   ☐ microscope
   ☐ prepared microslides:
      ☐ thin skin section
      ☐ thick skin section
      ☐ hair follicles c.s.
   ☐ preserved specimen: cat or fetal pig (unskinned)
   ☐ dissection tools and trays
   ☐ storage container (if specimen is to be reused)
☐ Read the directions and safety tips for this exercise carefully before starting any procedure.

Study TIPS

Review the major tissues types of the body. The skin is an organ, and all four major tissues types are represented. Refer to Labs 7 to 9 and construct a table or chart that defines the role of each tissue type within the skin. To understand the relationship of the accessory organs (hair, nails, and glands), you may want to develop a concept map that illustrates the relationship of these structures and the function of the skin.

safety first
Don't forget the rules for safe use of the microscope. •

A. BASIC SKIN STRUCTURE

First in a model and then in prepared microscopic specimens, identify the elements of skin structure described in the following steps:

☐ 1 The skin has two distinct layers. The superficial layer is a sheet of keratinized stratified squamous epithelium called the **epidermis**. The epidermis is itself divided into distinct histological regions or **strata** (meaning "layers"):
   ☐ **Stratum basale** is the deepest stratum of the epidermis. It consists of a single sheet of columnar cells that continue to divide. As the daughter cells are formed, they are pushed upward, becoming part of the next stratum.
   ☐ **Stratum spinosum** is noted for its multilayer of distorted ("spined") cells. The cells become distorted as they are pushed up from the deeper stratum basale. Stratum basale and stratum spinosum together are often called stratum germinativum.
   ☐ **Stratum granulosum** is superficial to stratum spinosum. It contains flattened cells pushed up from the deeper strata. As the cells are pushed up through this stratum, they form the protein granules that give it the name granulosum. By the time the cells leave this stratum, they have died.
   ☐ **Stratum lucidum** (meaning "light layer") is a very thin layer present only in **thick skin**. Thick skin is found only in high-wear areas such as the palms and soles. The more flexible **thin skin** is found over most other areas of the body. This stratum's name comes about because it is translucent, allowing light to pass through it easily.
   ☐ **Stratum corneum** is the layer of dead, keratinized tissue already identified in Lab Exercise 7. Stratum corneum is extremely thick in thick skin, providing a great deal of protection. Stratum corneum protects deeper tissues from mechanical injury, from inward or outward diffusion of water and other molecules, and from invasion by microorganisms.
☐ 2 The layer of skin deep to the epidermis is a sheet of irregular fibrous connective tissue called the **dermis**. The dermis is usually much thicker than the epidermis. Like most connective tissues, the dermis has a scattering of blood vessels and nerves. The blood vessels supply both the dermis and epidermis. Because blood cools when it travels through the skin, the body varies the amount of blood sent to the skin to regulate loss of heat by the entire body. The dermis

contains many sensory nerve endings. Sensations such as heat, cold, touch, and pressure are mediated by dermal nerve endings. There are two regions of the dermis:

☐ The **reticular layer** of the dermis is a thick region of irregularly arranged protein fibers. Most of the fibers are collagenous, but a few are made of elastin.

☐ The **papillary layer** is the bumpy superficial portion of the dermis attached to the epidermis. The bumps, called **papillae** (meaning "nipples"), form regular rows in thick skin but are rather irregularly arranged in thin skin. For this reason, thick skin can be observed to have distinct ridges, such as fingerprints. These ridges give the hands and feet better gripping ability.

☐ 3 Deep to the skin is a layer of **subcutaneous tissue**, sometimes called the **hypodermis** or **superficial fascia**. Although not a part of the skin, it is often studied along with skin. Subcutaneous tissue is loose, fibrous (areolar) connective tissue that connects the skin to underlying muscles and bone. Some of the areolar tissue has been modified to become adipose tissue. Adipose tissue's protective and insulating characteristics complement the protection and temperature regulation roles of the skin.

Study TIPS

To remember the layers of the epidermis from the innermost to outermost layer, use the following mnemonic: **B**ragging **S**ure **G**ains **L**ittle **C**ooperation.

| Hint | **Figure 10-1** shows light micrographs of skin structures. • |

B. HAIR, NAILS, AND GLANDS

The skin has a variety of accessory structures, including **hair** and **nails**. Both hair and nails are modified forms of stratum corneum, or keratinized tissue. A hair is a cylinder of compact keratinized material, and a nail is a plate of compact keratinized material. Identify the structures described in the following in a model and in prepared specimens.

☐ 1 Each hair is formed within a separate **hair follicle**. The follicle is a sheathlike indentation of the epidermis (see

Figure 10-1, *D*). At the bottom of the follicle, a **hair papilla** covered with stratum germinativum produces the hair. The portion of each hair within the follicle is called the **hair root**, whereas the portion that has been pushed out of the follicle is called the **hair shaft**. The hair has a very dense cortex and a less dense medulla.

☐ 2 Attached to each follicle is an exocrine (ducted) sebaceous gland (see Figure 10-1, *D*). This gland produces the fatty substance, **sebum**, that coats the hair and skin. Sebum prevents moisture loss and conditions the hair and skin so that they do not become brittle and easily broken.

☐ 3 The **arrector pili** muscle is a strap of smooth muscle tissue connecting the side of a follicle to the superficial surface of the dermis. When contracted, the muscle pulls the follicle so that it is nearly perpendicular to the skin's surface **(Figure 10-2)**. This increases the air spaces among the hairs, improving their insulation quality. Contraction of the arrector pili also dimples the epidermis, raising a ridge at the edge of the follicle (a "goose pimple" or "goose bump").

☐ 4 The toenail or fingernail is also formed by a modified portion of stratum germinativum. In the case of either hair or nail, this modified tissue is often called **matrix**. A portion of the **nail bed** (skin under the nail) is matrix that produces the nail plate. Part of the matrix may be visible through the nail as a pale crescent, or **lunula**. Nail formation begins under a fold of epidermis. The portion of the nail under the fold is the **root**, and the visible portion is the nail **body**. A **cuticle**, or **eponychium**, may extend from the fold onto the nail body **(Figure 10-3)**.

☐ 5 **Sweat glands** are found in many areas of the skin. They are exocrine glands that produce a watery solution, sweat, that coats the skin. Sweat serves primarily to improve heat loss by the skin through evaporation. Eccrine sweat glands produce thin, watery sweat in many areas of the body. Apocrine sweat glands, found in the axillary and pubic regions, secrete a thicker sweat that is rich in complex organic molecules.

> ❗ *safety first*
> Observe the usual precautions for dissection activities. Use gloves and take care to avoid injuries. Use safety goggles to avoid injury during dissections. •

Epidermis   Dermis

Hypodermis   Hair follicle   Sebaceous gland

Epidermis

Keratinized stratified squamous epithelial cells (stratum corneum)

Dermis   Germinal layers of epithelial cells

Epidermis   Dermis

Duct of sweat gland   Stratum corneum

Dermis   Papillae of dermis   Epidermis

Duct of sweat gland   Sweat gland (coiled tube)

FIGURE 10-1 Light micrographs of skin structures. **A** and **B**, Thin skin. **C**, Thick skin. **D**, Skin with hair follicles and other accessory structures. **E**, Skin with sweat glands.

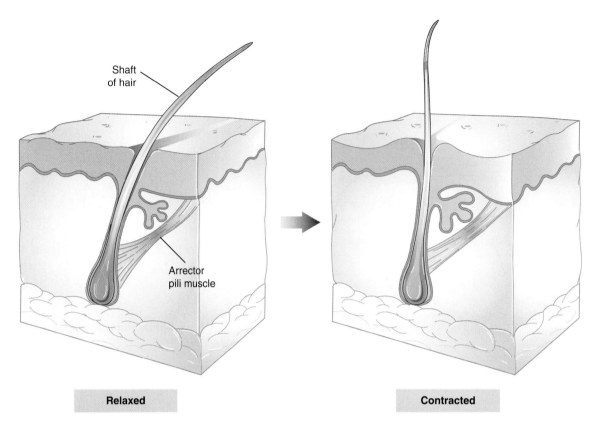

Relaxed

Contracted

FIGURE 10-2 When the arrector pili contracts, it pulls the follicle and hair into a perpendicular position, improving the insulation quality of the hair. Notice how a "goose pimple" is raised around the follicle opening.

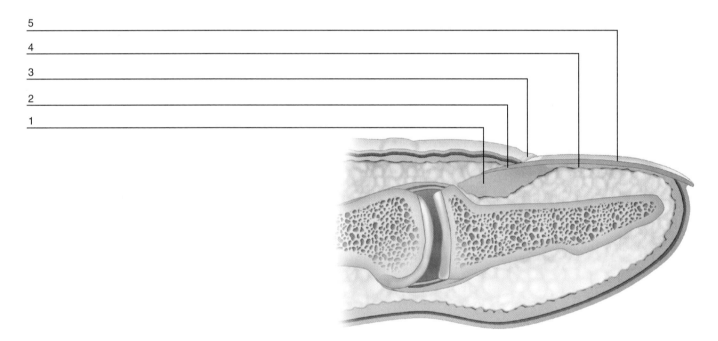

FIGURE 10-3 Label this section of a finger with the appropriate terms on the lines provided and on the blanks in the Lab Report at the end of this exercise.

Coloring Exercises: Skin and Hair

Use colored pens or pencils to shade in both the figure and the labels. Each red numeral in the figure corresponds to a matching red numeral following the appropriate label.

Skin

Epidermis

STRATUM CORNEUM₁
STRATUM LUCIDUM₂
STRATUM GRANULOSUM₃
STRATUM SPINOSUM₄
STRATUM BASALE₅

Dermis

PAPILLARY LAYER₆
RETICULAR LAYER₇
SWEAT GLAND₈
BLOOD VESSEL₉
NERVE₁₀

Hair

ROOT₁₁
SHAFT₁₂
FOLLICLE₁₃
PAPILLA₁₄
MATRIX₁₅
ARRECTOR PILI₁₆
SEBACEOUS GLAND₁₇
HYPODERMIS₁₈

FIGURE 10-4 Structures of the skin. **A,** Thin skin. **B,** Thick skin.

C. DISSECTION: CAT INTEGUMENT

If you are going to use the cat as a dissection specimen throughout this course, it must first be skinned. This exercise not only directs you on how to perform this essential step, but it also provides an excellent opportunity to practice identifying surface anatomy—as well as to see "the big picture" of the integumentary system **(Figure 10-4)**.

☐　1　Examine the external aspect of your specimen **(Figure 10-5)**:
　　☐　Determine the anatomical orientation of the specimen. Which direction is anterior? posterior? Which direction is ventral? dorsal? Identify sagittal, transverse, and frontal planes in your specimen.
　　☐　Identify these externally visible features:
　　　　☐　Pinna (auricle, or external ear)
　　　　☐　External nares (nostrils)
　　　　☐　Vibrissae (whiskers)
　　　　☐　Integument (skin)
　　　　☐　Forelimbs
　　　　☐　Hindlimbs
　　　　☐　Thoracic region
　　　　☐　Abdominal region
　　　　☐　Genitals (sex organs)
　　　　☐　Anus
　　　　☐　Tail
　　☐　Determine the sex of your specimen by examining the external genitals **(Figure 10-6)**:
　　　　☐　**Female**—Immediately anterior to the anus, on the ventral surface, is the **vulva** with an opening to the **vagina** and the **urethra**. The vulva is also called the urogenital opening.
　　　　☐　**Male**—In the male, there is a pouch of skin immediately ventral to the anus. This pouch—the **scrotum**—contains the **testes**, or male primary sex organs. Anterior to the scrotum is the end of the **penis** with its **prepuce**, or skinfold covering. Locate the opening of the **urethra** in the penis.

☐　2　Place the animal in the tray with its ventral surface facing you. Insert the tip of a scissors into the hole already present under the chin. This hole was used to inject the cat's vessels with latex. If you are using a cat that was not injected, then lift up a fold of skin and puncture it at the same site. Slide the bottom tip of the scissors into the **subcutaneous** area under the skin.

☐　3　Begin cutting along the lines indicated in Figure 10-5. Notice that you must cut all the way around the neck and the distal ends of each limb (just proximal to the feet, or paws). All the other cuts are to be made only on the ventral aspect of the cat. When you make the median cut along the posterior abdomen, toward the tail, cut around the genitals rather than through them. Be careful not to cut into the skeletal muscles under the skin.

☐　4　With your forceps, pull the flaps of skin over the neck away from the cat's body. Notice the **areolar tissue** under the skin that is pulled apart as you remove the skin. Sometimes it helps if you scrape at the loose connective tissue under the skin with your scalpel as you peel the skin away. The skinning process is not difficult if you have patience and proceed slowly. Peel the other flaps of skin in a similar fashion until the cat is completely skinned.

☐　5　Examine the skin, identifying these features:
　　☐　**Dermis**—The thick inner layer of the skin
　　☐　**Epidermis**—The thinner outer layer of the skin
　　☐　**Hypodermis**—The subcutaneous tissue under the skin proper, made of areolar and adipose tissue

☐　6　Wrap the skin around the cat again and place the entire animal in its storage bag or other container provided.

> **Hint** ▶ After each dissection activity later in this course, always wrap the skin around your specimen before storing it. This will help prevent your specimen from drying out—a common problem with preserved specimens. ●

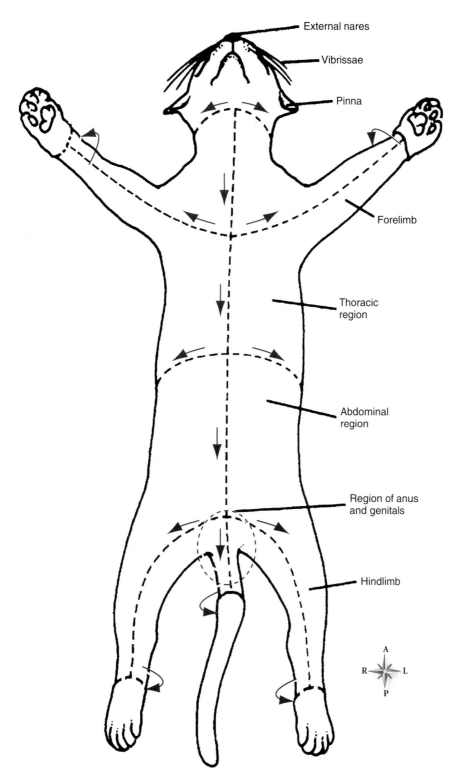

External nares

Vibrissae

Pinna

Forelimb

Thoracic region

Abdominal region

Region of anus and genitals

Hindlimb

A
R — L
P

FIGURE 10-5 Cat. External aspect, showing how skin is to be cut for removal.

D. DISSECTION: FETAL PIG INTEGUMENT

In this (and all succeeding) whole-animal dissection activities, the instructions for both cat and fetal pig specimens will be given. Both specimens are popular in anatomy and physiology courses.

☐ 1 Examine the external aspect of your specimen:
  ☐ Determine the anatomical orientation of the specimen. Which direction is anterior? posterior? Which direction is ventral? dorsal? Identify sagittal, transverse, and frontal planes in your specimen.
  ☐ Identify these externally visible features:
    ☐ Pinna (auricle, or external ear)
    ☐ External nares (nostrils)
    ☐ Integument (skin)
    ☐ Umbilicus (umbilical cord)
    ☐ Forelimbs
    ☐ Hindlimbs
    ☐ Thoracic region
    ☐ Abdominal region
    ☐ Nipples
    ☐ Anus
    ☐ Tail
  ☐ Determine the sex of your specimen by examining the external genitals:
    ☐ **Female**—Immediately anterior to the anus, on the ventral surface, is the **vulva** with an opening to the **vagina** and the **urethra**. The vulva is also called the urogenital opening.
    ☐ **Male**—In the male fetal pig, there is a rather loose area of skin immediately anterior to the anus, perhaps even hiding the anus from view. Around the time of birth, each **testis** will descend from its position inside the body into the space under this skin. The skin will

pouch out to form the outer wall of the **scrotum**. Just posterior to the umbilical cord is the distal end of the **penis** with its **prepuce**, or skinfold covering. Locate the opening of the **urethra** in the penis.

☐ 2 Place the animal in the tray with its ventral surface facing you. Pull up on the skin over the neck and puncture it with the tip of a scissors. Slide the bottom tip of the scissors into the **subcutaneous** area under the skin.

☐ 3 Begin cutting along the lines indicated in Figure 10-6. Notice that the posterior cuts are different for male and female specimens. Be careful not to cut into the skeletal muscles under the skin or through the base of the umbilical cord.

☐ 4 With your forceps, pull the two flaps of skin over the neck away from the animal's body. Notice the areolar tissue under the skin that is pulled apart as you remove the skin. Sometimes it helps if you scrape at the loose connective tissue under the skin with your scalpel as you peel the skin away. The skinning process is not difficult if you have patience and proceed slowly. Pull the flaps of skin over the abdomen and over the groin area away in a similar fashion. If you have a male pig, leave the skin posterior to the umbilical cord in place for now. Cut the skin away from the body entirely.

☐ 5 Examine the skin, identifying these features:
  ☐ **Dermis**—Thick inner layer of the skin
  ☐ **Epidermis**—Thinner outer layer of the skin
  ☐ **Hypodermis**—Subcutaneous tissue under the skin proper, made of areolar and adipose tissue

Hint After each dissection activity later in this course, always wrap the skin around your specimen before storing it. This will help prevent your specimen from drying out—a common problem with preserved specimens. •

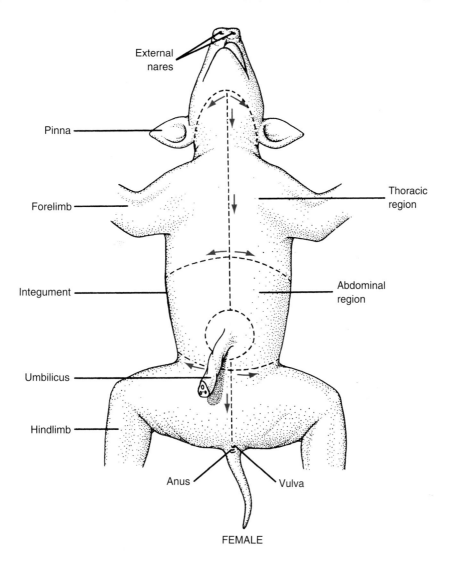

External
nares

Pinna

Forelimb

Thoracic
region

Integument

Abdominal
region

Umbilicus

Hindlimb

Anus

Vulva

FEMALE

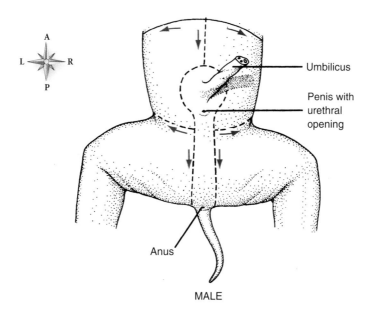

A

L — R

P

Umbilicus

Penis with
urethral
opening

Anus

MALE

FIGURE 10-6 Fetal pig. External aspect of the female (top) and male (bottom).

Name: _____ Date: _____ Section: _____

LAB REPORT 10
The Skin

Specimen: *thin skin section*
Total Magnification: _____

Specimen: *thick skin section*
Total Magnification: _____

Specimen: *hair follicles c.s.*
Total Magnification: _____

Specimen: _____
Total Magnification: _____

Figure 10-3 (from p. 96)

1. _____
2. _____
3. _____
4. _____
5. _____

Fill-in

1. _____
2. _____
3. _____
4. _____
5. _____
6. _____
7. _____
8. _____
9. _____
10. _____
11. _____
12. _____
13. _____
14. _____
15. _____
16. _____
17. _____
18. _____
19. _____
20. _____

Fill-in (complete each item with the correct term)

1. The _?_ is the superficial layer (of two) in the skin.

2. The hypodermis is mainly areolar and _?_ tissue.

3. Fingerprint ridges are formed as a result of the orderly arrangement of dermal _?_.

4. Stratum corneum is composed of dead cell parts and a tough, waterproof protein called _?_.

5. Stratum _?_ is the epidermal stratum in which one could find many phases of mitosis.

6. Cells are pushed into stratum _?_ from stratum basale.

7. When you sense cold air around you, nerve endings in the _?_ are probably involved.

8. When you sense cold air around you, bumps may appear on the skin. This is caused by the contraction of the _?_.

9. The subcutaneous tissue is also called the superficial fascia, or _?_.

10. Physiologists believe that some sweat glands produce aromatic, organic molecules called pheromones. The type of sweat gland (of the two discussed in this exercise) most likely to produce pheromones is _?_.

11. Strong shampoo tends to remove _?_ from the hair and scalp, making it dry and easily damaged.

12. The eponychium, or _?_, covers part of the nail plate.

13. When you have your hair cut, the portion of the hair trimmed is called the _?_.

14. Blood vessels that supply the epidermis are found in the _?_ region of the dermis.

15. Stratum basale and stratum spinosum together may be called stratum _?_.

16. Keratinized _?_ epithelium forms the epidermis.

17. The dermis is composed mainly of _?_ fibers, with a few elastic fibers.

18. Stratum _?_ is usually absent in thin skin.

19. _?_ glands produce sebum.

20. The most widely distributed type of sweat gland is the _?_ type of gland.

Name: _____ Date: _____ Section: _____

Fill in the blank spaces in **Table 10-1**.

TABLE 10-1   **Characteristics of the Skin Layers**

CHARACTERISTIC	EPIDERMIS	DERMIS
Tissue type		
Presence of blood vessels		
Relative thickness		
Permeability (to water)		
Relative strength		

Short Answer (write a few complete sentences)

How does thin skin differ from thick skin?

Overview of the Skeleton

This exercise is the first of several concerning the *skeletal system.* The skeletal system's major organs are the **bones** and **ligaments.** Ligaments are simply cords of regular dense fibrous tissue that bind the bones to one another. Bones are more complex in their structure, so we will spend some time investigating the nature of a typical bone. Before we move on to a detailed study of all the bones of the skeleton, we will survey the basic plan of the skeleton.

Investigation of the gross and microscopic structure of the typical bone and of the basic skeletal plan will be good preparation for the exercises that follow.

BEFORE YOU BEGIN

- ☐ Read the appropriate chapter in your textbook.
- ☐ Set your learning goals. When you finish this exercise, you should be able to:
  - ☐ describe the organs of the skeletal system
  - ☐ describe the gross and microscopic structure of bone tissue
  - ☐ list the primary functions of the skeletal system
  - ☐ outline the organization of the skeletal system
- ☐ Prepare your materials:
  - ☐ microscope
  - ☐ prepared microslides:
    - ☐ compact bone (ground bone) c.s.
    - ☐ cancellous bone
    - ☐ epiphyseal plate c.s.
  - ☐ human skeleton (disarticulated)
  - ☐ human skeleton (articulated)
  - ☐ long bone (fresh, whole)
  - ☐ whole long bone (fresh, l.s.)
- ☐ Read the directions and safety tips for this exercise carefully before starting any procedure.

> **Hint** The concepts of this exercise will be easier to understand if you briefly review the microscopic organization of bone tissue presented in Exercise 8. •

A. BONE TYPES

The 206 bones in the standard human skeleton can be classified by their shapes. The best way to learn this classification scheme is by trying to classify the bones yourself, as outlined in the following steps:

- ☐ 1 Unpack the bones of a disarticulated (taken apart) human skeleton, and spread the bones over your workplace.

- ☐ 2 Divide the group of bones into four piles according to the categories given here. Do not use books or other aids to help you.
  - ☐ **Long bones** are cylindrical bones that are longer than they are wide.
  - ☐ **Short bones** are as long as they are wide, sometimes having an almost cuboidal shape.
  - ☐ **Flat bones** arise when bone tissue invades and hardens fibrous membranes, so they are sheetlike in shape. They are usually curved rather than absolutely flat.
  - ☐ **Irregular bones** don't quite fit any of the other categories because of the complexity of their shapes.
- ☐ 3 Compare your results to the results of others in your lab section. Does everyone agree?

B. GROSS STRUCTURE OF A BONE

All bones have the same general structural pattern. Some bones have more "optional features" than other bones. The long bone is often used as a general specimen for study because it has all the features that any bone can have **(Figure 11-1)**.

> **!** **safety first**
> Because fresh animal tissues at room temperature can harbor dangerous bacterial colonies, specimens should only be handled when wearing disposable, nonporous gloves. •

- ☐ 1 Obtain fresh long bone specimens from a large animal. One should be whole (uncut), and the other cut along its long axis (l.s.).
- ☐ 2 Examine the external aspect of a whole bone. Find the features described.
  - ☐ **Ligament**—Although actually a separate organ, some bits of these fibrous straps that hold bones together may still be attached to your specimen.
  - ☐ **Periosteum**—The periosteum is a sheet of irregular, dense fibrous connective tissue continuous with the ligaments. It covers the shaft and part of the heads of a long bone. Try to scrape some of the periosteum away from the underlying bone. How strongly is it attached?
  - ☐ **Articular cartilage**—The articular cartilage is a smooth cap of hyaline cartilage found where the bone *articulates* (forms a joint) with another bone. Joints, or connections between bones, are often movable. Which function of

the skeletal system benefits by the presence of movable joints?

- ☐ **Diaphysis**—The diaphysis is the whole central shaft of the long bone. Only the external part of the shaft, made of solid bone tissue, is visible from the external aspect. For what skeletal functions is the hard shell of the diaphysis specialized?

- ☐ **Epiphysis**—The epiphyses are the "heads" of a long bone, one proximal to the diaphysis and one distal. Only the external portions are visible in a whole specimen.

☐ **3** Use the sectioned bone specimen to identify the structures listed.

- ☐ **Medullary cavity**—The medullary cavity, as its name implies, is a space within the center of the diaphysis. The walls surrounding the space are made of both cancellous and compact bone. In the adult, the cavity generally contains *yellow bone marrow*, which is a mass of fatty tissue. What is the purpose of yellow marrow?

- ☐ **Endosteum**—The endosteum is a thin epithelial membrane that lines the medullary cavity.

- ☐ **Cancellous bone**—The epiphyses, like diaphyses, have a compact bone cortex, but the medulla is often different. The inside of each epiphysis has cancellous, or spongy, bone. The soft tissue in the spaces of the cancellous bone is often *red bone marrow*, which produces blood cells.

C. MICROSCOPIC STRUCTURE OF A BONE

The microscopic structure of the long bone reflects the general nature of any type of bone **(Figure 11-2)**. As you learned in Exercise 8, there are two basic types of bone tissue within a bone organ: **compact bone** and **cancellous bone**. In this exercise, you will build on what you learned about these bone tissue types. Then you will be able to integrate this information with what you already know about the gross structure of bone so that you can see "the big picture" of bone structure and function.

☐ **1** **Compact bone**—Compact bone is found mainly in the hard outer shell of a bone organ. Compact bone tissue is formed by solid cylindrical units called **osteons** packed tightly together. The osteon, or *haversian system*, consists of multiple concentric layers of hard bone matrix, with cells sandwiched between each layer. This bone matrix is made up of collagen fibers encrusted with crystals of a calcium-containing mineral called *apatite*. Each layer of bone matrix is a **lamella** (plural *lamellae*). **Osteocytes** are literally trapped within lacunae between the lamellae. The osteocytes were once active **osteoblasts** but have trapped themselves in the solid matrix they formed. Notice in **Figure 11-3** that the **periosteum** that surrounds each bone is made up of an inner layer that contains active osteoblasts and an outer layer of dense fibrous connective tissue. The lamellae

are centered around the **central (haversian) canal's** blood vessels. There are also transverse canals connecting the central canals of adjacent osteons. These transverse canals are called **transverse** or **Volkmann canals**. They are also sometimes called **perforating canals**. The osteocytes trapped within lacunae transport materials to and from the canal by way of tiny **canaliculi** ("small canals") that connect the osteocytes to one another and to the canal. Observe a prepared slide of ground bone (compact bone), and try to identify as many features as possible.

> ! **safety first**
> Avoid electrical hazards while using the microscope. Be sure to exercise care in dealing with broken glass slides. Do not reach for slides or other objects while you are looking into the ocular, or you may knock over something (or someone). •

> 📌 **landmark characteristics**
> A cross section of compact bone has rings of lamellae surrounding several adjacent haversian, or *central*, canals. The lamellae resemble rings in an onion slice. The central canals are either clear or nearly black, the lamellae are buff to orange, and the osteocytes are brown or black. The canaliculi often appear as wavy hairlines radiating from the lacunae (see Figure 11-3). •

☐ **2** **Cancellous bone and hematopoietic tissue**—*Cancellous bone* is found in the inner portions of a bone organ. Cancellous bone is easily identified by its open, latticelike structure. Thin plates of bone matrix, with a scattering of osteocytes trapped within lacunae, form structural beams that have great strength despite the open spaces. These branching beams of hard bone are called **trabeculae**. Because cancellous bone has open spaces, it is sometimes called **spongy bone**. This name can be misleading because one might think spongy bone is as soft as a bath sponge; it is not soft at all because it has hard trabeculae. The spaces are filled with *hematopoietic* or *myeloid tissue*, a special type of blood tissue that produces new blood cells. Hematopoietic tissue is also called *red bone marrow*.

> 📌 **landmark characteristics**
> Cancellous bone is distinguished by its rather disorganized array of trabecular beams of bone surrounded by myeloid tissue. The bone pieces may look like slivers of compact bone, with lamellae that often do not form complete circles. The myeloid tissue is a scattering of blood cells, which appear as tiny dark circles. Myeloid (hematopoietic) tissue may also have a netlike formation of very thin collagen fibers called *reticular fibers*. •

Coloring Exercises: Long Bone Structure

Use colored pens or pencils to shade in both the figure and the labels. Each red numeral in the figure corresponds to a matching red numeral following the appropriate label.

EPIPHYSIS₁
EPIPHYSEAL PLATE₂
DIAPHYSIS₃
PERIOSTEUM₄
ARTICULAR CARTILAGE₅
MEDULLARY CAVITY₆
ENDOSTEUM₇
CANCELLOUS BONE₈
COMPACT BONE₉
BLOOD VESSEL₁₀

FIGURE 11-1 Structures of the long bone.

Coloring Exercises: **Bone Tissue**

Use colored pens or pencils to shade in both the figure and the labels. Each red numeral in the figure corresponds to a matching red numeral following the appropriate label.

COMPACT BONE₁
SPONGY BONE₂
BLOOD VESSEL₃
CANALICULI₄
CENTRAL CANAL₅
LACUNA₆
LAMELLA₇
MYELOID TISSUE₈
OSTEOCYTE₉

OSTEON₁₀
PERIOSTEUM₁₁
TRABECULA₁₂
TRANSVERSE CANAL₁₃

FIGURE 11-2 Microscopic structure of bone.

- Osteon
- Lamella
- Central canal
- Lacunae

FIGURE 11-3 Compact bone (ground bone) in cross section. High power.

☐ 3 **Epiphyseal plate**—Until a long bone has stopped growing in length, a layer of cartilage called the **epiphyseal plate** remains between each epiphysis and the diaphysis **(Figure 11-4)**. During periods of growth, proliferation of epiphyseal cartilage cells brings about a thickening of this layer. **Ossification** (bone formation) of the additional cartilage nearest the diaphysis then follows; that is, osteoblasts make new bone matrix. As a result of this process, the bone becomes longer.

- Epiphyseal plate

A

- Stacks of chondrocytes
- Proliferating zone
- Zone of hypertrophy
- Calcified cartilage
- Ossification zone

B

FIGURE 11-4 Epiphyseal plate. **A,** Localization of the epiphyseal plate between the epiphyses and diaphyses of a long bone. **B,** Zones of the epiphyseal plate.

📌 *landmark characteristics*

The epiphyseal plate shown in Figure 11-4 is made up of four regions; each region, in turn, is made of several layers of cells. The layer closest to the epiphysis (top of figure) is not changing or growing, so the cells are said to be at rest. The *zone of proliferation*, which includes cells undergoing mitotic division, is where the plate becomes thicker. The *zone of hypertrophy* is where older, enlarged cells degenerate before calcification. In the *zone of calcification*, new cancellous bone can be seen. Typically, the epiphyseal plate is seen as a region of hyaline cartilage separated from a region of cancellous bone by a region of degenerating chondrocytes (cartilage cells) in lacunae that seem to be "stacked" in roughly parallel rows. •

A　　　　　　B

FIGURE 11-5 **A,** Sesamoid bone at the base of the thumb. **B,** Sutural (wormian) bones along a suture joint.

D. THE PLAN OF THE SKELETON

The usual number given for bones in the human skeleton is 206. This is by no means the absolute exact number, however. Most people have more bones, but each person has different types, locations, and numbers of "extra" bones **(Figure 11-5)**. Some people may be missing a bone or two. In this activity, you will examine both the standard 206 bones and the extra bones that may be present **(Table 11-1)**.

☐ 1 Obtain an articulated (connected) human skeleton.

☐ 2 The standard **axial skeleton** consists of 80 bones that form the central axis of the skeleton **(Figure 11-6)**. These 80 bones include 28 skull bones, 1 unattached bone in the

throat, 26 vertebrae, and 25 rib cage bones. Locate the bones of the axial skeleton in your specimen. Do not worry about learning the names of individual bones now. That will come later. For now, concentrate on "the big picture" of skeletal organization.

---

safety first

Be cautious when handling the articulated skeleton. The bones or mounting hardware may become loose and fall from the support frame, injuring you or your lab mates. •

TABLE 11-1   Bones of Skeleton (206 Total)*

PART OF BODY	NAME OF BONE	PART OF BODY	NAME OF BONE
Skull (28 Bones Total) Cranium (8 bones)	Frontal (1) Parietal (2) Temporal (2) Occipital (1) Sphenoid (1) Ethmoid (1)	**Upper Extremities** (including shoulder girdle) (64 bones total)	Clavicle (2) Scapula (2) Humerus (2) Radius (2) Ulna (2) Carpals (16) Metacarpals (10) Phalanges (28)
Face (14 bones)	Nasal (2) Maxillary (2) Zygomatic (malar) (2) Mandible (1) Lacrimal (2) Palatine (2) Inferior conchae (turbinates) (2) Vomer (1)	**Lower Extremities** (62 bones total)	Coxal bones (2) Femur (2) Patella (2) Tibia (2) Fibula (2) Tarsals (14) Metatarsals (10) Phalanges (28)
Ear bones (6 bones)	Malleus (hammer) (2) Incus (anvil) (2) Stapes (stirrup) (2)		
Hyoid Bone (1)			
Spinal Column (26 bones total)	Cervical vertebrae (7) Thoracic vertebrae (12) Lumbar vertebrae (5) Sacrum (1) Coccyx (1)		
Sternum and Ribs (25 bones total)	Sternum (1) True ribs (14) False ribs (10)		

*Excluding variable sesamoid and wormian bones.

Coloring Exercises: Overview of the Skeleton

Use colored pens or pencils to shade in both the figure and the labels. Each red numeral in the figure corresponds to a matching red numeral following the appropriate label.

AXIAL SKELETON₁
APPENDICULAR SKELETON₂

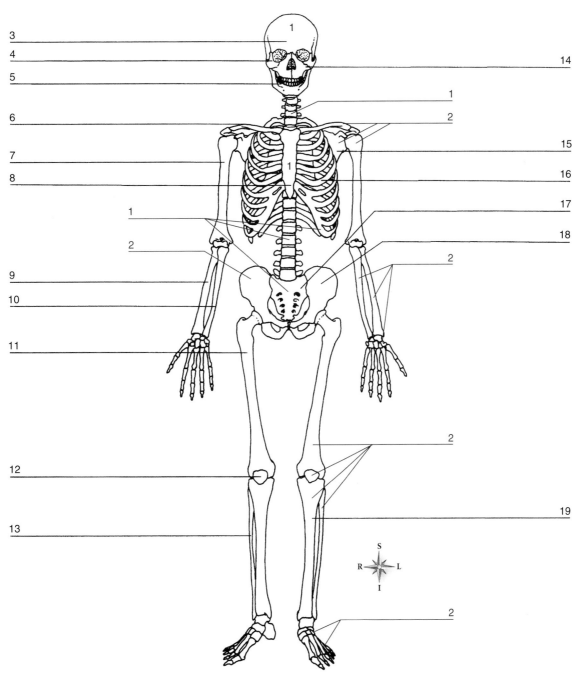

FIGURE 11-6 Bones of the human skeleton.

☐ **3** Locate the bones of the **appendicular skeleton** in your specimen. The appendicular skeleton, comprised of the 126 nonaxial bones, includes the bones of the appendages, or extremities (arms and legs). Sixty-four of these bones are in the *upper extremities* (shoulders and arms). Sixty-two bones are in the *lower extremities* (hips and legs).

☐ **4** Ask your lab instructor if there are any extra standard bones or any standard bones missing in your specimen. What difficulties could such differences have caused the individual during life?

☐ **5** Determine whether your specimen has any of the extra bone types typically found in skeletons (see Figure 11-5):

☐ **Sesamoid bones** are so called because they resemble sesame seeds: tiny rounded specks. Sesamoid bones are often found within tendons of the hand and foot.

☐ **Wormian bones,** also called *sutural bones,* are flat bones that form in the sutures (joints) between the cranial bones of the skull.

E. BONE MARKINGS AND FEATURES

As you have already observed on your specimen, bones do no generally have a smooth surface. There are many bumps, hole and projections on the bones of the human skeleton. These *bon markings* are named with terms that describe their shape and loca tion. As a preview to the next few exercises, review the terms use to name bone markings listed in **Table 11-2**.

Study TIPS

Bone markings may be difficult to identify. An effective strategy to identify the various bone markings would be to develop flash cards that have the bone marking on one side and a meaning or illustration/photo on the opposite side, or refer to *Mosby's Anatomy & Physiology Study and Review Cards*. Also, take advantage of the skeletal models in the lab, and with a partner, quiz each other on the various bone markings. Use your textbook lab manual, the *A&P Survival Guide*, or atlas as a reference.

TABLE 11-2   Bone Markings

MARKING	MEANING
Angle	A corner
Body	The main portion of a bone
Condyle	Rounded bump; usually fits into a fossa on another bone, forming a joint
Crest	Moderately raised ridge; generally a site for muscle attachment
Epicondyle	Bump near a condyle; often gives the appearance of a "bump on a bump"; for a muscle attachment
Facet	Flat surface that forms a joint with another facet or flat bone
Fissure	Long, cracklike hole for blood vessels and nerves
Foramen	Round hole for vessels and nerves (pl. *foramina*)
Fossa	Depression; often receives an articulating bone (pl. *fossae*)
Head	Distinct epiphysis on a long bone, separated from the shaft by a narrowed portion (or neck)
Line	Similar to a crest but not raised as much (is often rather faint)
Margin	Edge of a flat bone or flat portion of an irregular bone
Meatus	Tubelike opening or channel (pl. *meati*)
Neck	A narrowed portion, usually at the base of a head
Notch	A V-like depression in the margin or edge of a flat area
Process	A raised area or projection
Ramus	Curved portion of a bone, like a ram's horn (pl. *rami*)
Sinus	Cavity within a bone
Spine	Similar to a crest but raised more; a sharp, pointed process; for muscle attachment
Sulcus	Groove or elongated depression (pl. *sulci*)
Trochanter	Large bump for muscle attachment (larger than tubercle or tuberosity)
Tubercle	Smaller version of a tuberosity
Tuberosity	Oblong, raised bump, usually for muscle attachment

Name: _____ Date: _____ Section: _____

LAB REPORT 11
Overview of the Skeleton

Multiple Choice

1. _____
2. _____
3. _____
4. _____
5. _____
6. _____

Figure 11-6 (from p. 113)

1. _____
2. _____
3. _____
4. _____
5. _____
6. _____
7. _____
8. _____
9. _____
10. _____
11. _____
12. _____
13. _____
14. _____
15. _____
16. _____
17. _____
18. _____
19. _____

Multiple Choice (only one response is correct)

1. The inner lining of the medullary cavity is
   a. made of compact bone
   b. called the *endosteum*
   c. called the *periosteum*
   d. a and c are correct
2. Which of these tissues is present in a typical long bone?
   a. blood tissue
   b. cancellous bone
   c. compact bone
   d. dense fibrous tissue
   e. hyaline cartilage
   f. all of the above
3. In the coloring figure of the long bone, the epiphyseal plate is shown. What is the reason for its presence?
   a. It is scar tissue from a previous fracture.
   b. It is an area of growth between the epiphysis and diaphysis during bone development.
   c. It is callous tissue from overuse of the bone.
   d. It is the site of a current fracture.
4. The human skeleton functions to
   a. produce blood tissue
   b. store fat and minerals
   c. protect vital organs
   d. allow movement of the body
   e. provide a supporting framework
   f. all of the above
5. Your physician has just informed you that you have 40 bones in your skull. This means
   a. you have the standard number of skull bones
   b. you have some sesamoid bones in your skull
   c. you have some sutural bones in your skull
   d. you are missing some skull bones
6. The same physician tells you that all of your knee ligaments have been severed. This means that
   a. your leg bones are not being held together very well
   b. your leg muscles have become separated from the bone
   c. your patella (kneecap) is fractured
   d. your femur (thigh bone) is fractured

Fill-in

1. _____
2. _____
3. _____
4. _____
5. _____
6. _____
7. _____
8. _____
9. _____
10. _____
11. _____
12. _____
13. _____
14. _____
15. _____

Axial Bones

1. _____
2. _____
3. _____
4. _____
5. _____
6. _____
7. _____

Appendicular Bones

1. _____
2. _____
3. _____
4. _____
5. _____
6. _____
7. _____
8. _____

Fill-in (complete each item with the correct term)

1. Tiny round specks of bone found in a tendon are often called _?_ bones.
2. The fibrous covering of a long bone is called the _?_.
3. The shaft portion of a long bone is termed the _?_ of the bone.
4. The head region on the end of a long bone shaft is the _?_.
5. The _?_ on the outside of the long bone is made of hyaline cartilage.
6. Yellow bone marrow is made of _?_ tissue.
7. A bone that is as long as it is wide is classified as a _?_ bone.
8. When classified according to shape, the pelvic bone is considered to be _?_.
9. A human skeleton that is taken apart is called a(n) _?_ skeleton.
10. There are _?_ bones in a standard human skeleton.
11. The bones of the upper and lower extremities make up the _?_ skeleton.
12. Red bone marrow is associated with _?_ bone tissue.
13. The _?_ cartilage articulates with another bone or bone process.
14. When classified according to shape, the femur is a(n) _?_ bone.
15. The _?_ is the central space of the long bone.

Skeletal Plan (proceed through this list of bones, beginning at the top, and sort them according to how they fit in the skeletal plan [axial or appendicular]; you may need to refer to your textbook or later exercises in this manual)

femur
fifth metatarsal
humerus
hyoid
mandible
occipital
patella
pelvic (coxal)
radius
rib
sacrum
scapula
second thoracic vertebra
sternum
tibia

The Skull

This exercise is the first of four exercises that challenge you to learn the bones and important markings of the human skeleton.

The **skull** is the superior portion of the *axial skeleton*. For ease of study, the 28 bones of the skull are divided into three categories. The **cranial bones** form a roughly spherical case for the brain called the *cranium*. The **facial bones** include most of the remaining skull bones, except the six **auditory ossicles** of the middle ear. In this exercise, all 28 skull bones are presented for study.

BEFORE YOU BEGIN

☐ Read the appropriate chapter in your textbook.
☐ Set your learning goals. When you finish this exercise, you should be able to:
  ☐ distinguish between cranial bones and facial bones of the skull
  ☐ identify all the bones of the skull and their important markings in a specimen or figure
  ☐ describe the important features of a fetal skull
  ☐ name the major joints of the skull and identify them in a specimen or figure
☐ Prepare your materials:
  ☐ atlas or chart of the skull (or your textbook)
  ☐ articulated human skull (removable top)
  ☐ articulated fetal skull
  ☐ demonstration pointer
☐ Read the directions and safety tips for this exercise *carefully* before starting any procedure.

Study TIPS

The use of flash cards is recommended when learning to identify the different bones and their bone markings. You can develop your own or refer to *Mosby's Anatomy & Physiology Study and Review Cards*. The use of mnemonic devices can also help you remember the bones and their location. For example, when learning the bones that make up the orbit of the eye (from medial to lateral), a simple mnemonic would be:

No	Nasal
Man	Maxilla
Likes	Lacrimal
Every	Ethmoid
Single	Sphenoid
Zoo	Zygomatic

Hint Refer to Figures 12-3 through 12-6 for color photographs of the skull's bones and markings. Figures in your textbook and brief atlas will also be useful. •

A. BONES OF THE CRANIUM

Eight of the 28 skull bones form the cranium of the skull. Locate in a specimen and in a figure each bone and marking listed, noting the distinguishing characteristics of each.

As with all bones and markings studied in this course, try to understand the structural and functional relationships with surrounding structures.

! *safety first*
Use a disposable plastic pipette (dropper), a pipe cleaner, or another soft *demonstration pointer* to study the features of the skeleton. If you use a pen or pencil, you may mark the skull or damage its delicate parts. •

☐ 1 The single **frontal** bone forms the anterior third of the cranial dome. Locate these features on your specimen:
  ☐ **Supraorbital foramen**—Hole on the superior edge of the orbit
  ☐ **Frontal sinus**—Air space on the midline, between and superior to the orbits
☐ 2 The left and right **parietal** bones form the middle segment of the cranial dome, joined with each other along the midline by the **sagittal suture**. They form a **coronal suture** with the frontal bone and a **lambdoidal suture** with the occipital bone.
☐ 3 The **sphenoid** bone is a butterfly-shaped bone that forms part of the anterior floor and sides of the cranium. The **body** is the hollow, cubelike central portion. Locate some of the sphenoid bone's other features:
  ☐ **Greater wings**—Lateral winglike extensions of the body that form part of the lateral wall of the orbit (eye socket) wall
  ☐ **Lesser wings**—Narrow winglike extensions of the upper part of the body that form the posterior part of the orbit's roof
  ☐ **Optic foramen**—Round hole (for the optic nerve) through the back wall of the orbit

□ **Superior orbital fissure**—Cracklike opening lateral to the optic foramen

□ **Inferior orbital fissure**—Cracklike opening in the inferior back wall of the orbit

□ **Foramen rotundum**—Round opening seen from the inside of the skull, anterior to the foramen ovale

□ **Foramen ovale**—Oval opening seen from the inside of the skull, posterior to the foramen rotundum

□ **Foramen spinosum**—Small opening, often with a small, spinelike bump protruding into it, posterior to the foramen ovale

□ **Sella turcica**—Literally "Turkish saddle," a double projection on the superior aspect of the sphenoid

□ **Sphenoid sinus**—Air space inferior to the sella turcica, within the body of the sphenoid

□ **4** The paired **temporal** bones are at the sides of the cranium, extending inward to form part of the cranial floor. Find these temporal structures:

□ **Zygomatic process**—Narrow bridgelike projection of the temporal bone; articulates with the temporal process of the zygomatic bone

□ **Mastoid process**—Large bump posterior and inferior to the external auditory meatus

□ **Styloid process**—Thin process anterior to the mastoid process

□ **External auditory meatus**—Tubelike opening of the ear canal

□ **Petrous portion**—Can only be seen from the inside of the skull; looks like a "rocky cliff" anterior to the occipital bone

□ **Squamosal suture**—Joint along the top, curved edge of the temporal bone

□ **Mandibular fossa**—Depression that receives the condyle of the mandible

□ **Temporomandibular joint (TMJ)**—Joint formed by the mandibular fossa and the mandibular condyle

□ **Internal auditory meatus**—Tubelike opening in the petrous portion

□ **Jugular foramen**—Round hole at the junction of the petrous portion and the occipital bone

□ **Carotid foramen**—Canal through the petrous portion, slightly medial to the jugular foramen

□ **5** The **occipital** bone forms the posterior portion of the cranial dome, curving inferiorly to the base of the cranium. Locate these important features:

□ **Foramen magnum**—Very large hole for the spinal cord

□ **Occipital condyle**—Flattened bump lateral to the foramen magnum

□ **6** The **ethmoid** bone forms the middle portion of the anterior cranial floor, extending inferiorly between the eye *orbits* to also form the roof of the nasal cavity. Find these important ethmoid structures:

□ **Ethmoid sinuses (air cells)**—Air spaces within the main portion of the bone

□ **Perpendicular plate**—Thin plate projecting downward along the midsagittal plane; it forms the upper nasal septum

□ **Crista galli**—Literally "cock's comb," it is a crest on the superior midline of the ethmoid

□ **Superior nasal concha (turbinate)**—Superior of three curved projections from the nasal cavity's lateral wall

□ **Middle nasal concha (turbinate)**—Middle of three curved projections from the nasal cavity's lateral wall

□ **Cribriform plate**—Thin perforated plate forming the ethmoid's superior surface

□ **Olfactory foramina**—Tiny holes in the cribriform plate (for olfactory nerves from the upper nasal cavity)

> **Hint**   Use the summary tables in the appropriate chapter of your textbook; they summarize the information in this exercise.

B. BONES OF THE FACE

Fourteen bones of the skull are classified as facial bones. Find each facial bone and the markings listed in a specimen and figure.

□ **1** The two **maxillae**, or maxillary bones, are also called the upper jawbones. They support the face from the eyes down to the mouth, across the front of the cheek. Locate these maxillary features:

□ **Palatine process**—Platelike posterior projection of the upper jaw; forms the anterior part of the hard palate

□ **Incisive foramen**—Anterior hole in the palatine process near the body's midline

□ **Alveolar process**—Ridge in which the teeth of the upper jaw are anchored

□ **Infraorbital foramen**—Hole on the anterior "cheek," below the orbit

□ **Maxillary sinus**—Air space within the maxilla's "cheek" portion

□ **2** Each of the two **lacrimal bones** is on the medial margin of an eye orbit, between the ethmoid bone and an upward projection of the maxilla. Each has a sulcus where a tear duct is located (in life).

□ **3** The left and right **nasal** bones are joined at the midline, forming the superior margin of the nasal opening.

□ **4** The two **palatine** bones join together at the midline to form the posterior third of the *hard palate* (roof of the mouth). Locate these features:

□ **Transverse palatine suture**—Joint between the palatine bone and the maxilla's palatine process

□ **Greater palatine foramen**—Larger, anterior of two holes in each palatine bone

□ **5** The **inferior nasal conchae**, or turbinate bones, are a pair of thin, curved bones. They project medially from the lateral walls of the nasal cavity, curving toward the nasal floor.

□ **6** The **mandible**, or lower jawbone, is an oddly shaped bone forming the lower part of the face. Locate these elements of the mandible:

□ **Mandibular arch (notch)**—Large, U-shaped curve of the superior edge of the ramus

- □ **Mandibular condyle**—Rounded, posterior of two projections on the superior part of the ramus
- □ **Coronoid process**—Anterior of two superior projections of the ramus
- □ **Alveolar process**—Ridge along which the teeth are anchored
- □ **Ramus**—The posterior arms of the mandible that angle upward
- □ **Angle**—The corner formed where the ramus begins its upward angle
- □ **Body**—The entire anterior portion of the mandible, to which the rami are attached
- □ **Mandibular foramen**—Hole on the inside surface of the ramus, near the angle
- □ **Mental foramen**—Hole on the outside surface of the body, just lateral to the midline

- □ 7 Each of two **zygomatic** bones forms the upper lateral corner of a cheek, from the lower eye orbit around to the temporal bone. Locate these features:
  - □ **Temporal process**—Wedge-shaped process that joins the zygomatic process of the temporal bone
  - □ **Zygomatic arch**—Complete bridgelike structure formed by the zygomatic process of the temporal bone and the temporal process of the zygomatic bone

- □ 8 The single **vomer** forms the lower portion of the *nasal septum* that divides the nasal cavity.

C. AUDITORY OSSICLES

Each middle ear, within the petrous portion of the temporal bone, contains three auditory ossicles. They are listed here, but we will postpone studying them until Lab Exercise 28. (They are not visible in your specimen.)

- □ 1 The **malleus** is also called the *hammer*.
- □ 2 The **incus** is also called the *anvil*.
- □ 3 The **stapes** is known as the *stirrup*.

D. THE FETAL SKULL

The fetal skull features partly ossified skull bones and a large proportion of fibrous and cartilaginous tissue. Because the flat bones of the cranium have not met to form sutures, there are six fibrous areas called **fontanels**. Identify each in a fetal skull specimen or figure **(Figure 12-2)**.

- □ 1 The two **anterolateral**, or sphenoid, fontanels are at the junction of the sphenoid, temporal, parietal, and frontal bones.
- □ 2 The two **posterolateral**, or mastoid, fontanels are at the junction of the temporal, parietal, and occipital bones.
- □ 3 The **anterior**, or coronal, fontanel can be found where the right and left parietal bones are to meet the frontal bone.
- □ 4 The **posterior** fontanel forms where the parietal bones are to meet the occipital bone.

Study TIPS

Identifying the bones and their unique markings involves harnessing specific memory capabilities. Initially, you may find this a daunting task; however, the more you practice, the better you will be at identifying the bones. It is extremely difficult to remember something when you are exposed to it only once. *Why do you remember your own phone number?* It is because you have used it or said it out loud so many times that you have committed it to memory. Remember this mantra: repeat it, repeat it, and repeat it! During the lab or during study time, take advantage of articulated and disarticulated skeletons, and with a partner, quiz each other over the different bones. Obtain unlabeled illustrations and use them to identify the bones. There are many Internet sites that offer tutorials. An example of a very good interactive site is www.getbodysmart.com. This site has interactive links to all systems of the body. Use your text, lab manual, *A&P Survival Guide*, and *Mosby's Anatomy & Physiology Study and Review Cards* for reference.

Coloring Exercises: Skull

Use colored pens or pencils to shade in both the figure and the labels. Each red numeral in the figure corresponds to a matching red numeral following the appropriate label.

FRONTAL1   LACRIMAL8
PARIETAL2   NASAL9
OCCIPITAL3   PALATINE10
TEMPORAL4   INFERIOR NASAL CONCHA11
SPHENOID5   MANDIBLE12
ETHMOID6   ZYGOMATIC13
MAXILLA7   VOMER14

FIGURE 12-1 A, Anterior view of the skull. After coloring the diagram, label the specific structures noted on the lines provided and on the blanks in the Lab Report at the end of this exercise.

FIGURE 12-1, cont'd B, *Top,* left lateral view of the skull. *Bottom,* skull viewed from below. After coloring the diagram, label the specific structures noted on the lines provided and on the blanks in the Lab Report at the end of this exercise. *Continued*

FIGURE 12-1, cont'd C, Floor of the cranial cavity. After coloring the diagram, label the specific structures noted on the lines provided and on the blanks in the Lab Report at the end of this exercise.

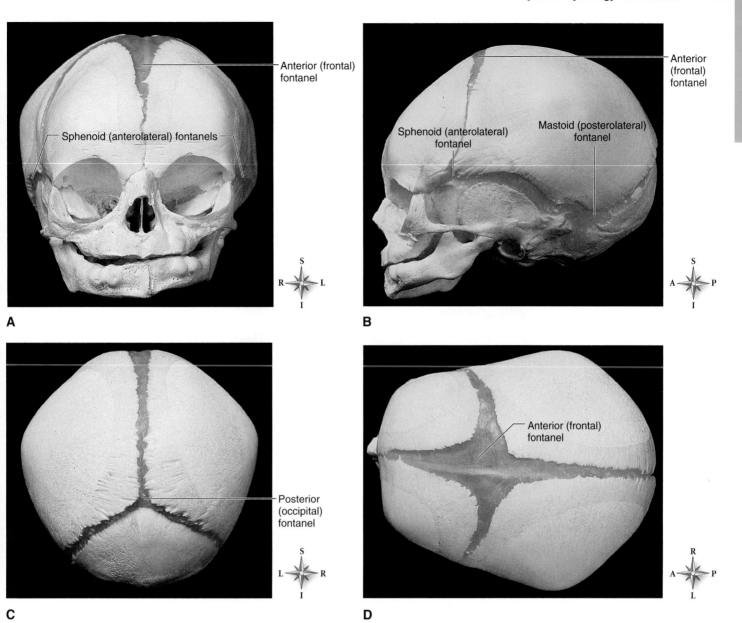

FIGURE 12-2 The fetal skull. **A,** From the front. **B,** From the left and slightly below. **C,** From behind. **D,** From above.

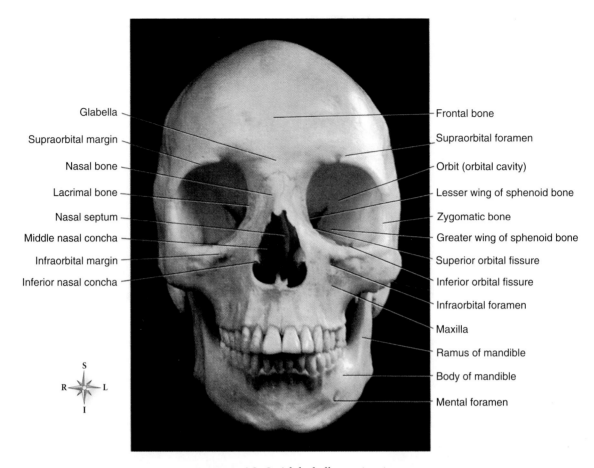

FIGURE 12-3 Adult skull, anterior view.

Glabella
Supraorbital margin
Nasal bone
Lacrimal bone
Nasal septum
Middle nasal concha
Infraorbital margin
Inferior nasal concha

Frontal bone
Supraorbital foramen
Orbit (orbital cavity)
Lesser wing of sphenoid bone
Zygomatic bone
Greater wing of sphenoid bone
Superior orbital fissure
Inferior orbital fissure
Infraorbital foramen
Maxilla
Ramus of mandible
Body of mandible
Mental foramen

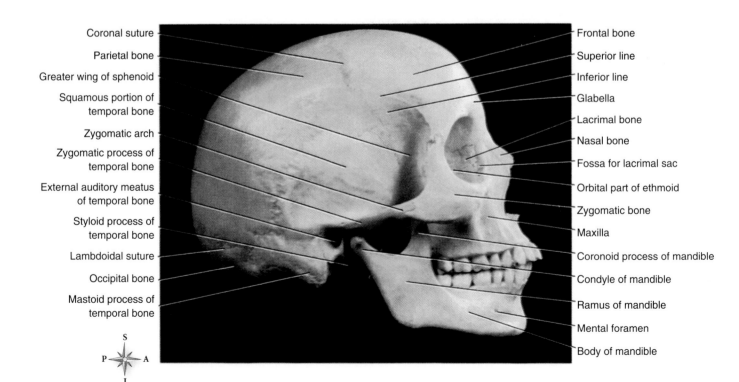

FIGURE 12-4 Adult skull, lateral view from subject's right.

Coronal suture
Parietal bone
Greater wing of sphenoid
Squamous portion of temporal bone
Zygomatic arch
Zygomatic process of temporal bone
External auditory meatus of temporal bone
Styloid process of temporal bone
Lambdoidal suture
Occipital bone
Mastoid process of temporal bone

Frontal bone
Superior line
Inferior line
Glabella
Lacrimal bone
Nasal bone
Fossa for lacrimal sac
Orbital part of ethmoid
Zygomatic bone
Maxilla
Coronoid process of mandible
Condyle of mandible
Ramus of mandible
Mental foramen
Body of mandible

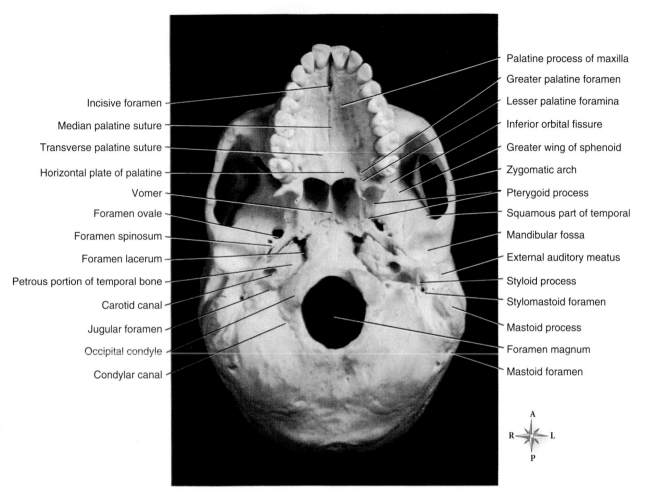

Incisive foramen

Median palatine suture

Transverse palatine suture

Horizontal plate of palatine

Vomer

Foramen ovale

Foramen spinosum

Foramen lacerum

Petrous portion of temporal bone

Carotid canal

Jugular foramen

Occipital condyle

Condylar canal

Palatine process of maxilla

Greater palatine foramen

Lesser palatine foramina

Inferior orbital fissure

Greater wing of sphenoid

Zygomatic arch

Pterygoid process

Squamous part of temporal

Mandibular fossa

External auditory meatus

Styloid process

Stylomastoid foramen

Mastoid process

Foramen magnum

Mastoid foramen

FIGURE 12-5 Adult skull, inferior view.

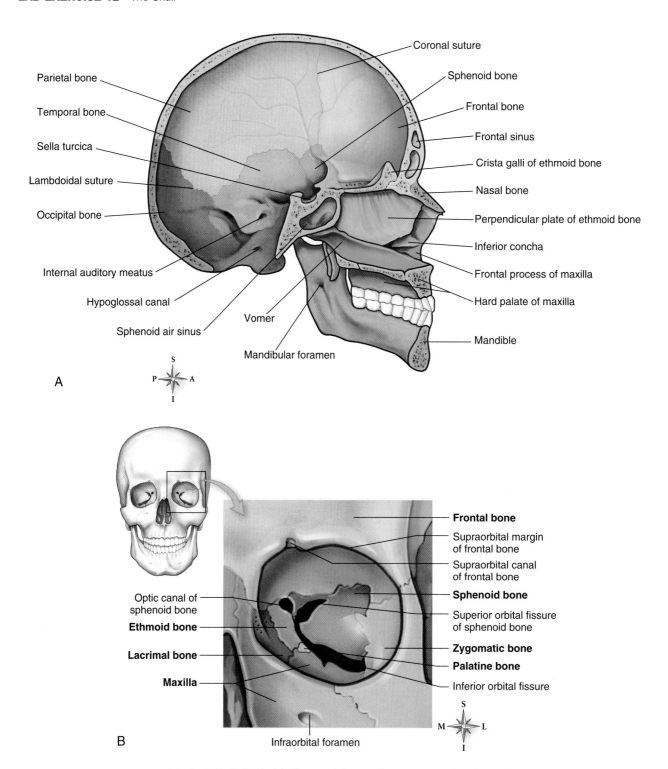

FIGURE 12-6 **A,** Right half of skull viewed from within. **B,** Bones that form right orbit.

Name: _____ Date: _____ Section: _____

LAB REPORT 12
The Skull

Figure 12-1 (from pp. 120-122)

(NOTE: Numbers 1 through 14 are used for coloring labels.)

15. _____
16. _____
17. _____
18. _____
19. _____
20. _____
21. _____
22. _____
23. _____
24. _____
25. _____
26. _____
27. _____
28. _____
29. _____
30. _____
31. _____
32. _____
33. _____
34. _____
35. _____
36. _____
37. _____
38. _____
39. _____
40. _____
41. _____
42. _____
43. _____
44. _____
45. _____
46. _____
47. _____
48. _____
49. _____
50. _____

List the Bones of the Cranium

1. _____
2. _____
3. _____
4. _____
5. _____
6. _____

Name the Facial Bones

1. _____
2. _____
3. _____
4. _____
5. _____
6. _____
7. _____
8. _____

Name the Auditory Ossicles

1. _____
2. _____
3. _____

Name the Major Fontanels

1. _____
2. _____
3. _____
4. _____

Sutures

1. _____
2. _____
3. _____
4. _____

Markings

1. _____
2. _____
3. _____
4. _____
5. _____
6. _____
7. _____
8. _____
9. _____
10. _____

Anatomical Relationships

1. _____
2. _____
3. _____
4. _____
5. _____
6. _____
7. _____
8. _____
9. _____
10. _____

Sutures (determine the name of the suture joint described)

1. Joins the parietal bones together
2. Joins the superior margin of the temporal bone to the frontal, parietal, and occipital bones
3. Joins the palatine bone to the maxilla
4. Joins the frontal bone to the two parietal bones

Markings (give the name of the bone marking or feature described in each item)

1. Large process of the temporal bone, just posterior to the external auditory meatus; it contains sinuses
2. A smaller, needle-shaped process just medial to the process described in the previous statement
3. A hole in the sphenoid bone that allows the optic nerve to exit the eye orbit
4. Same name for ridgelike processes on both the maxilla and mandible in which the teeth are embedded
5. A crest or projection on the superior surface of the ethmoid bone
6. A curved plate of bone projecting from the lateral wall of the nasal cavity, just above the inferior nasal conchae (part of the ethmoid bone)
7. One of two holes on the anterior portion of the mandibular body
8. A hole in the maxilla just below the orbit of the eye
9. The upper portion of the nasal septum is formed by this part of the ethmoid
10. This structure is formed by both the zygomatic process of the temporal bone and the temporal process of the zygomatic bone

Anatomical Relationships (use a directional term to complete each item correctly)

1. The frontal bone is _?_ to the occipital bone.
2. The lacrimal bones are on the _?_ margin of the orbit.
3. The mandible is mostly _?_ to the maxilla.
4. The occipital condyles are _?_ to the foramen magnum.
5. The palatine bones are _?_ to the maxilla.
6. The superior conchae are _?_ to the nasal septum.
7. The mandibular condyle is _?_ to the coronoid process.
8. The parietal bones are _?_ to the frontal bone.
9. The coronal fontanel is _?_ to the posterior fontanel.
10. The incisive foramen is _?_ to the transverse palatine suture.

The Vertebral Column and Thoracic Cage

As you recall, the axial skeleton is comprised of the skull, the vertebral column, the thoracic cage, and one unattached bone. All these structures form the central core, or *axis*, of the skeleton. In the previous exercise, we explored the skull in some detail. This exercise presents the remainder of the axial skeleton.

The **vertebral column** is a set of 26 bones stacked one on another to form a slightly curved, flexible support rod. The 25 bones of the rib cage, or **thoracic cage,** protect the lungs and heart within the thorax. The **hyoid** bone is not attached to any other bone but is very close to the skull and vertebral column and lies along the central axis of the body.

BEFORE YOU BEGIN

- ☐ Read the appropriate chapter in your textbook.
- ☐ Set your learning goals. When you finish this exercise, you should be able to:
  - ☐ name the component bones of the vertebral column and thoracic cage
- ☐ Prepare your materials:
  - ☐ human skeleton (disarticulated)
  - ☐ human skeleton (articulated)
  - ☐ human vertebrae set (optional)
  - ☐ demonstration pointer
- ☐ Read the directions and safety tips for this exercise *carefully* before starting any procedure.

> ❗ *safety first*
> Be careful when handling skeletal specimens. Loose hardware can injure both you and the specimen. Do not forget to use only approved demonstration pointers. •

Study TIPS

Since there are no distinct lines that separate the regions of the vertebra, the general features (lamina, pedicles, neural arch, processes, etc.) of each vertebra are often difficult to identify. You may want to obtain a photo or illustration of a vertebra and color/label each feature. It might be useful to do the same for the sacrum. Use your textbook, lab manual, the *A&P Survival Guide, Mosby's Anatomy & Physiology Study and Review Cards*, or atlas for reference.

A. THE VERTEBRAL COLUMN

The 26 bones of the vertebral column are grouped among the bones listed here. Find each bone and its important features on both an articulated skeleton and among the separate bones of a disarticulated skeleton or vertebrae set.

- ☐ 1 The seven **cervical** vertebrae at the superior end of the vertebral column are designated individually by number. The most superior is C1 (cervical number one), the next is C2, and so on. Of C1 through C7, only the first two have commonly used alternate names:
  - ☐ **Atlas**—C1, or the atlas, is a ringlike vertebra that supports the skull by forming a joint with the occipital condyles. The atlas has an **anterior arch** and **posterior arch** fused to left and right **lateral masses** to form a circle. Flat articulating **facets** are found on both the superior and inferior aspects.
  - ☐ **Axis**—C2, or the axis, is remarkable for its **dens** or *odontoid* (toothlike) process. The dens points superiorly through the atlas to act as a pivot for the rotation of C1 and the skull.
  - ☐ In an articulated skeleton or figure, notice the **cervical curve** of the vertebral column produced by these seven vertebrae.
- ☐ 2 The 12 **thoracic** vertebrae (T1 through T12) are inferior to the cervical vertebrae. As a group, they curve in the opposite direction of the cervical curve to form the **thoracic curve.**
- ☐ 3 Five large **lumbar** vertebrae (L1 through L5) form the curve of the lower back, or **lumbar curve.**
- ☐ 4 All vertebrae from C3 to L5 have certain common features. Find each of these features on examples of all three vertebral types.
  - ☐ **Vertebral foramen**—Large hole (for the spinal cord) in the center
  - ☐ **Spinous process**—Spine projecting posteriorly (a *bifid* or forked spinous process in cervical vertebrae)
  - ☐ **Body**—Thick disk of bone forming the anterior arch
  - ☐ **Lamina**—Thin, platelike section forming each leg of the posterior arch
  - ☐ **Pedicle**—Lateral section joining the lamina to the body
  - ☐ **Intervertebral foramen**—Hole formed between laminae of successive vertebrae (for spinal nerves)
  - ☐ **Transverse process**—Spine that projects laterally

☐ **Transverse foramen**—Hole in a transverse process
☐ **Superior articular facets**—Flat surfaces on the superior aspect
☐ **Inferior articular facets**—Flat surfaces on the inferior aspect

☐ 5 The **sacrum** is a bone that develops as a set of five vertebrae that fuse to form one large bone inferior to L5. A slight **sacral** curve can be seen from the lateral perspective. Find these sacral features:

☐ **Dorsal foramina**—Double row of holes between fused segments that form the sacrum (dorsal aspect)
☐ **Pelvic foramina**—Similar to dorsal foramina, but on the ventral aspect
☐ **Sacral canal**—Canal formed by the vertebral foramina of the fused sacral segments
☐ **Sacral hiatus**—Open space at the caudal end of the sacral canal (where the last two sacral segments have incomplete spinous processes)
☐ **Median sacral crest**—Bumpy ridge formed by fusion of sacral spinous processes
☐ **Sacral promontory**—Jutting ventral lip of the superior sacral segment

☐ 6 The most inferior bone of the vertebral column is the **coccyx**, or tailbone. This bone, like the sacrum, is actually a fusion of several vertebrae.

☐ 7 The **hyoid** bone is not really part of the vertebral column but will be considered here. This bone is a U-shaped bone in the throat. It serves as an attachment for tongue muscles and connective tissue associated with the larynx (voice box). In most articulated skeletal specimens, it is suspended by wire or plastic in a position anterior to the cervical curve.

B. THE THORACIC CAGE

The 25 bones of the rib cage, or **thoracic cage**, form a partially flexible, protective shield for the heart, lungs, and other thoracic organs. The thoracic cage also helps protect some organs of the upper abdomen, such as the liver and spleen. Locate the major structures of the thoracic cage.

☐ 1 Each of the 12 pairs of **ribs** articulates with the vertebral column. The ribs curve around anteriorly. The superior seven pairs of ribs attach directly to the *sternum* by way of **costal cartilages.** These 14 ribs are also called **true ribs.** The inferior five pairs, or **false ribs,** do not directly connect to the sternum. The upper three pairs of false ribs indirectly connect to the sternum via the costal cartilages of true ribs. The last two pairs of false ribs do not connect in any way, so they are also called **floating ribs.**

☐ 2 The **sternum,** or *breastbone*, receives the costal cartilages of the true ribs on the anterior aspect of the thoracic cage. In life, it forms an anterior protective wall over the heart and associated structures. Find these structures of the sternum **(Figure 13-4)**:

☐ **Body (gladiolus)**—Main (middle) portion of the sternum
☐ **Manubrium**—Superior segment
☐ **Xiphoid process**—Inferior, pointed segment

Coloring Exercises: Typical Vertebra

Use colored pens or pencils to shade in both the figure and the labels. Each red numeral in the figure corresponds to a matching red numeral following the appropriate label.

VERTEBRAL ARCH₁
LAMINA₂
PEDICLE₃
SPINOUS PROCESS₄
TRANSVERSE PROCESS₅
INFERIOR ARTICULAR
 PROCESS₆
INFERIOR ARTICULAR
 FACET₇

SUPERIOR ARTICULAR
 PROCESS₈
SUPERIOR ARTICULAR
 FACET₉
VERTEBRAL FORAMEN₁₀
BODY OF VERTEBRA₁₁

FIGURE 13-1 Structures of the vertebrae.

Coloring Exercises: Vertebral Column

Use colored pens or pencils to shade in both the figure and the labels. Each red numeral in the figure corresponds to a matching red numeral following the appropriate label.

CERVICAL VERTEBRA₁
CERVICAL CURVE₂
THORACIC VERTEBRA₃
THORACIC CURVE₄
LUMBAR VERTEBRA₅
LUMBAR CURVE₆
INTERVERTEBRAL DISKS₇
SACRUM₈

SACRAL CURVE₉
COCCYX₁₀

FIGURE 13-2 Structures of the vertebral column. After coloring the diagram, label the specific structures noted on the lines provided and on the blanks in the Lab Report at the end of this exercise. (Please color all intervertebral disks [7]; only a few have been labeled.)

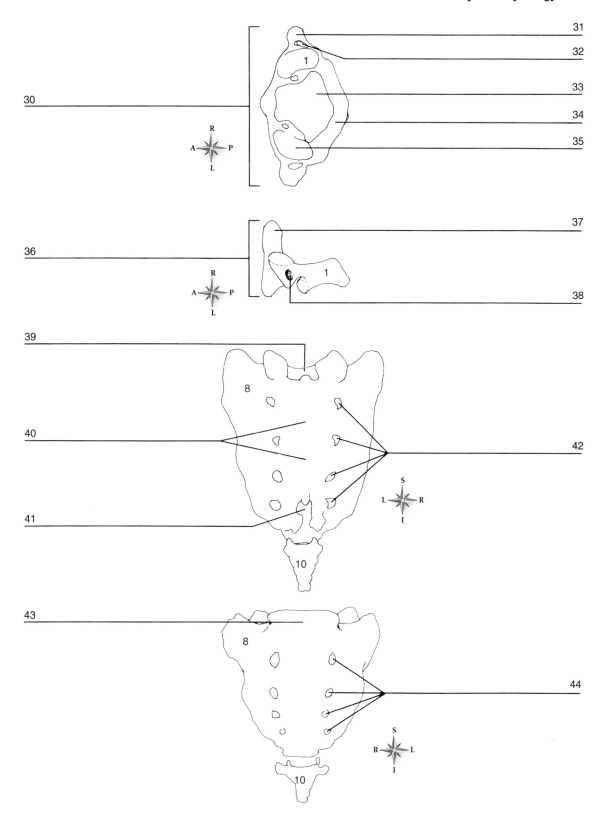

30

31
32
33
34
35

36

37

38

39

40

42

41

43

44

FIGURE 13-3 Structures of the atlas, axis, and sacrum. After coloring the diagram, label the specific structures noted on the lines provided and on the blanks in the Lab Report at the end of this exercise.

Coloring Exercises: Thoracic Cage

Use colored pens or pencils to shade in both the figure and the labels. Each red numeral in the figure corresponds to a matching red numeral following the appropriate label.

Ribs

TRUE RIB₁
FALSE RIB₂
COSTAL CARTILAGE₃

Sternum

MANUBRIUM₄
BODY₅
XIPHOID PROCESS₆
THORACIC VERTEBRA₇

FIGURE 13-4 Structures of the thoracic cage.

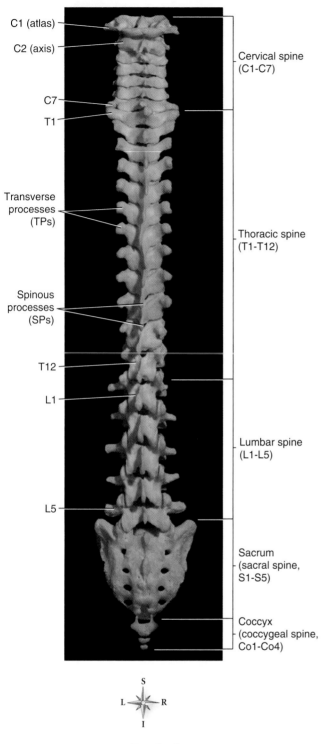

C1 (atlas)

C2 (axis)

C7

T1

Transverse
processes
(TPs)

Spinous
processes
(SPs)

T12

L1

L5

Cervical spine
(C1-C7)

Thoracic spine
(T1-T12)

Lumbar spine
(L1-L5)

Sacrum
(sacral spine,
S1-S5)

Coccyx
(coccygeal spine,
Co1-Co4)

S
L — R
I

FIGURE 13-5 Spinal column, posterior view.

Superior

C1
C2

C7
T1

Transverse
processes
(TPs)

Spinous
processes
(SPs)

Facet joints

Disc spaces

T12

L1

Intervertebral
foramina

L5

Cervical spine
(C1-C7)

Thoracic spine
(T1-T12)

Lumbar spine
(L1-L5)

Sacrum
(sacral spine,
S1-S5)

Coccyx
(coccygeal spine,
Co1-Co4)

Inferior

S
P — A
I

FIGURE 13-6 Spinal column, right lateral view.

clinical applications: anatomical images

Perhaps the oldest method of producing images of internal structures of the human body is sketching dissected specimens. More recent technology has produced a number of advanced techniques of producing images of human structures. One such technique, first produced by Wilhelm Roentgen around the turn of the last century, is **radiography.** This technique, which is also called x-ray photography, uses radiation waves that pass through the specimen and onto photographic film. Because the waves pass more easily through soft tissue than through dense tissue, such as bone, shadows of some structures are visible when the film is developed. **Figure 13-7, *A*,**

shows a radiograph, or x-ray photograph, of the lumbar region. Can you identify the structures indicated?

A more recent variation of this technique is computed tomography (CT). A CT scanner emits a beam of x-rays in a circular path around the subject. After passing through the body, the beams are processed by a computer that is able to reconstruct a three-dimensional image of internal structures. The operator can view different sections of the body on a video monitor. Figure 13-7, *B*, shows a CT image of a horizontal section of the upper abdomen. A vertebra is clearly shown; can you identify its parts?

FIGURE 13-7 A, Standard radiograph of the lumbar region (notice the "diagonal" perspective). **B,** CT image of the abdomen. Label the structures noted on the lines provided and on the blanks in the Lab Report at the end of this exercise.

Name: _____ Date: _____ Section: _____

The Vertebral Column and Thoracic Cage

Figures 13-2 and 13-3 (from pp. 132-133)

(NOTE: Numbers 1 through 10 are used for coloring labels.)

1. _____
2. _____
3. _____
4. _____
5. _____
6. _____
7. _____
8. _____
9. _____
10. _____
11. _____
12. _____
13. _____
14. _____
15. _____
16. _____
17. _____
18. _____
19. _____
20. _____
21. _____
22. _____
23. _____
24. _____
25. _____
26. _____
27. _____
28. _____
29. _____
30. _____
31. _____
32. _____
33. _____
34. _____

Table 13-1 (fill in the numbers as indicated)

TABLE 13-1   Count of Bones in the Vertebral Column

NUMBER	STRUCTURES
	Bones in the vertebral column
	Unfused vertebrae
	Cervical vertebrae
	Thoracic vertebrae
	Lumbar vertebrae
	Spinal curves
	Bones in the thoracic cage
	Pairs of ribs
	Pairs of true ribs
	Pairs of false ribs
	Pairs of floating ribs

Figure 13-7 (from p. 136)

1. _____
2. _____
3. _____
4. _____
5. _____
6. _____
7. _____
8. _____
9. _____
10. _____

Fill-in

1. _____
2. _____
3. _____
4. _____
5. _____
6. _____
7. _____
8. _____
9. _____
10. _____
11. _____
12. _____
13. _____
14. _____
15. _____
16. _____
17. _____
18. _____
19. _____
20. _____

Fill-in (complete each statement with the appropriate term)

1. The first cervical vertebra is called C1, or _?_.

2. The second cervical vertebra is called C2, or _?_.

3. The inward curve of the lower back is called the _?_ curve.

4. All ribs articulate with the _?_.

5. Both radiographs and CT scans use _?_ to form images of anatomical structures.

6. Kyphosis is a condition in which the vertebral column is distorted, giving a person a humpback. This condition involves an exaggerated _?_ curve.

7. Both the coccyx and _?_ are vertebral bones that are actually fused vertebrae.

8. The thoracic vertebrae are _?_ to the lumbar vertebrae.

9. The superior portion of the sternum is called the _?_.

10. The only bone that does not articulate with another bone is the _?_.

11. The _?_ is a vertical tunnel through the sacrum for the passage of nerves descending from the spinal cord.

12. The medial bumps along the midline of your back are caused by the _?_ of each vertebra.

13. The _?_ ribs do not articulate, even indirectly, with the sternum.

14. The _?_ ribs connect directly to the sternum.

15. Costal cartilages are composed of _?_ cartilage tissue.

16. _?_ disks (appearing in Figure 13-2) form a type of joint between the bodies of vertebrae.

17. The _?_ is a horseshoe-shaped bone.

18. The tailbone is more properly known as the _?_.

19. Spinal nerves leave the protection of the vertebral column by way of lateral holes or gaps between the vertebrae called the _?_ foramina.

20. The medial ridge along the posterior surface of the sacrum is called the _?_.

The Upper Extremities

Remember that the human skeleton is divided into the *axial skeleton* and the *appendicular skeleton* (extremities). You are now ready to begin learning about the *upper* extremities.

The appendicular skeleton consists of all 126 bones that form the upper and lower extremities. The *shoulder girdle* and upper extremities have 64 bones altogether, whereas the *pelvic girdle* and lower extremities have a total of 62 bones. This exercise presents all the bones and many important bone features of the upper extremities.

BEFORE YOU BEGIN

☐ Read the appropriate chapter in your textbook.
☐ Set your learning goals. When you finish this exercise, you should be able to:
  ☐ name the bones of the upper extremity skeleton
  ☐ identify upper extremity bones and markings on a specimen and in figures
☐ Prepare your materials:
  ☐ human skeleton (disarticulated)
  ☐ human skeleton (articulated)
  ☐ demonstration pointer
☐ Read the directions and safety tips for this exercise *carefully* before starting any procedure.

 safety first
Beware of loose parts in the articulated skeleton. Remember to use only approved demonstration pointers. •

Study TIPS

As discussed in Lab 12, learning the bones will require harnessing your memorization capabilities. The more you practice, the better you will be at identifying the bones. It is extremely difficult to remember something when you are exposed to it only once. Remember this mantra: repeat it, repeat it, and repeat it! During the lab or during study time, take advantage of articulated and disarticulated skeletons, and with a partner, quiz each other over the different bones. Obtain unlabeled illustrations and use them to identify the bones. You can use your cell phone to photograph various bones and then print the photos and label them. There are many Internet sites that offer tutorials. An example of a very good interactive site is www.getbodysmart.com. This site has interactive links to all systems of the body. Use your text, lab manual, *A&P Survival Guide*, and *Mosby's Anatomy & Physiology Study and Review Cards* for reference.

A. THE SHOULDER GIRDLE

Find each bone and marking listed in a specimen and in figures.

☐ 1 The **scapula,** or shoulder blade, forms part of the shoulder girdle that supports the arms. It is an irregular bone on the superior, posterior aspect of the rib cage that extends laterally to form a joint with the arm. Find these features of the scapula:
  ☐ **Axillary border**—Edge of the triangular scapula that faces the armpit region
  ☐ **Vertebral border**—Scapular edge that faces the vertebral column
  ☐ **Superior border**—Superior edge of the scapula
  ☐ **Acromion process**—Large process projecting laterally from the scapular spine to form part of the shoulder joint
  ☐ **Coracoid process**—Process anterior to, but smaller than, the acromion process
  ☐ **Glenoid cavity**—Depression at the upper, lateral corner of the scapular triangle; it forms part of the shoulder socket
  ☐ **Spine**—Large dorsal crest extending from the vertebral border to the acromion process
☐ 2 The **clavicle,** or collarbone, is the other bone of the shoulder girdle. The clavicle is a long bone whose long axis lies along a horizontal axis on the anterior, superior aspect of the thoracic cage.

B. THE ARM

Identify the bones and markings listed.

☐ 1 The **humerus** is the large, long bone of the arm. Find these parts of the humerus:
  ☐ **Head**—Enlarged proximal portion
  ☐ **Anatomical neck**—Diagonal line just inferior to the articular surface of the head
  ☐ **Surgical neck**—The point at which the bone narrows significantly distal to the head
  ☐ **Greater tubercle**—Large bump near the lateral aspect of the head
  ☐ **Lesser tubercle**—Bump near the midline of the head's anterior aspect
  ☐ **Intertubercular sulcus**—Groove between the greater and lesser tubercles
  ☐ **Deltoid tuberosity**—Rough muscle attachment site near the middle of the lateral surface of the shaft

☐ **Coronoid fossa**—Depression on the anterior, distal surface (between the epicondyles) that articulates with the ulna's coronoid process

☐ **Olecranon fossa**—Depression on the posterior, distal surface that articulates with the ulna's olecranon

☐ **Medial epicondyle**—Blunt projection of bone on the medial aspect of the distal end

☐ **Lateral epicondyle**—Blunt projection of bone on the lateral aspect of the distal end

☐ **Trochlea**—Spool-shaped articulating surface on the distal end that articulates with the ulna's trochlear notch

☐ **Capitulum**—Ball-like articulating surface on the distal end, lateral to the trochlea, that articulates with the head of the radius

☐ 2 The **radius** is one of two long bones of the forearm. It is lateral to the other forearm bone (when in the anatomical position) and articulates with the capitulum of the humerus. Find these features:

☐ **Head**—Proximal disklike enlargement

☐ **Radial tuberosity**—Oval bump just distal to the head, on the medial surface (facing the ulna)

☐ **Styloid process**—Pointed bump on the lateral aspect of the distal end

☐ 3 The **ulna,** the other long bone of the forearm, articulates with the trochlea of the humerus. Find these markings of the ulna:

☐ **Olecranon**—Large proximal process that forms the blunt point on the posterior aspect of the flexed elbow joint

☐ **Semilunar (trochlear) notch**—Curved anterior indentation on the olecranon that articulates with the trochlea of the humerus

☐ **Coronoid process**—Sharp anterior lip of the trochlear notch that articulates with the coronoid fossa of the humerus

☐ **Head**—Distal enlargement

☐ **Styloid process**—Pointed bump on the medial aspect of the head

C. THE WRIST AND HAND

Identify the bones and markings listed.

☐ 1 The **carpus,** or wrist, is composed of eight small bones:

☐ **Pisiform**

☐ **Triquetrum (triangular)**

☐ **Lunate**

☐ **Scaphoid (navicular)**

☐ **Hamate**

☐ **Capitate**

☐ **Trapezoid**

☐ **Trapezium**

☐ 2 The hand **(Figure 14-1)** consists of five similar **metacarpal** bones, numbered one through five (starting from the thumb side). Articulating with these are the **phalanges,** or finger bones. The phalanges are named *proximal, middle,* and *distal* and numbered one through five, according to their position. The first middle phalanx (of the thumb) is not present.

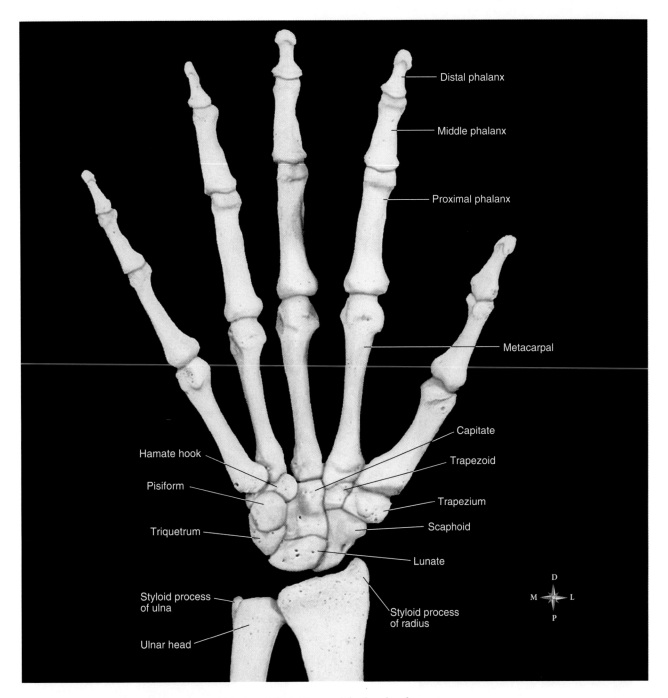

FIGURE 14-1 Bones of the hand, palmar view.

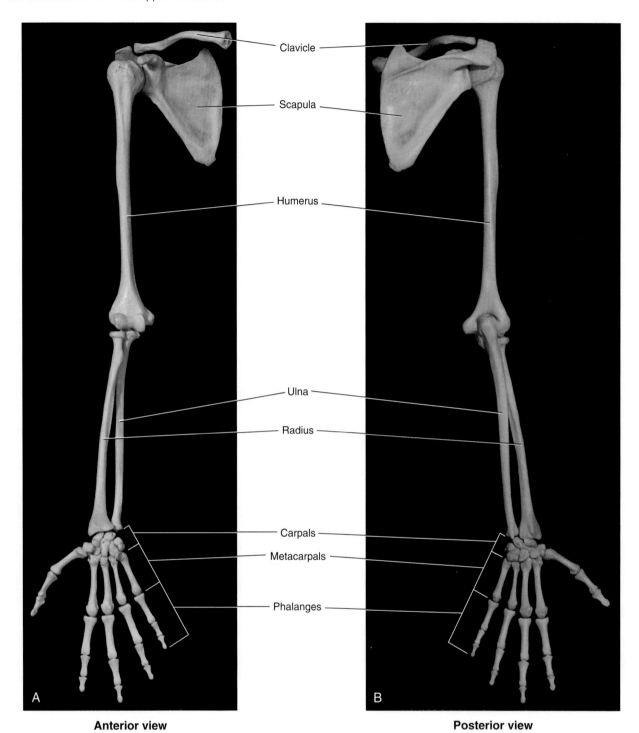

Clavicle

Scapula

Humerus

Ulna

Radius

Carpals

Metacarpals

Phalanges

Anterior view

Posterior view

A

B

FIGURE 14-2 Right upper extremity. **A,** Anterior view. **B,** Posterior view.

Coloring Exercises: Upper Extremity

Use colored pens or pencils to shade in both the figure and the labels. Each red numeral in the figure corresponds to a matching red numeral following the appropriate label.

SCAPULA₁
CLAVICLE₂
HUMERUS₃
RADIUS₄
ULNA₅
PISIFORM₆
TRIQUETRUM₇
LUNATE₈
SCAPHOID₉

HAMATE₁₀
CAPITATE₁₁
TRAPEZOID₁₂
TRAPEZIUM₁₃
METACARPAL₁₄
PROXIMAL PHALANX₁₅
MIDDLE PHALANX₁₆
DISTAL PHALANX₁₇

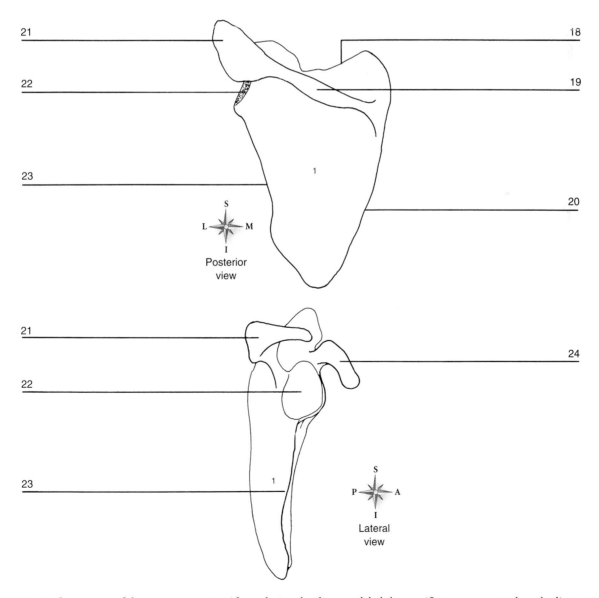

FIGURE 14-3 Proximal structures of the upper extremity. After coloring the diagram, label the specific structures noted on the lines provided and on the blanks in the Lab Report at the end of this exercise.

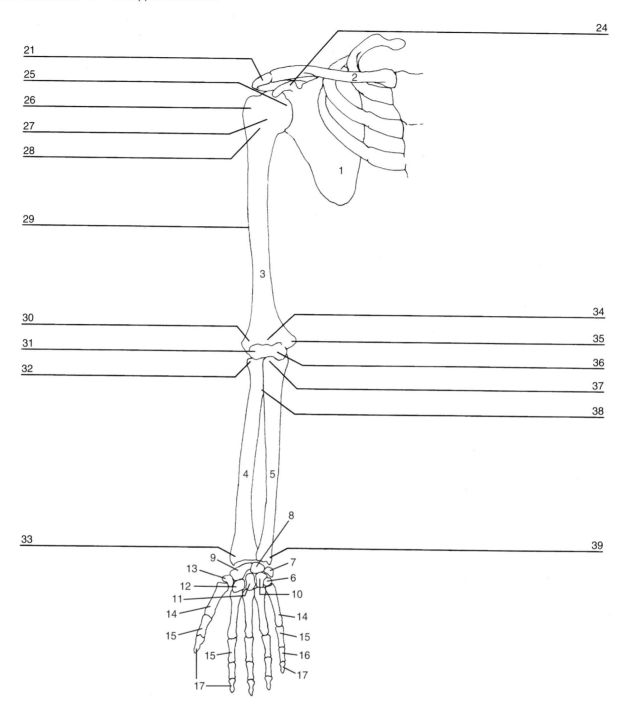

FIGURE 14-4 Anterior view of the upper extremity. After coloring the diagram, label the specific structures noted on the lines provided and on the blanks in the Lab Report at the end of this exercise.

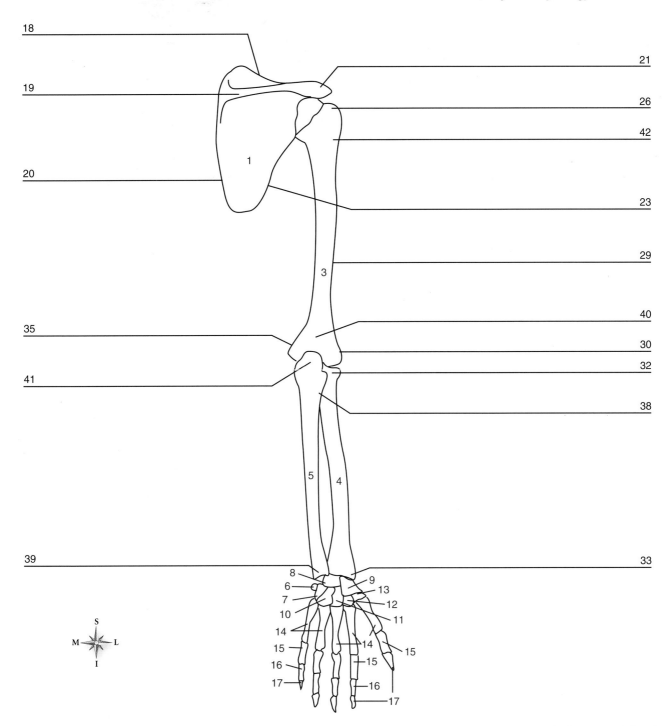

FIGURE 14-5 Posterior view of the upper extremity. After coloring the diagram, label the specific structures noted on the lines provided and on the blanks in the Lab Report at the end of this exercise.

Name: _____ Date: _____ Section: _____

LAB REPORT 14
The Upper Extremities

Figures 14-3, 14-4, and 14-5
(from pp. 143-145)

(NOTE: Numbers 1 through 17 are used for coloring labels.)

18. _____
19. _____
20. _____
21. _____
22. _____
23. _____
24. _____
25. _____
26. _____
27. _____
28. _____
29. _____
30. _____
31. _____
32. _____
33. _____
34. _____
35. _____
36. _____
37. _____
38. _____
39. _____
40. _____
41. _____
42. _____

Multiple Choice

1. _____
2. _____
3. _____
4. _____
5. _____
6. _____

Multiple Choice (only one response is correct in each item)

1. Jeb accidentally smashed his hand in a car door, breaking one of his bones. If the injury is near the middle of his palm, which type of bone must be involved?
   a. proximal phalanx
   b. metacarpal
   c. metatarsal
   d. distal phalanx
   e. carpal

2. The humeral process that articulates with the ulna is the
   a. trochlea
   b. capitulum
   c. lateral epicondyle
   d. medial epicondyle
   e. a and b are correct

3. The largest long bone of the upper extremities is the
   a. humerus
   b. tibia
   c. femur
   d. ulna
   e. clavicle

4. The forearm contains the
   a. ulna
   b. tibia
   c. radius
   d. humerus
   e. a and b are correct
   f. a and c are correct

5. The large, proximal process of the ulna that forms the posterior "point" of the flexed elbow is the
   a. head
   b. styloid process
   c. trochlea
   d. olecranon
   e. radial tuberosity

6. While skiing in the Alps last winter, Laura fell and fractured her collarbone. To which bone(s) does this collarbone attach?
   a. scapula
   b. sternum
   c. floating rib
   d. a and b are correct
   e. a, b, and c are correct

Table 14-1 (fill in the numbers as indicated)

TABLE 14-1   Bone Count in the Appendicular Skeleton

NUMBER	STRUCTURES
	Bones in the appendicular skeleton
	Bones in the upper extremities
	Wrist bones (total)
	Hand/finger bones (total)

15

The Lower Extremities

Recall that the appendicular skeleton consists of all 126 bones that form the upper and lower extremities. The *shoulder girdle* and arms (upper extremities) have 64 bones altogether, whereas the *pelvic girdle* and legs (lower extremities) have a total of 62 bones. This exercise presents all the bones and many important bone features of the lower extremities.

BEFORE YOU BEGIN

☐ Read the appropriate chapter in your textbook.
☐ Set your learning goals. When you finish this exercise, you should be able to:
  ☐ name the bones of the lower extremity
  ☐ identify lower extremity bones and markings on a specimen and in figures
☐ Prepare your materials:
  ☐ human skeleton (disarticulated)
  ☐ human skeleton (articulated)
  ☐ demonstration pointer
☐ Read the directions and safety tips for this exercise *carefully* before starting any procedure.

safety first

Beware of loose parts in the articulated skeleton. Remember to use only approved demonstration pointers. •

Study TIPS

As discussed in Labs 12 and 14, learning the bones will require harnessing your memorization capabilities. The more you practice, the better you will be at identifying the bones. It is extremely difficult to remember something when you are exposed to it only once. Remember this mantra: repeat it, repeat it, and repeat it! During the lab or during study time, take advantage of articulated and disarticulated skeletons, and with a partner, quiz each other over the different bones. Obtain unlabeled illustrations and use them to identify the bones. You can use your cell phone to photograph various bones and then print the photos and label them. There are many Internet sites that offer tutorials. An example of a very good interactive site is www.getbodysmart.com. This site has interactive links to all systems of the body. Use your text, lab manual, the *A&P Survival Guide*, and *Mosby's Anatomy & Physiology Study and Review Cards* for reference.

A. THE PELVIC GIRDLE

Find the bones and markings listed.

☐ 1 A left and right **coxal bone**, or pelvic bone, join to form the pelvic girdle. The *coxae* articulate with the sacrum and support the legs. The coxae are formed by the fusion of three bones early in development: the **ilium, ischium,** and **pubis**. These bones are still identifiable as pelvic regions:
  ☐ **Ilium**—Lateral, superior region of the bone; it includes the bowl-like wall of the upper pelvis
  ☐ **Ischium**—Inferior, posterior, lateral coxal region
  ☐ **Pubis**—Inferior, medial region, comprising an upper and lower *ramus*; forms the pubic arch at the body's anterior midline

☐ 2 Find these other features of the coxal bone:
  ☐ **Acetabulum**—Cuplike socket formed where the ilium, ischium, and pubis articulate with the head of the femur
  ☐ **Iliac crest**—Upper, curving "lip" of the "bowl" formed by the iliac portion
  ☐ **Iliac spines**—The "corners" of the iliac portion:
  ☐ **Anterior superior spine**—Blunt anterior point at the end of the iliac crest
  ☐ **Anterior inferior spine**—Smaller blunt point a short distance below the anterior superior spine
  ☐ **Posterior superior spine**—Point at the posterior end of the iliac crest
  ☐ **Posterior inferior spine**—Point a short distance below the posterior superior spine
  ☐ **Ischial spine**—Pointed process on the inferior edge of the ischial region that protrudes into the pelvic outlet
  ☐ **Obturator foramen**—Large hole formed by the curve of the pubis (medially) and the ischium
  ☐ **Pubic arch**—Arch formed by both the left and right pubis's lower angles, or rami
  ☐ **Pelvic brim (inlet)**—Boundary of the opening into the **true pelvis**; formed by the upper margins (**pubic crests**) of the superior pubic rami, the *ileopectineal lines* that run along the inside face of the ileum, and the *sacral promontory*
  ☐ **True pelvis**—Also called the *pelvis minor*, it is the space below the pelvic brim in which the pelvic organs usually lie
  ☐ **False pelvis**—Also called the *pelvis major*, it is the broad, shallow space above the pelvic brim and below the iliac crests (actually part of the abdominal cavity)

□ 3 Each coxal bone forms a joint directly with two other bones: the sacrum (posteriorly) and the opposite coxal bone (anteriorly).

□ **Symphysis pubis**—Joint between the left and right pubis; also called the *pubic symphysis*

□ **Sacroiliac joint**—Joint between the coxal's ilium and the lateral surface of the sacrum

B. THE LEG

Find the bones and markings listed.

□ 1 The **femur** is the long bone of the thigh **(Figure 15-3)**. Find these features of the femur:

□ **Head**—Large spherical enlargement at the proximal end

□ **Neck**—Narrow region just distal to the head

□ **Greater trochanter**—Large bump that forms a lateral, proximal "corner"

□ **Lesser trochanter**—Bump on the medial, proximal aspect (just distal to the neck)

□ **Intertrochanteric line**—Line that runs between the greater and lesser trochanter

□ **Linea aspera**—Ridge that runs lengthwise along the posterior surface of the shaft

□ **Medial condyle**—Medial, distal bump that articulates with the tibia

□ **Lateral condyle**—Lateral, distal bump that articulates with the tibia

□ **Medial epicondyle**—Blunt projection from the side of the medial condyle

□ **Lateral epicondyle**—Blunt projection from the side of the lateral condyle

□ 2 The **patella** is a large sesamoid bone forming the anterior bone of the knee joint (see Figure 15-3).

□ 3 The **tibia** is one of two long bones of the leg (see Figure 15-3). The tibia is the larger, medial leg bone. Find these tibial features:

□ **Lateral condyle**—Lateral, proximal articular surface

□ **Medial condyle**—Medial, proximal articular surface

□ **Crest**—Sharp ridge running longitudinally along the anterior surface

□ **Tibial tuberosity**—Rough bump on the anterior aspect just distal to the condyles

□ **Medial malleolus**—Pointed bump on the medial aspect of the distal end

□ 4 The **fibula** is the narrower, lateral bone of the leg, having these parts (see Figure 15-3):

□ **Head**—Proximal enlargement

□ **Lateral malleolus**—Pointed bump on the lateral aspect of the distal end

C. THE ANKLE AND FOOT

Find the bones and markings listed.

□ 1 The seven **tarsal** bones form the ankle **(Figures 15-1 and 15-2)**:

□ Talus

□ Calcaneus

□ Cuboid

□ Navicular

□ Medial cuneiform

□ Intermediate cuneiform

□ Lateral cuneiform

□ 2 The foot comprises five **metatarsal bones**, similar to the metacarpals of the hand. Also like the hand, the foot has 28 **phalanges**.

clinical applications: radiograph of the foot

_____ 1	_____ 5	
_____ 2	_____ 6	
_____ 3	_____ 7	
_____ 4	_____ 8	

FIGURE 15-1 Radiograph of the foot. This radiographic, or x-ray, image is a medial view of the left foot. Try to identify the noted structures and label them on the lines provided and on the blanks on the Lab Report at the end of this exercise.

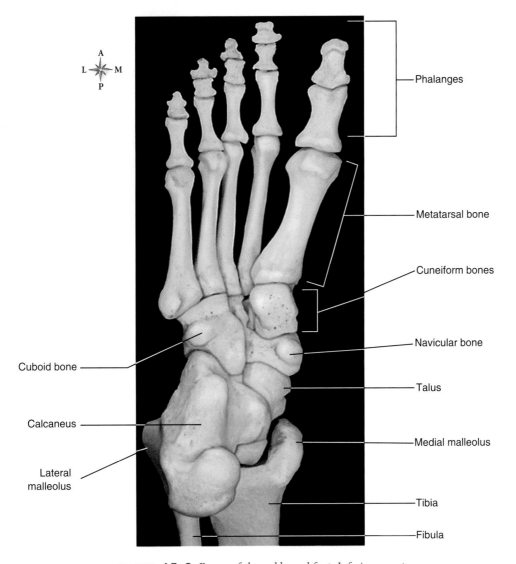

Phalanges

Metatarsal bone

Cuneiform bones

Navicular bone

Talus

Medial malleolus

Tibia

Fibula

Cuboid bone

Calcaneus

Lateral malleolus

FIGURE 15-2 Bones of the ankle and foot. Inferior aspect.

FIGURE 15-3 A, Anterior view of right lower extremity. **B,** Right lateral view of right lower extremity.

Coloring Exercises: Lower Extremity

Use colored pens or pencils to shade in both the figure and the labels. Each red numeral in the figure corresponds to a matching red numeral following the appropriate label.

COXAL₁

ILIUM₂

ISCHIUM₃

PUBIS₄

FEMUR₅

PATELLA₆

TIBIA₇

FIBULA₈

TALUS₉

CALCANEUS₁₀

CUBOID₁₁

NAVICULAR₁₂

MEDIAL CUNEIFORM₁₃

INTERMEDIATE CUNEIFORM₁₄

LATERAL CUNEIFORM₁₅

METATARSAL₁₆

PROXIMAL PHALANX₁₇

MIDDLE PHALANX₁₈

DISTAL PHALANX₁₉

FIGURE 15-4 Structures of the lower extremity. After coloring the diagram, label the specific structures noted on the lines provided and on the blanks in the Lab Report at the end of this exercise.

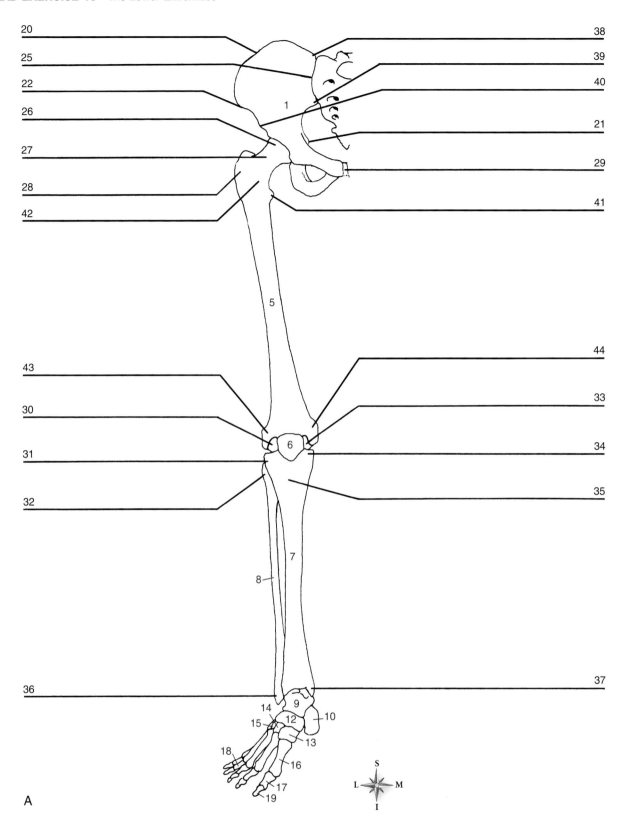

FIGURE 15-5 **A,** Anterior view of lower extremity. After coloring the diagram, label the specific structures noted on the lines provided and on the blanks in the Lab Report at the end of this exercise.

25
20
38
39
22
40
21
26
28
27
41
45
44
43
33
30
31
34
32
1
5
7
8
37
36
9
11
10
16

S
M — L
I

B

FIGURE 15-5, cont'd B, Posterior view of the left lower extremity. After coloring the diagram, label the specific structures noted on the lines provided and on the blanks in the Lab Report at the end of this exercise.

Name: _____ Date: _____ Section: _____

LAB REPORT 15
The Lower Extremities

Multiple Choice

1. _____

2. _____

3. _____

4. _____

5. _____

6. _____

Multiple Choice (only one response is correct in each item)

1. The leg is comprised of the
   a. tibia
   b. radius
   c. ulna
   d. fibula
   e. b and c are correct
   f. a and d are correct

2. Lynn has lost quite a bit of weight recently and now notices that a bump is visible in each side of her lower abdomen. Palpating it, she feels that her pelvic bone is protruding. Which part?
   a. ischial spine
   b. symphysis pubis
   c. anterior superior spine
   d. iliac crest
   e. acetabulum

3. The sacrum and coxal bone are joined at the
   a. sacroiliac joint
   b. hip joint
   c. sacrocoxal joint
   d. ischial tuberosity
   e. symphysis pubis

4. The coxal bone's cuplike socket for the head of the femur is called the
   a. trochlear notch
   b. ischial notch
   c. acetabulum
   d. obturator foramen
   e. femoral fossa

5. Which one of these is not a tarsal bone?
   a. calcaneus
   b. navicular
   c. cuneiform
   d. hamate
   e. talus

6. The long ridge that runs along the front of the tibia is called the
   a. tibial tuberosity
   b. intertrochanteric line
   c. iliac crest
   d. tibial crest
   e. fibular ridge

Figures 15-1 (from p. 151)

1. _____
2. _____
3. _____
4. _____
5. _____
6. _____
7. _____
8. _____

Figures 15-4 and 15-5
(from pp. 153-155)

(NOTE: Numbers 1 through 19 are used for coloring labels.)

20. _____
21. _____
22. _____
23. _____
24. _____
25. _____
26. _____
27. _____
28. _____
29. _____
30. _____
31. _____
32. _____
33. _____
34. _____
35. _____
36. _____
37. _____
38. _____
39. _____
40. _____
41. _____
42. _____
43. _____
44. _____
45. _____

Table 15-1 (fill in the numbers as indicated)

T A B L E   1 5 - 1   Bone Count in the Lower Extremities

NUMBER	STRUCTURES
	Bones in the appendicular skeleton
	Bones in the upper extremities
	Bones in the lower extremities
	Wrist bones (total)
	Ankle bones (total)
	Hand/finger bones (total)
	Foot/toe bones (total)

Joints

Joints, or articulations, are structures in the skeleton where two or more bones join together. Because different joints are built differently and therefore behave differently, anatomists have devised a scheme for classifying articulations. This exercise presents a common system of joint classification and challenges you to find examples of joint classes and the different types of movements that they allow. This exercise also offers you the opportunity to examine examples of specific joints of the body.

BEFORE YOU BEGIN

- ☐ Read the appropriate chapter in your textbook.
- ☐ Set your learning goals. When you finish this exercise, you should be able to:
  - ☐ distinguish the three classes of joints
  - ☐ describe examples of each joint class
  - ☐ identify different types of motions in joints
  - ☐ describe the structure of the different joints
- ☐ Prepare your materials:
  - ☐ human skeleton (articulated)
  - ☐ synovial joints (model or fresh animal specimen l.s., knee or shoulder)
- ☐ Read the directions and safety tips for this exercise *carefully* before starting any procedure.

Study TIPS

The use of a concept map is an effective strategy to learn and understand the different classifications of articulations and their locations. Refer to your text or the *A&P Survival Guide* as a reference.

A. CLASSIFYING JOINTS

Find an example of each type of joint described in the following steps. Try to find examples other than those given here.

safety first
Use caution when handling the articulated skeleton. •

- ☐ 1 **Fibrous joints** are found where fibrous connective tissue tightly binds the articulating bones. Identify these types of fibrous joints **(Figure 16-1)**:

- ☐ **Suture**—This is a joint between two flat bones, as between the left and right parietal bones (sagittal suture)
- ☐ **Syndesmosis**—These are bands of fibrous tissue that bind bones, as between the distal ends of the radius and ulna
- ☐ **Gomphosis**—A fibrous membrane that connects each tooth to its socket in a jaw's alveolar process
- ☐ 2 **Cartilaginous joints** are formed when a mass of cartilage joins bones.
  - ☐ **Synchondrosis**—Hyaline cartilage that connects bones; for example, the costal cartilage connection between a rib and the sternum
  - ☐ **Symphysis**—Fibrocartilage that forms the joint, as in the symphysis pubis, joining left and right coxae

> **Hint** Fibrous and cartilaginous joints can be classified according to function rather than structure. Thus, functional categories of **immovable** (synarthrotic) and **slightly movable** (amphiarthrotic) are sometimes used. Most fibrous joints are immovable, so they are called *synarthroses*. Likewise, many cartilaginous joints are slightly movable, so they are called *amphiarthroses*. •

- ☐ 3 **Synovial joints** are always **freely movable** (*diarthrotic*) joints. A flexible *joint capsule*, composed of ligaments and other connective structures and lined with a lubricating *synovial membrane*, allows a wide range of movement. Categories of synovial joints are based on the way in which the articulating bones fit together:
  - ☐ **Gliding joint**—Two flat surfaces that slide past each other, as between two carpal bones
  - ☐ **Hinge joint**—As with a door hinge, two bones are joined so that they can move in one plane only, as in the elbow
  - ☐ **Ellipsoid joint**—An oval condyle that fits into an oval fossa, allowing movement in two planes, as between the metatarsals and phalanges of the foot
  - ☐ **Pivot joint**—One bone that pivots on the axis of another, allowing rotation, as with the atlas and axis
  - ☐ **Saddle joint**—Two saddle-shaped processes that fit together to allow movement in two planes, as between the thumb's metatarsal and the trapezium of the wrist
  - ☐ **Ball-and-socket joint**—A ball-shaped process that fits into a rounded fossa, allowing almost unrestricted movement, as between the femur and the acetabulum

Study **TIPS**

Use a mnemonic device to help you remember the types of synovial joints. An example of this would be:

Getting	Gliding
Help	Hinge
Prepares	Pivot
Every	Ellipsoid
Student	Saddle
Better	Ball-and-socket

B. EXAMPLES OF SYNOVIAL JOINTS

In this activity, you are challenged to explore the detailed anatomy of the human knee joint and the human shoulder joint. Find the structures listed in models or charts.

> **Hint** Use the diagrams given in the figures here, as well as those found in your textbook, for help in locating the major structures listed in this activity. •

☐ 1 In a model or chart of the human knee, identify these features **(Figure 16-2)**:
  ☐ Articular cartilage
  ☐ Lateral meniscus
  ☐ Synovial membrane
  ☐ Patella
  ☐ Condyles of tibia
  ☐ Condyles of femur
  ☐ Prepatellar bursa
  ☐ Suprapatellar bursa
  ☐ Posterior cruciate ligament
  ☐ Anterior cruciate ligament
  ☐ Tibial collateral ligament
  ☐ Fibular collateral ligament
  ☐ Patellar ligament
  ☐ Head of fibula

How many of these features can you palpate in your own knee?

☐ 2 In a model or chart of the human shoulder joint, identify these features **(Figure 16-3)**:
  ☐ Acromion process of scapula
  ☐ Coracoid process of scapula
  ☐ Articular cartilage of humerus
  ☐ Glenoid cavity
  ☐ Articular cartilage of glenoid cavity
  ☐ Medial glenohumeral ligament
  ☐ Superior glenohumeral ligament
  ☐ Acromiocoracoid ligament
  ☐ Subdeltoid bursa
  ☐ Synovial membrane
  ☐ Synovial cavity

C. DISSECTION OF A JOINT

In a preserved or fresh animal specimen (l.s.) of a synovial joint such as the knee or shoulder, identify the features described Sketch your observations on a piece of paper and attach it to Lab Report 16.

> **safety first**
> Because fresh animal tissue at room temperature may harbor bacterial colonies, handle your specimen with gloved hands. •

☐ 1 Identify the *articulating bones*. Which joint is this?
☐ 2 Find the *articular cartilage* on the articulating surfaces of the joint. How would you describe its texture? What is the function of articular cartilage?
☐ 3 Locate the *ligaments* and other connective tissues of the *joint capsule* holding the joint together. Note how strong and how flexible they are.
☐ 4 The *synovial membrane* lines the joint capsule. What is its consistency? Is any *synovial fluid* still in the *synovial cavity* formed by this membrane? What is this fluid's function?

Coloring Exercises: Joint Classification

Use colored pens or pencils to shade in both the figure and the labels. Each red numeral in the figure corresponds to a matching red numeral following the appropriate label.

Joint Classification

FIBROUS JOINT₁
CARTILAGINOUS JOINT₂

Synovial Joint

ARTICULATING BONE₃
ARTICULAR CARTILAGE₄
SYNOVIAL MEMBRANE₅
SYNOVIAL CAVITY₆
SYNOVIAL CAPSULE₇

Synovial Joint Types

GLIDING₈
HINGE₉
ELLIPSOID₁₀
PIVOT₁₁
SADDLE₁₂
BALL AND SOCKET₁₃

FIGURE 16-1 Joint structures and types.

D. JOINT MOVEMENT

Although synovial, or *diarthrotic*, joints can allow a wide range of motion, they are limited by the structure of the joint and the surrounding body parts.

Demonstrate the types of joint movement listed by performing them yourself.

> **! safety first**
> Be careful to avoid accidentally hitting someone as you do this activity. Do not attempt this activity if you have a physical condition that may be worsened by joint movements. •

☐ 1 Some skeletal movements involve movement of body parts relative to a coronal (frontal) plane **(Figure 16-4)**:
  ☐ **Flexion**—Decreasing the angle of a joint
  ☐ **Extension**—Increasing the angle of a joint
  ☐ **Hyperextension**—Moving a joint beyond its normal range or beyond the anatomical position
  ☐ **Dorsiflexion**—Bending the ankle so that the toes point upward
  ☐ **Plantar flexion**—Bending the ankle so that the toes point downward
  ☐ **Protraction**—Moving a part anteriorly, along a horizontal plane
  ☐ **Retraction**—Moving a part posteriorly, along a horizontal plane

> **Hint** The angle of movement in joints is measured in the manner shown:

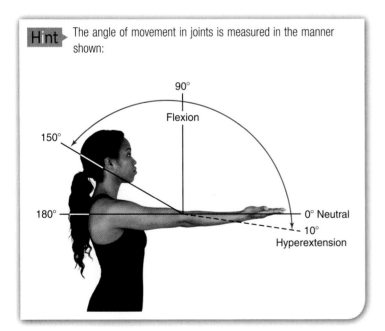

☐ 2 Some motions are done relative to a sagittal plane **(Figure 16-5)**:
  ☐ **Abduction**—Moving an appendage's distal end away from the midsagittal plane
  ☐ **Adduction**—Moving an appendage's distal end toward the midsagittal plane
  ☐ **Inversion**—Moving the foot from the anatomical position (sole downward) to a position in which the sole is facing the midsagittal plane
  ☐ **Eversion**—Moving the foot from the anatomical position to a position in which the sole faces away from the midsagittal plane
☐ 3 Try these circular movements **(Figure 16-6)**:
  ☐ **Circumduction**—Moving the distal end of an appendage in a circle, making a cone-shaped sweep
  ☐ **Rotation**—Moving a bone on its axis, as if on a pivot or axle
  ☐ **Pronation**—Rotating the forearm from the anatomical position (palm forward) to reverse it (palm facing the posterior)
  ☐ **Supination**—Rotating the forearm from the pronated position back to the anatomical position
☐ 4 Try these special movements **(Figure 16-7)**:
  ☐ **Elevation**—Raising a part
  ☐ **Depression**—Lowering a part

Study TIPS

Demonstrate these joint movements by performing them in front of a mirror. You can also identify them as a partner demonstrates them.

> **Hint** These joint movements are commonly classified in other ways as well. For example, what scheme of classification is used in the textbook? •

A

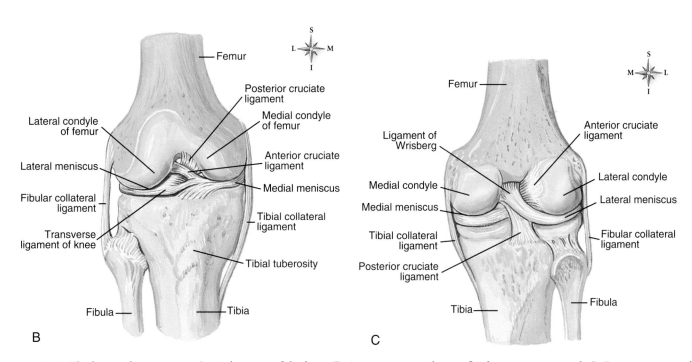

B

C

FIGURE 16-2 The human knee joint. **A,** Sagittal section of the knee. **B,** Anterior view, with superficial structures removed. **C,** Posterior view, with superficial structures removed.

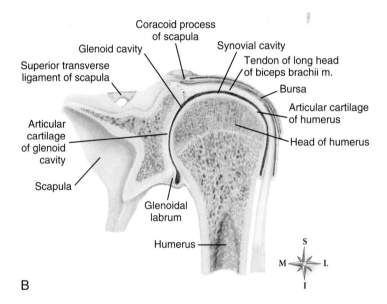

FIGURE 16-3 The shoulder joint. **A**, Anterior view. **B**, Viewed from behind through shoulder joint.

FIGURE 16-4 Movements relative to a coronal (frontal) plane. **A,** Flexion and extension of the elbow. **B,** Flexion, extension, and hyperextension of the neck. **C,** Dorsiflexion and plantar flexion. **D,** Protraction and retraction of the jaw.

FIGURE 16-5 Movements relative to a sagittal plane. **A,** Adduction and abduction of the thigh. **B,** Eversion and inversion of the foot.

FIGURE 16-6 Circular movements. **A,** Rotation of the head. **B,** Circumduction of the arm. **C,** Pronation and supination of the hand.

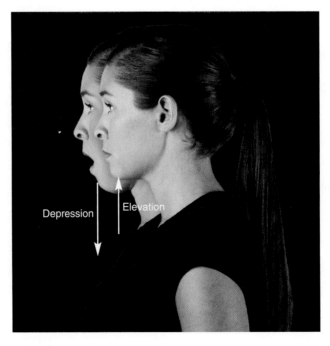

FIGURE 16-7 Special movements, temporomandibular joint (TMJ).

clinical application: *arthrography*

Radiographic examination of the soft tissues that form joints is called **arthrography**. In one method of arthrography, a **contrast medium** that absorbs x-rays is injected into the joint. The liquid contrast medium coats the surfaces of the cartilage, ligaments, and other soft structures of the joint. When a regular radiograph is taken, the coated soft tissues clearly appear because the x-rays do not penetrate the coating. The resulting image is called an **arthrogram**.

In the knee arthrograms shown in **Figure 16-8**, several features that are invisible in a regular radiograph can be seen:

☐ **Bursa**—A "pillow" made of synovial membrane and filled with synovial fluid
☐ **Meniscus**—A piece of cartilage shaped like a disk with a curved surface
☐ **Articular cartilage**—A cartilage coating on the articulating surfaces of bone

FIGURE 16-8 Arthrograms of the knee joint. Label the structures noted on the lines provided and also on the blanks in the Lab Report at the end of this exercise.

Can you identify these three joint structures in the arthrograms above?

1. What advantages does using contrast medium give when doing radiography?

2. Computed tomography (CT) has been more recently used to study joints. What advantages does the CT method have over the method described here?

Name: _____ Date: _____ Section: _____

LAB REPORT 16
Joints

Figure 16-8 (from p. 167)

1. _____
2. _____
3. _____

Matching I

1. _____
2. _____
3. _____
4. _____
5. _____
6. _____
7. _____
8. _____
9. _____
10. _____

Matching II

1. _____
2. _____
3. _____
4. _____
5. _____
6. _____
7. _____
8. _____
9. _____
10. _____

Matching I (may be used more than once)

a. Fibrous joint
b. Synovial joint
c. Cartilaginous joint

1. Gliding joint
2. Synchondrosis
3. Freely movable
4. Suture
5. Gomphosis
6. Saddle joint
7. Hinge joint
8. Symphysis
9. Mainly hyaline cartilage or fibrocartilage
10. Ellipsoid joint

Matching II (match these examples to their types)

a. Suture
b. Syndesmosis
c. Gomphosis
d. Synchondrosis
e. Symphysis
f. Hinge
g. Gliding
h. Pivot
i. Saddle
j. Ball and socket

1. Between bodies of vertebrae
2. Between the distal ends of the tibia and fibula
3. At the base of the thumb's proximal phalanx
4. Between the articular facets of the vertebrae's processes
5. Between the true ribs and sternum
6. Between the talus and leg
7. Between C1 and C2, at the dens
8. The shoulder
9. The transverse palatine suture
10. Between the tooth and jaw

Identify

1. _____

2. _____

3. _____

4. _____

5. _____

6. _____

7. _____

8. _____

9. _____

10. _____

Identify (in the blanks to the left, write the type of motion illustrated in the matching figure to the right. For example, in number 1, is abduction or adduction shown?)

1

2

3

4

5

6

7

8

9

10

17

Organization of the Muscular System

The muscular system is comprised of all the skeletal muscles, sometimes called *muscle organs* to distinguish them from muscle tissue and muscle cells. Skeletal muscles are attached to the skeleton in ways that move skeletal parts when the muscles contract. The chief function of this system, then, is skeletal movement. Secondarily, this system helps in temperature regulation by providing a source of metabolic heat.

This exercise presents some preliminary information about the muscular system. Although we have seen some of the histology of skeletal muscle tissue, we have not yet explored the muscle cell or the muscle organ. In this exercise we do both. We also take a brief look at how muscle organs are named so that the next exercise, which involves muscle identification, will be easier.

BEFORE YOU BEGIN

- ☐ Read the appropriate chapter in your textbook.
- ☐ Set your learning goals. When you finish this exercise, you should be able to:
  - ☐ describe the structure of the skeletal muscle cell
  - ☐ identify and describe the principal structures of a skeletal muscle organ
  - ☐ define the terms *origin* and *insertion*
  - ☐ interpret the meaning of muscle names
- ☐ Prepare your materials:
  - ☐ model or chart of a skeletal muscle cell
  - ☐ model or chart of a skeletal muscle organ
  - ☐ animal muscle specimen (fresh meat section)
  - ☐ dissection tools
- ☐ Read the directions and safety tips for this exercise *carefully* before starting any procedure.

A. THE SKELETAL MUSCLE CELL

Skeletal muscle cells provide the basic functional capability of the muscle organ because they can contract with great force. Such contraction requires a rather unusual structural pattern in muscle cells if it is to be efficient. Study these features of the skeletal muscle cell in a model or figure **(Figures 17-1, 17-2, and 17-3)**:

- ☐ 1 The **sarcolemma** is the plasma membrane of the long, cylindrical **muscle fiber**, or muscle cell. The sarcolemma has a *resting potential*, or electrical charge. This charge temporarily reverses during an *action potential*, or impulse, when the muscle fiber is stimulated.
- ☐ 2 The sarcolemma dips inward at several points to form internal *transverse tubules* called **T tubules.** An impulse traveling along the sarcolemma can thus also travel inside the cell.
- ☐ 3 Inside the cell are a number of membranous networks similar to endoplasmic reticulum (ER). They are all part of the **sarcoplasmic reticulum (SR).** The SR receives the impulse from the T tubules, which are nearby, and releases calcium ions into the **sarcoplasm** in response.
- ☐ 4 The calcium ions released from the SR diffuse through the sarcoplasm among parallel bundles of protein **myofilaments.** Each bundle is called a **myofibril** and is composed of an orderly arrangement of **thin filaments** and **thick filaments.**
- ☐ 5 The myofilaments are arranged in a repeating pattern called a **sarcomere.** When calcium ions react with some of the myofilament molecules, they slide past one another, shortening each sarcomere. Because all the sarcomeres in the cell's myofibrils shorten, the cell contracts.
- ☐ 6 As you recall, a muscle fiber has multiple **nuclei.** The nuclei are against the inside of the sarcolemma.

Coloring Exercises: Muscle Cell

Use colored pens or pencils to shade in both the figure and the labels. Each red numeral in the figure corresponds to a matching red numeral following the appropriate label.

SARCOPLASMIC
  RETICULUM1
NUCLEUS2
SARCOLEMMA3

BLOOD CAPILLARY4
MYOFIBRIL5
MITOCHONDRION6
TRANSVERSE TUBULE7

FIGURE 17-1 Structure of a muscle cell.

B. STRUCTURE OF A MUSCLE ORGAN

Each muscle organ has a unique shape and size, but the principal components of each are the same (see Figure 17-3). Identify each of these in a model or chart. Some structures may be visible in a fresh muscle specimen.

> **!** **safety first**
> Use gloved hands when handling fresh meat at room temperature. You may wish to use dissection tools. If so, be careful to avoid cuts and puncture wounds. •

☐ 1 The entire organ is covered with fibrous connective tissue that forms a sheath called the **epimysium.**

☐ 2 The fibrous tissue of the epimysium extends inward to form sheaths around bundles, or **fasciculi,** of muscle cells. This inner fibrous sheath is called the **perimysium.**

☐ 3 The perimysium's fibrous tissue continues inside each fascicle to wrap around each individual muscle cell. The connective tissue sheath around individual muscle fibers is called the **endomysium.** Just deep to the endomysium is the sarcolemma.

☐ 4 All the fibrous sheaths are continuous with one another and contain blood vessels that supply the muscle fibers. At the ends of the muscle organ, the muscle fibers stop, while the connective sheaths continue. This forms an extension of dense fibrous connective tissue that attaches to the periosteum of a bone (or to another muscle). If the fibrous connection is in the shape of a strap or band, it is called a **tendon.** If it is a broad, flat sheet, it is called an **aponeurosis.**

☐ 5 Generally a muscle attaches to the skeleton at two ends. The end that attaches to the more stationary bone is called the **origin.** The other end, or **insertion,** attaches to the bone that moves as the muscle contracts.

Study TIPS

As you study the organizational structure of a muscle, think of its structure as a tube within a tube, within a tube, within a tube. In other words, the entire muscle is a tube. Within this tube are numerous "tubes" (fasciculi). Within the fasciculi are "tubes" (muscle fibers). As you examine the muscle fibers, you will note that they too are divided into "tubes" (myofibrils). Finally, the myofibrils are divided into even smaller "tubes" (myofilaments).

C. NAMING SKELETAL MUSCLES

Muscle **nomenclature** is the system of naming skeletal muscle organs. The names of muscles, as with many organs, are in Latin rather than in English. By using only a handful of descriptive Latin words, in combinations of two or three, anatomists have named all the muscles of the human body. Review these terms used to name muscles because they will come in handy when you learn specific muscle names in the next exercise.

☐ 1 Muscles can be named for their overall shape. Review these terms related to muscle shape:

deltoid	shaped like **delta** (Δ)
orbicularis	circular
platy	flattened; platelike
quadratus	square
rhomboideus	diamond-shaped
trapezius	trapezoidal
triangularis	triangular

☐ 2 Some muscles are named for their points of attachment (*origin* and *insertion*). For example, the *sternocleidomastoid* muscle has attachments on the sternum, clavicle, and mastoid process of the temporal bone.

☐ 3 Muscles can be named according to relative size:

brevis	short
longus	long
magnus	large
maximus	largest
medius	moderately sized
minimus	small

☐ 4 The direction of fibers visible in a muscle can be a basis for its name, using these terms:

oblique	diagonal to the body's midline
rectus	parallel to the midline
sphincter	circling an opening
transversus	at a right angle to the midline

☐ 5 Some muscle names are derived from the action(s) produced:

abductor	abducts a part
adductor	adducts a part
depressor	depresses a part
extensor	extends a part
flexor	flexes a part
levator	elevates a part
rotator	rotates a part

Coloring Exercises: **Skeletal Muscle**

Use colored pens or pencils to shade in both the figure and the labels. Each red numeral in the figure corresponds to a matching red numeral following the appropriate label.

TENDON₁
EPIMYSIUM₂
PERIMYSIUM₃
ENDOMYSIUM₄
MYOFIBRIL₅
THIN FILAMENT₆
THICK FILAMENT₇
SARCOMERE₈
A BAND₉
I BAND₁₀

FIGURE 17-2 Structure of skeletal muscle.

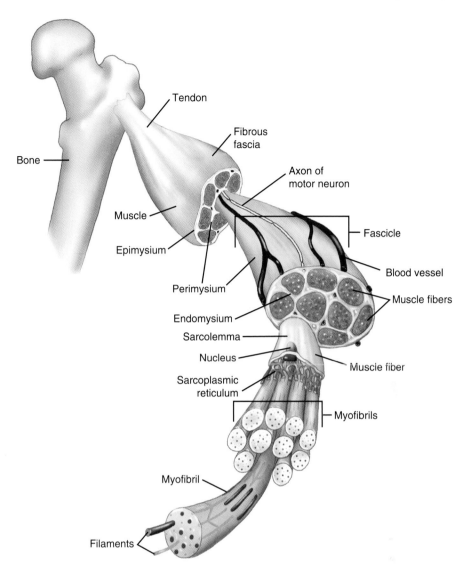

FIGURE 17-3 Architecture of a muscle.

□ 6 Some muscles are named for the region in which they are found. Some of these terms should be familiar to you:

brachialis	arm
frontalis	frontal (bone)
femoris	femur
gluteus	posterior of hip/thigh
oculi	eye
radialis	radius
ulnaris	ulna

T A B L E 1 8 - 2 **Muscles of the Trunk**

MUSCLE	ORIGIN	INSERTION	ACTION
ERECTOR SPINAE₁₂ (DIVIDES INTO THREE)	Vertebrae, pelvis	Superior vertebrae, ribs	Holds body upright
DEEP BACK MUSCLES	Vertebrae	Vertebrae	Flexes or extends trunk
EXTERNAL INTERCOSTALS₁₃	Ribs	Edge of next rib (inferiorly)	Expands thorax
INTERNAL INTERCOSTALS₁₄	Ribs	Edge of next rib (superiorly)	Compresses thorax
RECTUS ABDOMINIS₁₅	Pubis	Inferior thoracic cage	Flexes waist
EXTERNAL ABDOMINAL OBLIQUE₁₆	Inferior thoracic cage	Midline of abdomen	Compresses abdomen
INTERNAL ABDOMINAL OBLIQUE₁₇	Pelvis	Midline of abdomen	Compresses abdomen
TRANSVERSUS ABDOMINIS₁₈	Vertebrae, pelvis, ribs	Midline of abdomen	Compresses abdomen
TRAPEZIUS₁₁	Skull, upper vertebral column	Scapula	Extends head, neck; elevates, depresses, or rotates scapula
LEVATOR SCAPULAE₁₉	Vertebrae	Scapula	Elevates scapula
RHOMBOIDEUS₂₀ (TWO)	Vertebrae	Scapula	Retracts scapula
SERRATUS ANTERIOR₂₁	Ribs	Scapula	Protracts scapula
PECTORALIS MINOR₂₂	Ribs	Scapula	Depresses scapula
PECTORALIS MAJOR₂₃	Ribs, clavicle	Humerus	Adducts, flexes arm
TERES MAJOR₂₄	Scapula	Humerus	Extends, adducts, rotates arm
LATISSIMUS DORSI₂₅	Vertebrae	Humerus	Extends, adducts arm
INFRASPINATUS₂₆	Scapula	Humerus	Extends, rotates arm
SUPRASPINATUS₂₇	Scapula	Humerus	Abducts arm
SUBSCAPULARIS	Scapula	Humerus	Extends, rotates arm
TERES MINOR	Scapula	Humerus	Adducts, rotates arm
DELTOID₂₈	Scapula, clavicle	Humerus	Abducts arm

Use terms in OUTLINE type as coloring labels. Terms in **SOLID** type do not appear in the coloring plate.

Coloring Exercises: Muscles of the Upper Extremity

Use colored pens or pencils to shade in both the figure and the labels. Each red numeral in the figure corresponds to a matching red numeral following the appropriate label.

FIGURE 18-3 Muscles of the arm.

TABLE 18-3   **Muscles of the Upper Extremity**

MUSCLE	ORIGIN	INSERTION	ACTION
TRICEPS BRACHII₍29₎	Scapula	Ulna	Extends forearm
BICEPS BRACHII₍30₎	Humerus, scapula	Radius	Flexes, supinates forearm
BRACHIALIS₍31₎	Humerus	Ulna	Flexes forearm
PRONATORS₍32₎ (TWO)	Ulna, humerus	Radius	Pronates forearm
FLEXOR CARPI ULNARIS₍33₎	Humerus (medial epicondyle)	Carpal bone	Flexes, abducts wrist
FLEXOR CARPI RADIALIS₍34₎	Humerus (medial epicondyle)	Metacarpal bones	Flexes, abducts wrist
FLEXOR DIGITORUM₍35₎ (TWO)	Humerus (medial epicondyle, ulna, radius)	Phalanges	Flexes fingers
BRACHIORADIALIS₍36₎	Humerus	Radius (distal)	Flexes forearm
SUPINATOR	Ulna	Radius	Supinates forearm
EXTENSOR CARPI ULNARIS₍37₎	Humerus (lateral epicondyle)	Metacarpal bones	Extends, abducts wrist
EXTENSOR CARPI RADIALIS₍38₎ (TWO)	Humerus (lateral epicondyle)	Metacarpal bones	Extends, abducts wrist
EXTENSOR DIGITORUM₍39₎	Humerus (lateral epicondyle)	Phalanges	Extends fingers

Use terms in OUTLINE type as coloring labels. Terms in **SOLID** type do not appear in the coloring plate.

Coloring Exercises: **Mucles of the Lower Extremity**

Use colored pens or pencils to shade in both the figure and the labels. Each red numeral in the figure corresponds to a matching red numeral following the appropriate label.

FIGURE 18-4 Muscles of the leg.

TABLE 18-4   Muscles of the Lower Extremity

MUSCLE	ORIGIN	INSERTION	ACTION
ILIOPSOAS 40	Ilium, vertebrae	Femur	Flexes thigh
TENSOR FASCIAE LATAE 41	Hip	Tibia	Abducts thigh
GLUTEAL GROUP (A, B, C)			
A GLUTEUS MAXIMUS 42	Hip	Femur	Extends thigh
B GLUTEUS MEDIUS 43	Hip	Femur	Abducts thigh
C GLUTEUS MINIMUS	Hip	Femur	Abducts thigh
QUADRICEPS FEMORIS (A, B, C, D)			
A RECTUS FEMORIS 44	Ilium	Tibia	Extends leg, flexes thigh
B VASTUS LATERALIS 45	Femur	Tibia	Extends leg
C VASTUS MEDIALIS 46	Femur	Tibia	Extends leg
D VASTUS INTERMEDIUS	Femur	Tibia	Extends leg
SARTORIUS 47	Ilium	Tibia	Flexes thigh; flexes, rotates leg
HAMSTRING GROUP (A, B, C)			
A BICEPS FEMORIS 48	Ischium, femur	Fibula	Flexes leg, extends thigh
B SEMIMEMBRANOSUS 49	Ischium	Tibia	Flexes leg, extends thigh
C SEMITENDINOSUS 50	Ischium	Tibia	Flexes leg, extends thigh
ADDUCTOR GROUP (A, B)			
A ADDUCTOR LONGUS 51	Pubis	Femur	Adducts thigh
B GRACILIS 52	Pubis	Tibia	Adducts thigh
TIBIALIS ANTERIOR 53	Tibia	Metatarsal bones	Extends (dorsiflexes) foot
EXTENSOR DIGITORUM LONGUS 54	Tibia	Phalanges	Extends toes
GASTROCNEMIUS 55	Femur	Calcaneus	(Plantar) flexes foot
SOLEUS 56	Tibia, fibula	Calcaneus	(Plantar) flexes foot
FIBULARIS 57 (THREE)	Tibia, fibula	Tarsal, metatarsal bones	Flexes, everts foot

Use terms in OUTLINE type as coloring labels. Terms in **SOLID** type do not appear in the coloring plate.

Coloring Exercises: Muscles of the Pelvic Floor

Use colored pens or pencils to shade in both the figure and the labels. Each red numeral in the figure corresponds to a matching red numeral following the appropriate label.

> **Hint** ▶ By now you have noticed that several of the muscles illustrated in the coloring exercises do not have labels. Some of them are muscles that you were asked to identify but are not labeled for coloring because they are too far away from the outline labels. Go back to the figures and try to identify the unlabeled muscles. Use your textbook and anatomy reference books in your school library to help you.   •

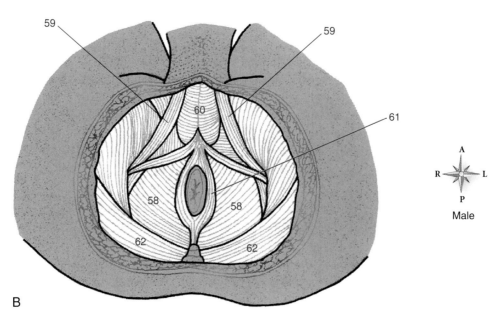

FIGURE 18-5 Inferior view of the pelvic muscles in the female (**A**) and male (**B**).

TABLE 18-5 **Muscles of the Pelvic Floor**

MUSCLE	ORIGIN	INSERTION	ACTION
LEVATOR ANI58	Pubis, ischium	Sacrum, coccyx	Elevates anus
ISCHIOCAVERNOSUS59	Ischium	Clitoris or penis	Compresses base of clitoris or penis
BULBOSPONGIOSUS60	MALE: bulb of penis FEMALE: central tendon of perineum	MALE: central tendon of perineum FEMALE: base of clitoris	MALE: constricts urethra; erects penis FEMALE: erects clitoris
SPHINCTER EXTERNUS ANI61	Coccyx	Central tendon (median raphe)	Closes anal canal
GLUTEUS MAXIMUS62	Hip	Femur	Extends thigh

Use terms in OUTLINE type as coloring labels.

☐ 3 Identify these muscles of the *upper extremity* **(Figure 18-3)**:
   ☐ Triceps brachii
   ☐ Biceps brachii
   ☐ Brachialis
   ☐ Pronators (two muscles, teres and quadratus)
   ☐ Flexor carpi ulnaris
   ☐ Flexor carpi radialis
   ☐ Flexor digitorum (two muscles)
   ☐ Brachioradialis
   ☐ Supinator
   ☐ Extensor carpi ulnaris
   ☐ Extensor carpi radialis (two muscles, profundus and superficialis)
   ☐ Extensor digitorum
☐ 4 Identify these muscles of the *lower extremity* **(Figure 18-4)**:
   ☐ Iliopsoas
   ☐ Tensor fasciae latae
   ☐ Gluteal group: gluteus maximus, gluteus medius, gluteus minimus
   ☐ Quadriceps femoris group: rectus femoris, vastus lateralis, vastus medialis, vastus intermedius
   ☐ Sartorius
   ☐ Hamstring group: biceps femoris, semimembranosus, semitendinosus
   ☐ Adductor group: adductor longus, gracilis
   ☐ Tibialis anterior
   ☐ Extensor digitorum longus

   ☐ Gastrocnemius
   ☐ Soleus
   ☐ Fibularis (three muscles, longus, brevis, and tertius)
☐ 5 Identify these muscles of the *pelvic floor* **(Figure 18-5)**:
   ☐ Levator ani
   ☐ Ischiocavernosus
   ☐ Bulbospongiosus
   ☐ Sphincter externus ani
   ☐ Gluteus maximus

B. DEMONSTRATING MUSCLE ACTION

For each of the muscles found in Activity A of this exercise, demonstrate its action with your own muscle (if possible). As you contract the muscle, palpate it and note its size and location.

! *safety first*
Be careful to avoid injuring yourself and others as you perform each muscle action. •

Hint For a more detailed description of the origin, insertion, action, and innervation of some of these muscles, please refer to your textbook. •

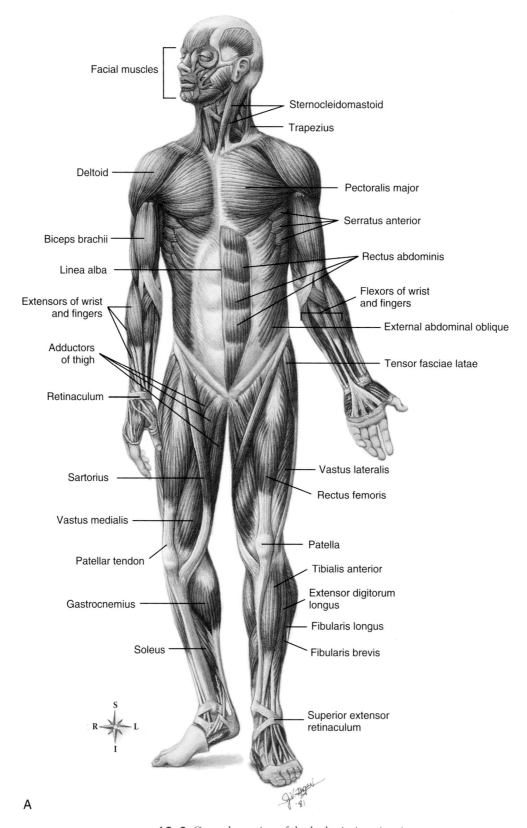

FIGURE 18-6 General overview of the body. **A,** Anterior view.

Sternocleidomastoid

Splenius capitis

Seventh cervical vertebra

Trapezius

Deltoid

Infraspinatus

Teres minor

Teres major

Triceps brachii

Latissimus dorsi

External abdominal oblique

Extensors of the wrist and fingers

Gluteus maximus

Hamstring group

Semitendinosus

Biceps femoris

Semimembranosus

Adductor magnus

Gracilis

Iliotibial tract

Gastrocnemius

Calcaneal tendon (Achilles tendon)

Fibularis longus

Soleus

Fibularis brevis

S

L   R

I

B

FIGURE 18-6, cont'd B, Posterior view.

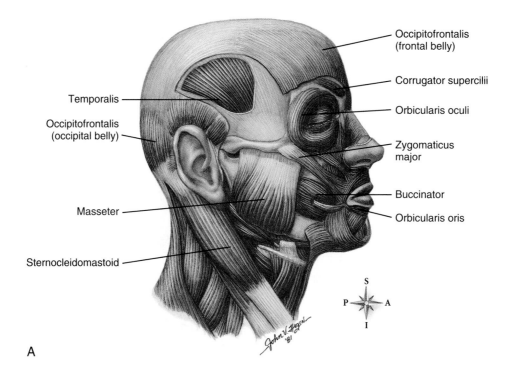

Occipitofrontalis
(frontal belly)

Corrugator supercilii

Orbicularis oculi

Zygomaticus
major

Buccinator

Orbicularis oris

Temporalis

Occipitofrontalis
(occipital belly)

Masseter

Sternocleidomastoid

A

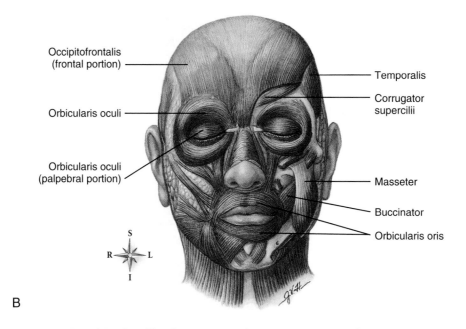

Occipitofrontalis
(frontal portion)

Orbicularis oculi

Orbicularis oculi
(palpebral portion)

Temporalis

Corrugator
supercilii

Masseter

Buccinator

Orbicularis oris

B

FIGURE 18-7 Muscles of facial expression and mastication. **A,** Lateral view. **B,** Anterior view.

Name: _____ Date: _____ Section: _____

LAB REPORT 18
Skeletal Muscle Identification

Table Completion (list each muscle name only once in the table below)

Adductor group
Latissimus dorsi
Biceps brachii
Pectoralis major
Deltoid
Pectoralis major/latissimus dorsi combination
Erector spinae
Quadriceps femoris group

Gastrocnemius
Rectus abdominis
Gluteus maximus
Tensor fasciae latae
Hamstring group
Tibialis anterior
Iliopsoas
Triceps brachii

PART MOVED	FLEXOR	EXTENSOR	ABDUCTOR	ADDUCTOR
Arm				
Forearm				
Thigh				
Leg				
Foot				
Trunk				

Fill-in

1. _____
2. _____
3. _____
4. _____
5. _____
6. _____
7. _____
8. _____
9. _____
10. _____
11. _____
12. _____
13. _____
14. _____
15. _____
16. _____
17. _____
18. _____
19. _____
20. _____
21. _____
22. _____
23. _____
24. _____
25. _____

Fill-in (complete each item with the correct term)

1. The occipitofrontalis, or epicranius, originates on the _?_ bone.
2. The masseter, temporalis, and pterygoids all insert on the _?_.
3. The sternocleidomastoid inserts on the _?_.
4. The temporalis closes the _?_.
5. The _?_ closes the eye.
6. The pectoralis _?_ inserts on the humerus.
7. The deltoid inserts on the _?_.
8. The _?_ intercostals help accomplish forced expiration.
9. The erector _?_ help maintain posture.
10. The pectoralis major is _?_ to the pectoralis minor.
11. The latissimus dorsi is on the _?_ side of the trunk.
12. The _?_ intercostals contract when you take a deep breath.
13. The rippling effect seen on the lower midline of the abdomens of some athletes is caused by hypertrophy of the _?_ muscle.
14. The origin of the brachialis is _?_ to its insertion.
15. In grasping a baseball tightly in the hand, one would likely use the _?_ muscle.
16. Both the biceps brachii and the _?_ flex the forearm.
17. The extensor digitorum inserts on the _?_.
18. The adductor longus and the _?_ are both part of the adductor group.
19. The hamstring muscles all _?_ the leg.
20. The muscle that pulls the leg so that you can cross it over the other leg while sitting is called the _?_ muscle.
21. Both the gastrocnemius and the _?_ plantar flex the foot.
22. Muscles of the quadriceps group all _?_ the leg.
23. In the male, the _?_ pulls the penis erect but also can constrict the urethra.
24. The large muscle that extends the thigh is the _?_.
25. The levator ani raises the _?_.

Dissection: Skeletal Muscles

In the previous exercise, you identified the components of the human musculature on models and/or charts of the human muscular system. In this exercise, you are challenged to find some of the major muscles in a preserved mammalian specimen. While the musculature of these animals may differ somewhat from human musculature, a dissection exercise stimulates an appreciation for the highly variable, three-dimensional nature of muscular anatomy that no other type of learning activity can.

Activity A provides directions for studying the musculature of the cat. Activity B is an alternate activity, providing directions for studying the musculature of the fetal pig.

BEFORE YOU BEGIN

❏ Read the appropriate chapter in your textbook.
❏ Set your learning goals. When you finish this exercise, you should be able to:
  ☐ dissect the musculature of a preserved cat or fetal pig
  ☐ identify the following in a dissected mammalian specimen:
    ☐ muscles of the head and neck
    ☐ muscles of the trunk
    ☐ muscles of the upper extremity
    ☐ muscles of the lower extremity
    ☐ muscles of the pelvic floor
❏ Prepare your materials:
  ☐ preserved (plain or injected) cat or fetal pig
  ☐ dissection tools and trays
  ☐ mounted skeleton of the cat or fetal pig
  ☐ storage container (if specimen is to be reused)
❏ Read the directions and safety tips for this exercise *carefully* before starting any procedure.

❗ safety first
Observe the usual precautions when working with a preserved specimen. Heed the safety advice accompanying the preservatives used with your specimen. Use protective gloves while handling your specimen. Use safety goggles to avoid injury during dissections. Avoid injury with dissection tools. Dispose of or store your specimen as instructed. •

Study **TIPS**
As you complete this dissection, refer to an illustration or atlas of the human body. Use the illustration or atlas to locate and compare the human musculature with your preserved specimen.

A. CAT MUSCULATURE

If your cat was not skinned in Exercise 10, it must be done before beginning this activity. Refer to Exercise 10 for directions regarding the removal of the skin (see Figure 10-5).

Hint ▶ The muscles are held in place by various connective tissues. The best way to dissect muscles is to first scrape or cut away any fascia that covers the muscle of interest, *taking care not to cut into the muscle itself.* Next, carefully slip a blunt probe under the muscle and slide it back and forth to break the loose fibers holding the muscle in place. It is best not to cut any of the muscles unless you absolutely must to see an important underlying muscle. When you do cut a muscle, cut it in a way that will permit you to later fold it back into its normal position. Remember, you will probably be studying these muscles over and over again as you prepare for your practical examination on cat musculature. A bag full of separate muscle organs will not help you identify them by location in another specimen. •

☐ 1 Identify the muscles of the *head and neck* **(Table 19-1)**. Before you begin, you must place the cat on its back and remove the skin and underlying connective tissue up to the chin **(Figure 19-2)**.
  ☐ Mylohyoid
  ☐ Masseter
  ☐ Digastric
  ☐ Sternohyoid
  ☐ Sternomastoid

Hint ▶ Refer to **Figures 19-2 to 19-6** for color photographs of dissected cat musculature. •

FIGURE 19-1 Skeletal system of the cat. Use this figure to locate muscle origins and insertions listed in the tables in this exercise.

TABLE 19-1 **Muscles of the Head and Neck of the Cat**

MUSCLE	ORIGIN	INSERTION	ACTION
Mylohyoid	Mandible (body)	Hyoid	Depresses mandible; elevates floor of mouth
Masseter	Zygomatic	Mandible	Elevates, protracts mandible
Digastric	Occipital	Mandible	Depresses, retracts mandible
Sternohyoid	Sternum	Hyoid	Depresses hyoid
Sternomastoid	Sternum	Temporal (mastoid)	Flexes, rotates head

☐ 2 With the cat still on its back, identify the superficial muscles of the *trunk and shoulder* (ventral aspect) **(Table 19-2)**.
  ☐ Clavobrachialis (clavodeltoid)
  ☐ Pectoantebrachialis
  ☐ Pectoralis major
  ☐ Pectoralis minor
  ☐ Xiphihumeralis
  ☐ External oblique
☐ 3 Make careful incisions near the midline to expose the following deeper muscles of the *trunk* (ventral aspect):
  ☐ Internal oblique
  ☐ Transversus abdominis
  ☐ Rectus abdominis
☐ 4 Turn the cat onto its ventral side and identify the following superficial muscles of the *trunk and shoulder* (dorsal aspect, as in Figure 19-4):
  ☐ Clavotrapezius
  ☐ Levator scapulae ventralis
  ☐ Acromiotrapezius
  ☐ Spinotrapezius
  ☐ Clavobrachialis
  ☐ Acromiodeltoid
  ☐ Spinodeltoid
  ☐ Latissimus dorsi
☐ 5 With your scissors, cut the three trapezius muscles (as shown in Figure 19-4, B) to expose the deeper muscles of the *trunk and shoulder*. Identify these muscles:
  ☐ Supraspinatus
  ☐ Infraspinatus
  ☐ Teres major
  ☐ Rhomboideus major
  ☐ Rhomboideus minor
  ☐ Rhomboideus capitis
  ☐ Splenius
☐ 6 Turn the cat so that it is again lying on its back and identify these muscles of the *forelimb* from the medial aspect (Figure 19-5, A & B, and **Table 19-3**):
  ☐ Triceps brachii
  ☐ Epitrochlearis
  ☐ Biceps brachii

☐ 7 Place the cat so that it is lying on its ventral surface and identify these muscles of the *forelimb* from the lateral aspect (Figure 19-5, C to E, and Table 19-3):
  ☐ Brachialis
  ☐ Triceps brachii

Hint ▶ You will have to cut some of the superficial muscles of the upper limb to see the deeper muscles. See Figure 19-5 for examples. •

☐ 8 Place the cat on its back and identify these superficial and deep muscles of the *hindlimb* from the medial aspect (Figure 19-6 and **Table 19-4**):
  ☐ Sartorius
  ☐ Gracilis
  ☐ Rectus femoris
  ☐ Vastus medialis
  ☐ Adductor longus
  ☐ Semimembranosus
  ☐ Semitendinosus
  ☐ Tensor fasciae latae
  ☐ Flexor digitorum longus
  ☐ Gastrocnemius
  ☐ Soleus
  ☐ Tibialis anterior
☐ 9 Place the cat on its ventral surface and identify these muscles of the *hindlimb* from the lateral aspect (Figure 19-6, C):
  ☐ Gluteus medius
  ☐ Gluteus maximus
  ☐ Caudofemoralis
  ☐ Tensor fasciae latae
  ☐ Biceps femoris
  ☐ Semimembranosus
  ☐ Semitendinosus
  ☐ Gastrocnemius
  ☐ Soleus
  ☐ Peroneus
  ☐ Tibialis anterior

FIGURE 19-2 Muscles of the head and neck of the cat.

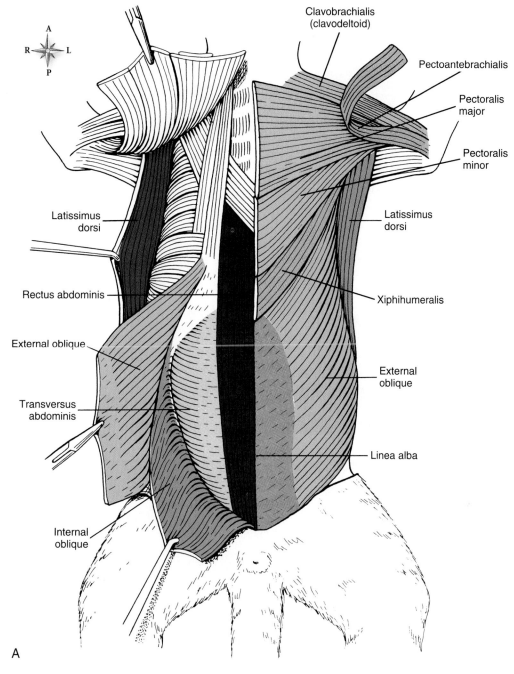

FIGURE 19-3 Muscles of the trunk and shoulder. **A,** Ventral view.

Continued

Clavobrachialis muscle

Epitrochlearis muscle

Serratus anterior muscle

Latissimus dorsi muscle (cut)

External oblique muscle (partially reflected)

Internal oblique muscle (partially reflected)

Pectoantebrachialis muscle

Pectoralis major muscle

Pectoralis minor muscle

Xiphohumeralis muscle (removed on right)

Linea alba

Rectus abdominis muscle

Peritoneum

Transverse abdominis muscle

B

Clavotrapezius muscle (reflected on left)

Clavobrachialis muscle

Acromiodeltoid muscle

Triceps brachii muscle (lateral head)

Triceps brachii muscle (long head)

Infraspinatus muscle

Rhomboideus major muscle

Rhomboideus capitis muscle

Splenius muscle

Supraspinatus muscle

Acromiotrapezius muscle (cut; removed on left)

Rhomboideus minor muscle

Spinotrapezius muscle

Latissimus dorsi muscle (reflected on left; partially removed on right)

Lumbodorsal fascia (largely removed)

C

FIGURE 19-3, cont'd B, Ventral view. C, Dorsal view.

TABLE 19-2   **Muscles of the Trunk and Shoulder of the Cat**

MUSCLE	ORIGIN	INSERTION	ACTION
Clavobrachialis	Clavicle	Ulna (proximal end)	Extends humerus; flexes elbow; rotates head
Pectoantebrachialis	Sternum (anterior)	Ulnar fascia	Adducts humerus
Pectoralis major	Sternum, clavicle	Humerus	Adducts humerus
Pectoralis minor	Sternum	Humerus	Adducts humerus
Xiphihumeralis	Sternum (xiphoid)	Humerus	Adducts humerus
External oblique	Lumbodorsal fascia, posterior ribs	Linea alba	Compresses abdomen; flexes, rotates vertebral column
Internal oblique	Lumbodorsal fascia, pelvis	Linea alba	Compresses abdomen; flexes, rotates vertebral column
Transversus abdominis	Lumbar vertebra, costal cartilage	Linea alba	Compresses abdomen
Rectus abdominis	Coxal (pubis)	Sternum, costal cartilages	Compresses abdomen
Clavotrapezius	Back of skull, dorsal midline of neck	Clavicle	Moves head and clavicle toward each other
Levator scapulae ventralis	Occipital and vertebra C1 (atlas)	Scapula	Moves scapula anteriorly
Acromiotrapezius	Vertebrae C2 to T3 (spinous processes)	Scapula (spine)	Moves scapula toward midline of body
Spinotrapezius	Vertebrae C1 to C4 and T1 to T12 (spinous processes)	Scapula	Moves scapula toward midline of body and posteriorly
Acromiodeltoid	Scapula (acromion)	Humerus (proximal end)	Adducts, rotates humerus
Spinodeltoid	Scapula (spine)	Humerus	Elevates, rotates humerus
Latissimus dorsi	Lumbodorsal fascia and vertebrae T4 to L6	Humerus	Adducts, rotates, extends humerus
Supraspinatus	Scapula (above spine)	Humerus (greater tubercle)	Extends humerus; moves scapula toward head
Infraspinatus	Scapula (below spine)	Humerus (greater tubercle)	Rotates humerus
Teres major	Scapula (lateral border)	Humerus (proximal end)	Rotates humerus
Rhomboideus major	Vertebrae (thoracic)	Scapula (inferior angle)	Pulls scapula toward vertebral column
Rhomboideus minor	Vertebrae (posterior cervical and thoracic)	Scapula (vertebral border)	Pulls scapula toward vertebral column
Rhomboideus capitis	Occipital	Scapula (vertebral border)	Pulls scapula forward and medially
Splenius	Vertebrae (T1 and T2) and fascia of neck	Occipital	Extends and turns head laterally

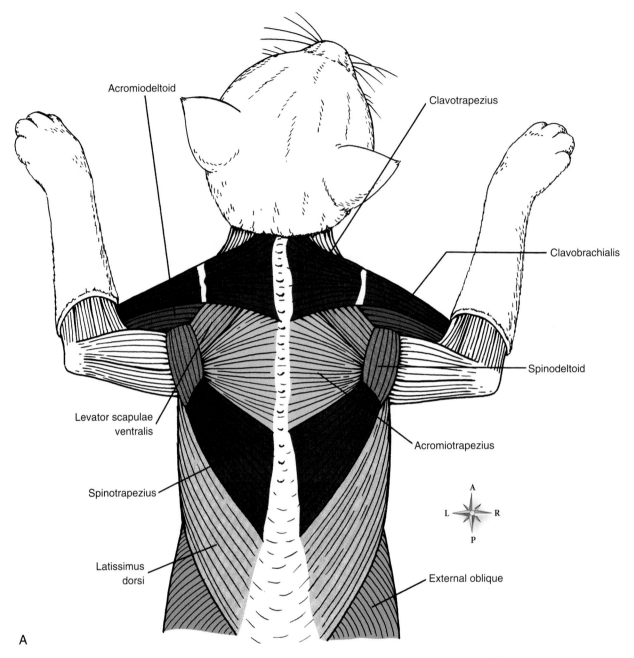

FIGURE 19-4 A, Superficial muscles of the trunk and shoulder (dorsal aspect) of the cat.

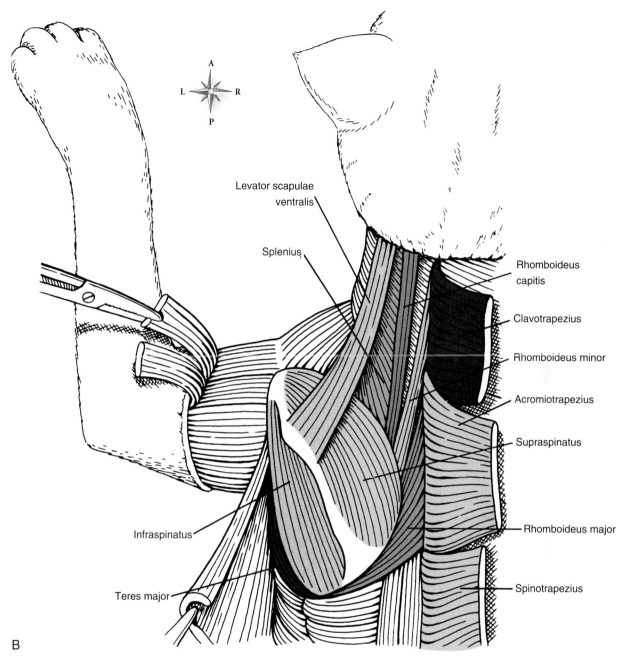

Levator scapulae ventralis

Splenius

Rhomboideus capitis

Clavotrapezius

Rhomboideus minor

Acromiotrapezius

Supraspinatus

Infraspinatus

Rhomboideus major

Teres major

Spinotrapezius

B

FIGURE 19-4, cont'd B, Deeper muscles of the trunk and shoulder (dorsal aspect) of the cat.

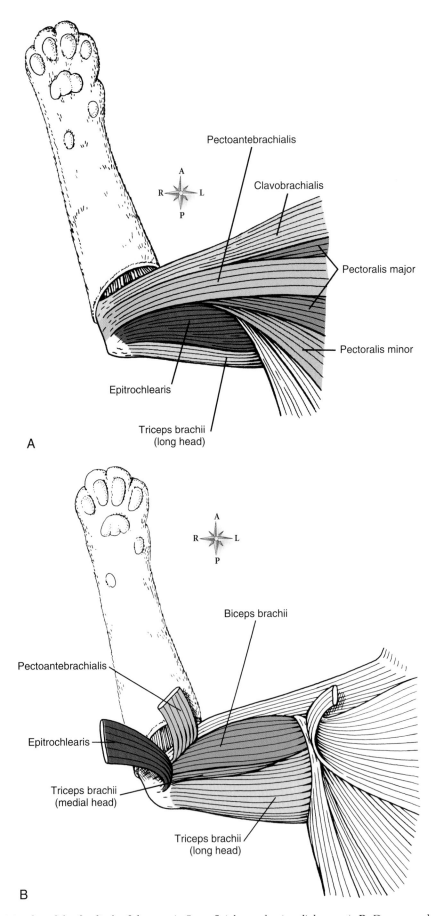

FIGURE 19-5 Muscles of the forelimb of the cat. **A,** Superficial muscles (medial aspect). **B,** Deep muscles (medial aspect).

Clavobrachialis muscle

Cephalic vein

Pectoantebrachialis muscle

Pectoralis major muscle

Epitrochlearis muscle

Pectoralis minor muscle

Latissimus dorsi muscle

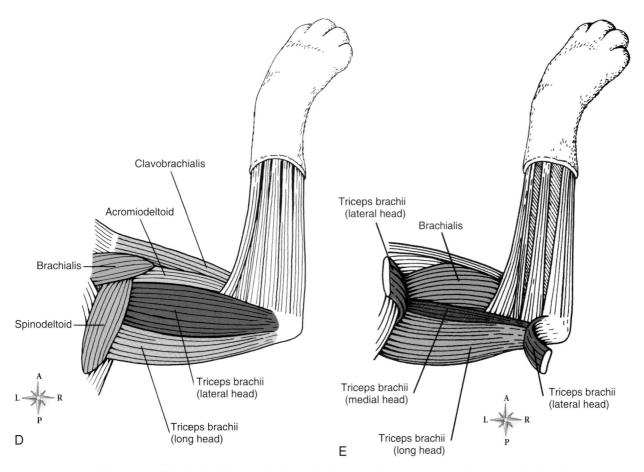

Clavobrachialis

Acromiodeltoid

Brachialis

Spinodeltoid

Triceps brachii
(lateral head)

Triceps brachii
(long head)

D

Triceps brachii
(lateral head)

Brachialis

Triceps brachii
(medial head)

Triceps brachii
(long head)

Triceps brachii
(lateral head)

E

FIGURE 19-5, cont'd C, Medial view. D, Superficial muscles (lateral aspect). E, Deep muscles (lateral aspect).

TABLE 19-3 **Muscles of the Forelimb of the Cat**

MUSCLE	ORIGIN	INSERTION	ACTION
Triceps brachii	Long head: scapula (edge of glenoid cavity) Medial head: humerus (shaft) Lateral head: humerus (deltoid tuberosity)	Ulna (olecranon)	Extends distal forelimb
Epitrochlearis	Fascia of latissimus dorsi	Ulna (olecranon)	Extends distal forelimb
Biceps brachii	Scapula (edge of glenoid cavity)	Radius (radial tuberosity)	Flexes distal forelimb
Brachialis	Humerus (lateral surface)	Ulna (proximal end)	Flexes distal forelimb

TABLE 19-4 **Muscles of the Hindlimb of the Cat**

MUSCLE	ORIGIN	INSERTION	ACTION
Sartorius hindlimb	Coxal (iliac crest)	Tibia, patella	Adducts, rotates thigh and extends distal
Gracilis	Coxal (pubis)	Tibia (medial surface)	Adducts hindlimb
Rectus femoris	Coxal (near acetabulum)	Patella	Extends hindlimb
Vastus medialis	Femur	Patella	Extends hindlimb
Adductor longus	Coxal (pubis)	Femur (proximal end)	Adducts hindlimb
Semimembranosus	Coxal (ischium)	Femur (distal end)	Extends hindlimb
Semitendinosus	Coxal (ischium)	Tibia	Flexes distal hindlimb
Tensor fasciae latae	Coxal (ilium)	Fascia of thigh	Extends hindlimb
Flexor digitorum longus	Tibia, fibula	Distal phalanges	Flexes digits
Gastrocnemius	Femur (epicondyles)	Calcaneus	Extends foot
Soleus	Fibula (proximal end)	Calcaneus	Extends foot
Tibialis anterior	Tibia, fibula (proximal ends)	Metatarsal I	Flexes foot
Gluteus medius	Coxal (ilium), vertebrae (sacral and caudal)	Femur (proximal end)	Abducts hindlimb
Gluteus maximus	Coxal (ilium), vertebrae (sacral and caudal)	Femur (proximal end)	Abducts hindlimb
Caudofemoralis	Vertebrae (caudal)	Patella	Abducts hindlimb; extends distal hindlimb
Biceps femoris	Coxal (ischium)	Tibia, patella	Abducts hindlimb; extends distal hindlimb
Peroneus	Fibula	Metatarsals	Flexes foot

External oblique

Adductor longus

Adductor femoris

Sartorius

Gracilis

Semitendinosus

Gastrocnemius

Soleus

Tibialis anterior

Flexor digitorum longus

A

FIGURE 19-6 Muscles of the hindlimb of the cat. **A,** Superficial muscles (medial aspect).

Continued

Femoral artery
Adductor longus muscle
Pectineus muscle
Adductor femoris muscle
Gracilis muscle (cut)
Semimembranosus muscle
Semitendinosus muscle
Biceps femoris muscle
Gastrocnemius muscle (reflected)
Soleus muscle
Achilles tendon

Tensor fasciae latae muscle
Femoral vein
Vastus lateralis muscle
Femoral nerve
Rectus femoris muscle
Sartorius muscle (cut)
Tibia
Tibialis anterior muscle

Adductor longus
Gracilis
Adductor femoris
Semimembranosus
Semitendinosus

Sartorius
Rectus femoris
Vastus lateralis
Vastus medialis
Tensor fasciae latae
Sartorius
Gracilis
Gastrocnemius
Soleus
Flexor digitorum longus
Tibialis anterior

B

FIGURE 19-6, cont'd B, Deep muscles (medial aspect).

Lumbodorsal fasciae
Gluteus medius muscle
Sartorius muscle
Tensor fasciae latae muscle
Gluteus maximus muscle
Caudofemoralis muscle
Biceps femoris muscle
Semitendinosus muscle
Semimembranosus muscle
Gastrocnemius muscle
Soleus muscle
Tibialis anterior muscle
Peroneus muscle
Achilles tendon

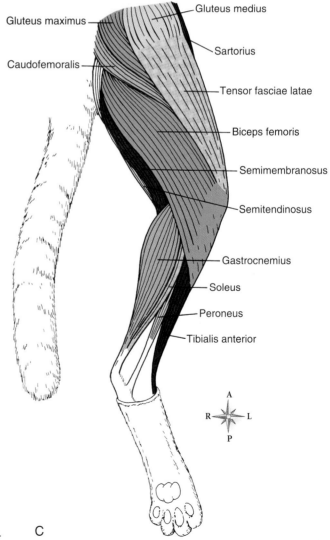

Gluteus maximus
Caudofemoralis
Gluteus medius
Sartorius
Tensor fasciae latae
Biceps femoris
Semimembranosus
Semitendinosus
Gastrocnemius
Soleus
Peroneus
Tibialis anterior

FIGURE 19-6, cont'd C, Superficial muscles (lateral aspect).   C

B. FETAL PIG MUSCULATURE

This activity is a brief alternative to the study of cat musculature offered in Activity A. If your fetal pig was not skinned in Exercise 10, it must be done before beginning this activity. Refer to Exercise 10 for directions regarding the removal of the skin. Before you study the muscles of the fetal pig, acquaint yourself with the skeletal system shown in **Figure 19-7**. This will help you to locate muscle origins and insertions.

> **Hint** The muscles are held in place by various connective tissues. Because the muscles of a fetal pig have not been used extensively by the animal, they often appear underdeveloped and are therefore difficult to distinguish. The best way to dissect muscles is to first scrape or cut away any large chunks of fat and fascia that cover the muscles of interest, taking care not to cut into the muscle itself. Next, carefully slip a blunt probe under the muscle and slide it back and forth to break the loose fibers holding the muscle in place. It is best not to cut any of the muscles unless you absolutely must to see an important underlying muscle. When you do cut a muscle, cut it in a way that will permit you to later fold it back into its normal position. Remember, you will probably be studying these muscles over and over again as you prepare for your practical examination on fetal pig musculature. A bag full of separate muscle organs will not help you identify them by location in another specimen. •

☐ 1 Identify the muscles of the *head and neck* **(Table 19-5)**. Before you begin, you must place the fetal pig on its back and remove the skin and underlying connective tissue up to the chin **(Figure 19-8, *B*)**.
  ☐ Mylohyoid
  ☐ Masseter
  ☐ Digastric
  ☐ Sternohyoid
  ☐ Sternomastoid

☐ 2 With the fetal pig still on its back, identify the superficial muscles of the trunk and shoulder (ventral aspect) **(Table 19-6)**:
  ☐ Clavobrachialis
  ☐ Superficial pectoral
  ☐ Serratus anterior
  ☐ External oblique
  ☐ Rectus abdominis

☐ 3 Make a careful cut across the superficial pectoral muscle near the midline, as shown in Figure 19-8, *B*, to expose the following deeper muscles of the *shoulder* (ventral aspect):
  ☐ Anterior deep pectoral
  ☐ Posterior deep pectoral
  ☐ Teres major

☐ 4 Make a cut along the midline of the abdomen to expose these deep muscles of the *trunk* (ventral aspect):
  ☐ Internal oblique
  ☐ Transversus abdominis

☐ 5 Turn the fetal pig onto its ventral side and identify the following superficial and deep muscles of the *trunk and shoulder*:
  ☐ Clavotrapezius
  ☐ Supraspinatus
  ☐ Acromiotrapezius
  ☐ Spinotrapezius
  ☐ Deltoid
  ☐ Latissimus dorsi

> **Hint** Often, the deeper muscles can be located easily by cutting through some of the superficial muscles. Be careful not to remove the superficial muscles, however. •

☐ 6 Turn the fetal pig so that it is again lying on its back and identify these muscles of the *forelimb* **(Table 19-7)**:
  ☐ Triceps brachii
  ☐ Biceps brachii
  ☐ Brachialis

☐ 7 With the fetal pig still on its back, identify these superficial and deep muscles of the *hindlimb* from the medial aspect **(Table 19-8)**:
  ☐ Sartorius
  ☐ Gracilis
  ☐ Rectus femoris
  ☐ Vastus medialis
  ☐ Pectineus
  ☐ Iliopsoas
  ☐ Adductor longus
  ☐ Semimembranosus
  ☐ Semitendinosus
  ☐ Tensor fasciae latae

☐ 8 Place the fetal pig on its ventral surface and identify these muscles of the *hindlimb* from the lateral aspect:
  ☐ Gluteus medius
  ☐ Tensor fasciae latae
  ☐ Biceps femoris

> **Hint** Refer to Figure 19-8 for a color photograph of dissected fetal pig musculature. •

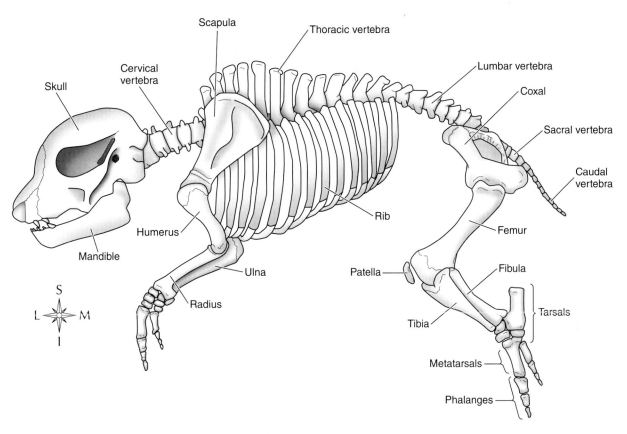

FIGURE 19-7 Skeletal system of the fetal pig. Use this figure to locate muscle origins and insertions listed in the tables in this exercise.

A

FIGURE 19-8 Fetal pig musculature. **A,** Lateral view.

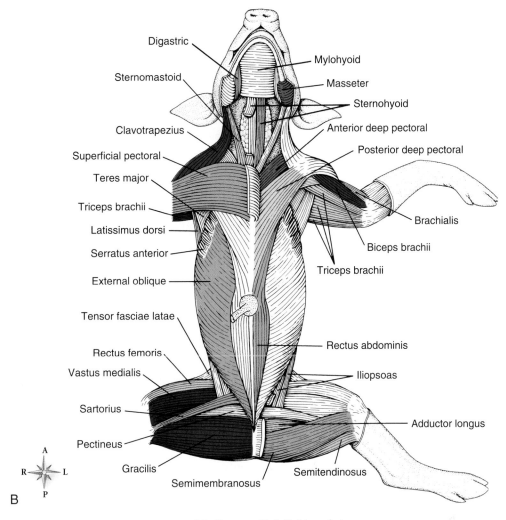

Digastric
Sternomastoid
Clavotrapezius
Superficial pectoral
Teres major
Triceps brachii
Latissimus dorsi
Serratus anterior
External oblique
Tensor fasciae latae
Rectus femoris
Vastus medialis
Sartorius
Pectineus
Gracilis
Semimembranosus

Mylohyoid
Masseter
Sternohyoid
Anterior deep pectoral
Posterior deep pectoral
Brachialis
Biceps brachii
Triceps brachii
Rectus abdominis
Iliopsoas
Adductor longus
Semitendinosus

B

FIGURE 19-8, cont'd B, Ventral view.

TABLE 19-5 **Muscles of the Head and Neck of the Fetal Pig**

MUSCLE	ORIGIN	INSERTION	ACTION
Mylohyoid	Mandible (body)	Hyoid	Depresses mandible; elevates floor of mouth
Masseter	Zygomatic	Mandible	Elevates, protracts mandible
Digastric	Occipital	Mandible	Depresses, retracts mandible
Sternohyoid	Sternum	Hyoid	Depresses hyoid
Sternomastoid	Sternum	Temporal (mastoid)	Flexes, rotates head

TABLE 19-6 **Muscles of the Trunk and Shoulder of the Fetal Pig**

MUSCLE	ORIGIN	INSERTION	ACTION
Clavobrachialis	Clavicle	Ulna (proximal end)	Extends humerus; flexes elbow; rotates head
Superficial pectoral	Sternum	Humerus	Adducts humerus
Serratus anterior	Ribs (4-8)	Scapula (vertebral border)	Depresses scapula
External oblique	Lumbodorsal fascia, posterior ribs	Linea alba	Compresses abdomen; flexes, rotates vertebral column
Rectus abdominis	Coxal (pubis)	Sternum, costal cartilages	Compresses abdomen
Anterior deep pectoral	Sternum, costal cartilages	Scapula	Pulls scapula toward midline of body
Posterior deep pectoral	Sternum, costal cartilages	Humerus (proximal end)	Adducts humerus
Teres major	Scapula (lateral border)	Humerus (proximal end)	Rotates humerus
Internal oblique	Lumbodorsal fascia, pelvis	Linea alba	Compresses abdomen; flexes, rotates vertebral column
Transversus abdominis	Lumbar vertebra, costal cartilages	Linea alba	Compresses abdomen
Clavotrapezius	Back of skull, dorsal midline of neck	Clavicle	Moves head and clavicle toward each other
Supraspinatus	Scapula (above spine)	Humerus (greater tubercle)	Extends humerus; moves scapula toward head
Acromiotrapezius	Vertebrae C2 to T3 (spinous processes)	Scapula (spine)	Moves scapula toward midline of body
Spinotrapezius	Vertebrae C1 to C4 and T1 to T12 (spinous processes)	Scapula	Moves scapula toward midline of body and posteriorly
Deltoid	Scapula	Humerus (proximal end)	Adducts humerus
Latissimus dorsi	Lumbodorsal fascia and vertebrae T4 to L6	Humerus	Adducts, rotates, extends humerus

TABLE 19-7   Muscles of the Forelimb of the Fetal Pig

MUSCLE	ORIGIN	INSERTION	ACTION
Triceps brachii	Long head: scapula (edge of glenoid cavity) Medial head: humerus (shaft) Lateral head: humerus (deltoid tuberosity)	Ulna (olecranon)	Extends distal forelimb
Biceps brachii	Scapula (edge of glenoid cavity)	Radius (radial tuberosity)	Flexes distal forelimb
Brachialis	Humerus (lateral surface)	Ulna (proximal end)	Flexes distal forelimb

TABLE 19-8   Muscles of the Hindlimb of the Fetal Pig

MUSCLE	ORIGIN	INSERTION	ACTION
Sartorius	Coxal (iliac crest)	Tibia, patella	Adducts, rotates thigh and extends distal hindlimb
Gracilis	Coxal (pubis)	Tibia (medial surface)	Adducts hindlimb
Rectus femoris	Coxal (near acetabulum)	Patella	Extends hindlimb
Vastus medialis	Femur	Patella	Extends hindlimb
Pectineus	Coxal (pubis)	Femur (proximal end)	Adducts hindlimb
Iliopsoas	Vertebrae (lumbar), coxal (ilium)	Femur (lesser trochanter)	Flexes, rotates hindlimb
Adductor longus	Coxal (pubis)	Femur (proximal end)	Adducts hindlimb
Semimembranosus	Coxal (ischium)	Femur (distal end)	Extends hindlimb
Semitendinosus	Coxal (ischium)	Tibia	Flexes distal hindlimb
Tensor fasciae latae	Coxal (ilium)	Fascia of thigh	Extends hindlimb
Gluteus medius	Coxal (ilium), vertebrae (sacral and caudal)	Femur (proximal end)	Abducts hindlimb
Biceps femoris	Coxal (ischium)	Tibia, patella	Abducts hindlimb; extends distal hindlimb

Name: _____ Date: _____ Section: _____

LAB REPORT 19
Dissection: Skeletal Muscles

A. Cat Musculature Dissection Checklist

☐ Muscles of the head and neck

  ☐ mylohyoid

  ☐ masseter

  ☐ digastric

  ☐ sternohyoid

  ☐ sternomastoid

☐ Muscles of the trunk and shoulder

  ☐ clavobrachialis

  ☐ pectoantebrachialis

  ☐ pectoralis major

  ☐ pectoralis minor

  ☐ xiphihumeralis

  ☐ external oblique

  ☐ internal oblique

  ☐ transversus abdominis

  ☐ rectus abdominis

  ☐ clavotrapezius

  ☐ levator scapulae ventralis

  ☐ acromiotrapezius

  ☐ spinotrapezius

  ☐ acromiodeltoid

  ☐ spinodeltoid

  ☐ latissimus dorsi

  ☐ supraspinatus

  ☐ infraspinatus

  ☐ teres major

  ☐ rhomboideus major

☐ rhomboideus minor

☐ rhomboideus capitis

☐ splenius

☐ Muscles of the forelimb

  ☐ triceps brachii

  ☐ epitrochlearis

  ☐ biceps brachii

  ☐ brachialis

☐ Muscles of the hindlimb

  ☐ sartorius

  ☐ gracilis

  ☐ rectus femoris

  ☐ vastus medialis

  ☐ adductor longus

  ☐ semimembranosus

  ☐ semitendinosus

  ☐ tensor fasciae latae

  ☐ flexor digitorum longus

  ☐ gastrocnemius

  ☐ soleus

  ☐ tibialis anterior

  ☐ gluteus medius

  ☐ gluteus maximus

  ☐ caudofemoralis

  ☐ biceps femoris

  ☐ peroneus

B. Fetal Pig Musculature Dissection Checklist

- ☐ Muscles of the head and neck
    - ☐ mylohyoid
    - ☐ masseter
    - ☐ digastric
    - ☐ sternohyoid
    - ☐ sternomastoid
- ☐ Muscles of the trunk and shoulder
    - ☐ clavobrachialis
    - ☐ superficial pectoral
    - ☐ serratus anterior
    - ☐ external oblique
    - ☐ rectus abdominis
    - ☐ anterior deep pectoral
    - ☐ posterior deep pectoral
    - ☐ teres major
    - ☐ internal oblique
    - ☐ transversus abdominis
    - ☐ clavotrapezius
    - ☐ supraspinatus
    - ☐ acromiotrapezius

- ☐ spinotrapezius
- ☐ deltoid
- ☐ latissimus dorsi
- ☐ Muscles of the forelimb
    - ☐ triceps brachii
    - ☐ biceps brachii
    - ☐ brachialis
- ☐ Muscles of the hindlimb
    - ☐ sartorius
    - ☐ gracilis
    - ☐ rectus femoris
    - ☐ vastus medialis
    - ☐ pectineus
    - ☐ iliopsoas
    - ☐ adductor longus
    - ☐ semimembranosus
    - ☐ semitendinosus
    - ☐ tensor fasciae latae
    - ☐ gluteus medius
    - ☐ biceps femoris

20
Skeletal Muscle Contractions

Now that you are familiar with the structure of the muscular system and its organs, it is time to take a closer look at the physiology of this system. The first activity demonstrates contraction at the cell level. The second and third activities challenge you to investigate concepts of muscle function at the organ level.

BEFORE YOU BEGIN

- ❏ Read the appropriate chapter in your textbook.
- ❏ Set your learning goals. When you finish this exercise, you should be able to:
  - ☐ describe some factors that influence the contraction of single skeletal muscle fibers
  - ☐ interpret a myogram of a single twitch, determining its three phases
  - ☐ understand the nature of the treppe phenomenon and tetanus
  - ☐ demonstrate how muscle contraction can be studied in a laboratory setting
- ❏ Prepare your materials:
  - ☐ glycerinated rabbit psoas muscle
  - ☐ watch glass or petri dish
  - ☐ microscopes (dissecting and regular)
  - ☐ fine glass probes
  - ☐ glass slides and coverslips
  - ☐ glycerin solution (50% in triple distilled water)
  - ☐ metric ruler (mm)
  - ☐ adenosine triphosphate (ATP) + salt solution
  - ☐ ATP solution
  - ☐ salt solution
- ❏ If Activity B is performed:
  - ☐ frog (live)
  - ☐ pithing needle
  - ☐ dissection pan or board
  - ☐ dissection tools
  - ☐ Ringer's solution (amphibian)
  - ☐ blunt glass probe or polished tube
  - ☐ string
  - ☐ kymograph or physiograph system
  - ☐ stimulator apparatus
- ❏ If Activity C is performed:
  - ☐ Physiogrip system
  - ☐ computer and access to a printer
  - ☐ electrode gel
  - ☐ flat plate electrode (and tape)
  - ☐ stimulator

- ☐ pen (washable ink)
- ☐ USB drive/thumb drive (if data are to be stored)
- ☐ Read the directions and safety tips for this exercise *carefully* before starting any procedure.

Study TIPS

Before you begin this lab, review the physiology of muscle contraction. Understand what chemicals are necessary for muscle contraction. Refer to your textbook or the *A&P Survival Guide*.

A. CONTRACTION OF SINGLE MUSCLE FIBERS

In this activity, you will observe contractions in single skeletal muscle fibers. Your specimen is a special glycerinated preparation of a rabbit psoas muscle.

> **safety first**
> Take the usual precautions when using a microscope. Protect your eyes and skin from laboratory solutions. Be careful to avoid injury when using the glass probes. •

- ☐ **1** Obtain a small piece (1-2 cm) of glycerinated muscle tissue in a watch glass or petri dish.
- ☐ **2** Focus on the specimen after placing it on the stage of a dissecting microscope. (You may use a hand lens instead.)
- ☐ **3** Using fine glass probes or micropipette tips, try to separate some individual fibers from the rest of the bundle. Avoid using your hands or metal instruments to manipulate the specimen. Note: metal will "discharge" the tissue. Be sure to use glass!

> **Hint** ▶ Although it may seem difficult to separate fibers at first, care and patience will get the job done quickly and efficiently. Individual fibers are best, but a few in an unseparated bundle will do. •

- ☐ **4** Remove one of the fibers and place it on a microscope slide with a coverslip. Observe the specimen on a compound microscope.

☐ **5** Observe the muscle fiber with low power, then high power. Make a sketch of your observation. Are the striations visible? Which parts of the muscle fiber form these stripes?

☐ **6** Put three or four separated fibers on a different microscope slide, straight and parallel to one another. Do not use a coverslip. With a metric ruler, measure the length of each fiber (in mm).

☐ **7** With the dropper built into the bottle, use the ATP + salt solution to bathe the fibers. Observe the fibers for 30 seconds and note any contraction.

☐ **8** Measure each fiber again and record the new length. Calculate the percentage of change in each fiber using the following formula:

$$\frac{(\text{Beginning Length}) - (\text{Ending Length})}{(\text{Beginning Length})} \times 100 = \%$$

What is the *average* percentage of change in the fibers? How do you account for the change? If there was no change, why not?

☐ **9** Repeat steps 6 through 8, using the ATP solution and again using the salt solution. Based on your observations, what chemicals are essential for contraction?

B. CONTRACTION IN A MUSCLE ORGAN

Before beginning this activity, review these basic principles of muscle physiology:

The normal stimulus for a muscle fiber contraction is a *neurotransmitter* chemical from a nerve cell. The nerve-muscle fiber connection is called a **neuromuscular** junction. Electrical or mechanical stimulation can also cause a contraction. Regardless of whether the stimulus is chemical or electrical, it must be strong enough to pass the threshold of stimulation—the point at which it is just strong enough to initiate a contraction.

Fibers that compose a muscle organ are divided into functional teams, or motor units. Each fiber in a motor unit is innervated by the same nerve cell and so contracts at the same time. The relative strength of contraction in a whole organ depends in part on how many motor units are stimulated at one time. **Recruitment** of more units increases the organ's strength of contraction.

We will demonstrate muscle organ contraction by stimulating many motor units in a prepared muscle organ. To record our observations, we will use a **myograph.** Myograms, or graphic representations of muscle contractions, can be produced for isotonic contractions and for isometric contractions. Isotonic contractions change muscle length (without changing tension), and isometric contractions change tension (without changing length). On myograms, time is the horizontal axis, and strength (or length) of contraction is the vertical axis.

The myogram of a single **twitch** contraction shows these features **(Figure 20-1, A)**:

☐ **Latent period**—Phase after stimulation has occurred but during which a contraction is not yet apparent

☐ **Contraction phase**—Period during which the myogram line rises, indicating that contraction is in progress
☐ **Relaxation phase**—Period when the line falls, indicating a return to the resting state

If restimulation of the muscle occurs soon enough after a twitch contraction, you may observe the **treppe** phenomenon, also called the *staircase effect* (Figure 20-1, B). The second in a series of contractions has a larger amplitude (size) than the first, the third an even greater amplitude, and so on. Eventually, a maximum is reached, and the waves reach a plateau. When the muscle can no longer sustain contractions, it is in a state of **muscle fatigue.**

When a muscle is continually restimulated before the relaxation phase is over, the myogram will not show the wave line returning to the baseline. Instead, the twitch waves will seem to fuse together. Wave summation, or fusion, is often termed **tetanus.** *Incomplete tetanus* occurs when a slight relaxation can be seen between waves. *Complete tetanus* occurs when the waves fuse into a line.

In this activity, you (or your instructor) will use the gastrocnemius muscle of a frog to demonstrate some of the major principles of muscle contraction.

Prepare a frog gastrocnemius muscle in the manner described in steps 1 through 7 and **Figure 20-2**.

> **!** **safety first**
> Avoid cuts and punctures when using the dissection tools. Check for damaged or improper wiring on the electrical equipment. Do not touch the stimulator electrode or other bare wires directly. •

☐ **1** Holding the frog in your hand, locate the joint between the base of the skull and the first vertebra by bending the head down until a notch along the posterior edge of the skull can be felt or is visible.

☐ **2** Quickly push a pithing needle into the groove and then into the cranial cavity. While rotating the needle, move it from side to side to destroy the brain tissue inside.

☐ **3** Pull out the needle partially so that you can insert the tip into the vertebral canal. Push the needle as far as you can, again rotating it to destroy the nerve tissue.

☐ **4** Place the frog on a dissection pan or board. Lift the skin around the hip joint with a forceps and puncture it with the tip of a scissors. Try not to damage the muscle tissue of the leg.

☐ **5** Using the scissors, cut the skin in a circle all the way around the base of the thigh. Grasp the cut edge of the thigh's skin with forceps and pull it toward the foot. The skin will pull away from the leg as if it were a stocking. Keep pulling until the ankle joint appears.

> **Hint** Keep the muscle tissue moist with Ringer's solution so that it will remain functional. •

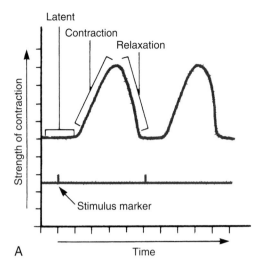

Latent

Contraction

Relaxation

Strength of contraction

Stimulus marker

A

Time

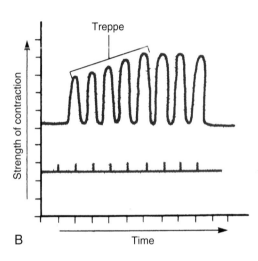

Treppe

Strength of contraction

B

Time

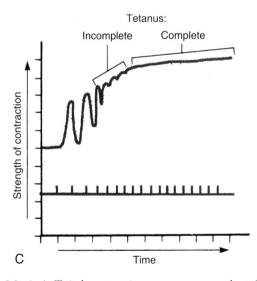

Tetanus:

Incomplete

Complete

Strength of contraction

C

Time

FIGURE 20-1 **A,** Twitch contractions on a myogram chart. **B,** Treppe phenomenon. **C,** Tetanus.

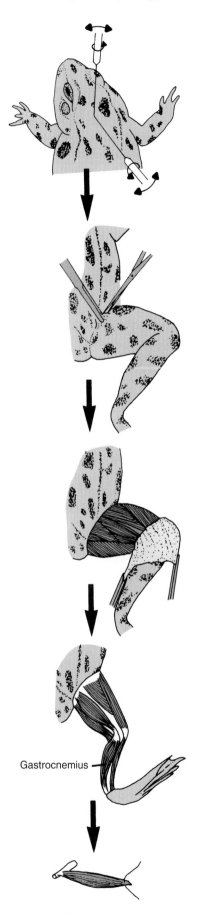

Gastrocnemius

FIGURE 20-2 Isolating frog gastrocnemius muscle.

☐ 6 Locate the *gastrocnemius muscle* (the fleshy part of the calf) and the *calcaneal* (Achilles) tendon, which attaches it to the ankle. Slip a blunt glass probe under the muscle, and slide it back and forth to detach the muscle from underlying connective tissue. While lifting the muscle with the probe, tie a 10- to 15-cm piece of string to the calcaneal tendon. Finally, cut the tendon distal to the knot.

☐ 7 Cut the thigh (bone and muscle) just proximal to the gastrocnemius muscle's attachment to the femur. Break the femur away from the knee joint and remove all muscles but the gastrocnemius. You now have a muscle ready to use in an experiment.

HUMANE USE OF ANIMALS

Animals used in research and education should be treated respectfully and humanely. Double pithing is an accepted method for destroying the central nervous system so that the animal will feel no pain. This method also ensures that certain tissues will remain functional and will not be damaged by spinal reflexes. The frogs that you use have been raised for research and educational purposes.

☐ 8 Set up a kymograph or physiograph according to the instructions accompanying the instrument **(Figure 20-3)**. You may be measuring the intensity of an isotonic contraction by using a movable lever attached to the muscle (as in a kymograph). Or you may be measuring an isometric contraction by means of the force with which it pulls on a transducer (as in a physiograph).

> **Hint** ▶ Different systems operate differently, but here is an easy way to calibrate just about any physiograph setup:
>
> ☐ suspend a 100-gram weight from the transducer
> ☐ adjust the signal amplifier SENSITIVITY or GAIN to produce a 5-cm deflection of the pen
>
> *Check the manufacturer's handbook for further details regarding your particular system.*

☐ 9 Set the stimulator *mode* to CONTINUOUS (REPEAT), *duration* (width) to 1 msec, *frequency* to 1 Hz (1 stimulus per second), and *voltage* to 0.1 volt (V). Stimulate the muscle with the stimulator probe. Continue increasing the voltage in 0.1-volt steps until a response is observed. This voltage is the *threshold of stimulation*. Record it here for later reference: _____ volts.

☐ 10 Change the stimulator *mode* to SINGLE, then continue to increase voltage over a series of twitches a few seconds apart. You have to trigger each stimulus manually when in the SINGLE mode. Does the amplitude of the myogram curve remain the same? Why or why not? Record the voltage at which a moderately sized twitch is observed: _____ volts.

☐ 11 Set the voltage to the level recorded in step 10, the *mode* to CONTINUOUS (REPEAT), and the *frequency* to 1 Hz. Keeping the voltage constant, record a series of twitches 1 second apart. Does the amplitude increase, decrease, or stay the same? Explain. Allow the muscle to rest for several minutes.

☐ 12 Keeping the voltage constant, increase the frequency slowly (from 1 Hz) until incomplete tetanus, then complete tetanus, is observed. Record the threshold frequencies for each phenomenon in Lab Report 20.

C. HUMAN MUSCLE CONTRACTION

This exercise may be done in addition to, or in place of, Activity B. Rather than using a laboratory animal as a subject, this activity calls for using *yourself* (or your lab partner) as an experimental subject. In this case, a muscle organ is used in vivo instead of being isolated from the subject's body. This activity is based on Intelitool's PHYSIOGRIP apparatus for use with Windows-based personal computers. If you are using a different operating system (e.g., Mac or DOS), the directions will be similar. Refer to the Intelitool manual if you have difficulty.

Please note: Depending on the version of the tool, the following instructions may vary. Please check with your instructor for any modifications.

> **!** *safety first*
> Do not participate in this activity as a subject if you have health problems that could be affected by this procedure (e.g., a heart condition). Be aware of electrical hazards. During the activity, the subject should not touch any person or object other than the pistol grip.   •

☐ 1 Set up the PHYSIOGRIP apparatus according to the user's manual provided by the manufacturer (Phipps & Bird, Intelitool). For more information, visit Intelitool's website (www.intelitool.com).

☐ 2 Locate the **motor point** of the flexor digitorum superficialis muscle of the right forearm **(Figure 20-4)**. The motor point is the spot most sensitive to external stimulation. Use this method to find it:

☐ Put electrode gel on the flat plate electrode and attach it to the dorsal surface of the right hand with a rubber strap (tape).

☐ With the power switched off, set the stimulator *frequency* to 1 Hz (stimulus/sec), *mode* to CONTINUOUS (REPEAT), *duration* to 1 msec, and *voltage* to 60 volts. Spread a tiny dab of gel on the stimulator probe, and then turn the power on.

☐ Have the subject move the probe around the ventral surface of the forearm close to the belly of the flexor digitorum superficialis muscle until the area of strongest stimulation is found. When the strongest contraction of the third finger is observed, the subject has the correct spot. The subject may want to mark this spot with washable ink.

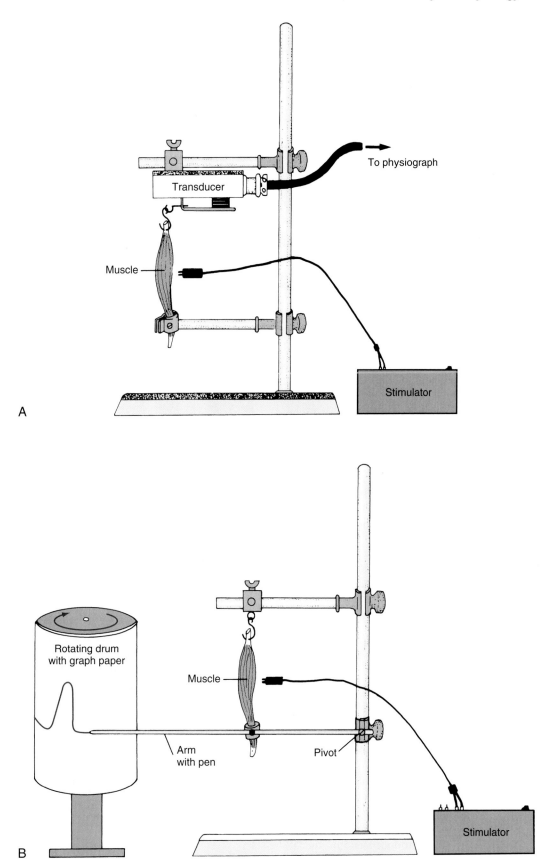

FIGURE 20-3 A, Typical physiograph setup. **B,** Typical kymograph apparatus. Refer to your system's owner's manual, or your instructor, for detailed instructions in setting up the apparatus.

> **Hint** Finding the correct motor point is critical to this activity. If you are having difficulty, try pressing rather hard with the stimulator. You may also try increasing the voltage gradually (but not exceeding 80 volts). Females, especially, may get better results with the alternate motor point (and resultant flexion of the fourth finger) (see Figure 20-4). •

☐ **3** Set up the PHYSIOGRIP program as directed.
  Windows users:
  ☐ Select NEW from the FILE menu.
  ☐ Set the controls in the FILE INFORMATION and FILE SETUP areas as shown:
    ☑ Stimulator Channel
    ☑ Auto Stop
    ☐ Metronome
      Rate: 200 Hz
      Size: 16k

☐ **4** Have the subject place the right hand on the PHYSIOGRIP pistol with the appropriate finger (third or fourth) around the trigger. Have the subject pull the trigger just enough to raise the monitor's graph line from the bottom of the screen.

☐ **5** At a setting of 10 volts, click the START button and stimulate the muscle at the motor point with the stimulator probe. The subject will feel a stimulation once per second. Increase the *voltage* gradually from 10 volts until a response is observed. This voltage is the *threshold of stimulation*. Record it here for later reference: _____ volts.

☐ **6** After the threshold has been reached, continue to increase the voltage slightly over a series of twitches. Does the amplitude of the myogram curve remain the same for each contraction? Why or why not?

> **Hint** Press [I] in EXPERIMENT MODE to erase data and start over.
> Press [P] in REVIEW/ANALYZE MODE to print data. A few other important keys:
> [S] = stop
> [F] = forward to next data frame
> [B] = backward to previous screen
> Measure the height of contractions in the ANALYZE screen by clicking on the D1 and D2 marker buttons and placing the markers on the minimal and maximal contractions.

☐ **7** Select NEW from the FILE menu and set up the file exactly as in Step 3. Set the stimulator voltage to the threshold level and the frequency to as low as possible.

☐ **8** Click on the START button and adjust the stimulator *voltage* and/or *duration* until the wave produced is 50% to 75% of the screen height. Click STOP after a few good-quality twitches.

☐ **9** Select REVIEW/ANALYZE from the main menu or click the ANALYZE button. Measure the length of the latent period, contraction phase, and relaxation phase (in msec).

FIGURE 20-4 Forearm, showing placement of flat plate electrode and likely motor points.

> **Hint** You may want to store your data on a memory stick and do your measurements at a later time. Both the PHYSIOGRIP manual and the program screens instruct you in how to do this. You may also wish to take your measurements from a *hard copy* printout. Make a printout by pressing [ESC] now (make sure your printer is online). •

☐ **10** Select RUN (CONTINUOUS) EXPERIMENT MODE. Use only as isolated stimulator and make sure that only the subject's lab partner, rather than the subject, touches the stimulator or the stimulator controls.

☐ **11** Set the stimulator *frequency* to 1 Hz, the *duration* to 1 msec, and adjust the *voltage* so that the wave is about 25% of the screen height. Click STOP after a few good-quality twitches. Gradually increase the *frequency* until incomplete tetanus, then complete tetanus, is observed. Sustain complete tetanus for only 1 or 2 seconds.

☐ **12** Select REVIEW/ANALYZE from the main menu or click the ANALYZE button. Make any measurements or observations that your instructor may suggest. At what frequency does incomplete tetanus occur? At what frequency does complete tetanus occur? Print out your results and attach them to Lab Report 20.

> **Hint** The PHYSIOGRIP manual contains additional experiments, as well as troubleshooting tips. •

clinical applications: exercise

The term **exercise** has many definitions, depending on the context in which it is used. For some *exercise physiologists*, the term refers to any significant use of skeletal muscles. Exercise physiology has many important applications in athletic training, injury prevention, *ergonomics* (study of body movement as it relates to work activities), physical therapy, and everyday health issues.

An interesting aspect of exercise physiology is that it involves the study of nearly every system and organ in the body, not just the skeletal muscles. When skeletal muscles contract, the sudden increase in metabolism affects many of the processes throughout the body.

1. List as many metabolic needs of skeletal muscles during exercise as you can. One has already been given to you: *oxygen.* (Think of things from the extracellular environment that are needed by cells as they work.)

2. For each need listed in question 1, name the body process that supplies that need. Think about *all* the processes that fulfill a need. In our example of *oxygen*, breathing is cited as a process that supports oxygen availability. However, blood flow is also required to deliver the oxygen.

For example, the increased use of oxygen in muscles usually triggers an increase in respiratory rate. Why? Because the rate of oxygen extraction from the blood by muscles increases. Respiratory control centers increase the respiratory rate in response to the low blood concentration of oxygen.

Answering the following questions will help you appreciate the whole-body aspect of exercise physiology. Read all the questions before answering. You may want to put your answers in the form of a table on a separate sheet.

3. Go back over each process listed in question 2. Next to each one, indicate how the process may change during exercise. Does its rate increase? Decrease?

4. During exercise, some processes slow or stop because metabolic necessities such as oxygen are diverted to the skeletal muscles. What processes must be "put on hold" until exercise is over?

Name: _____ Date: _____ Section: _____

Skeletal Muscle Contractions

Specimen: *psoas muscle (rabbit)*
Total Magnification: _____

Specimen: *psoas muscle (rabbit)*
Total Magnification: _____

Contraction of Single Muscle Fibers

TREATMENT	BEGINNING LENGTH	ENDING LENGTH	PERCENT CHANGE
ATP + salt solution			
	Average		
ATP solution			
	Average		
Salt solution			
	Average		

Explanation/Interpretation:

Contraction in a Muscle Organ

PHENOMENON	VALUE	EXPLANATION
Threshold level of stimulation	volts	What does this value represent?
Level of stimulation required for a standard twitch	volts	What does this value represent? How does knowing this value help you do the rest of the experiment?
Series of twitch contractions		Does the amplitude remain the same for each twitch in the series? Why or why not?
Threshold frequency or incomplete tetanus	Hz	What does this value represent? A common finding in the frog gastrocnemius is a threshold of about 70 Hz. Is your result higher or lower?
Threshold frequency or complete tetanus	Hz	What does this value represent? A common result is around 200 Hz. How does your result compare?
Duration of latent period (of one twitch)	msec	What does this value represent? Can you explain it in terms of the physiology of contraction?
Duration of contraction phase (of one twitch)	msec	What does this value represent?
Duration of relaxation phase (of one twitch)	msec	What does this value represent?
Total duration of one twitch contraction	msec	Looking at all your data, does this value seem to be constant or variable?

NOTE: Do not forget to attach copies of your myogram charts (with your measurements and notations) to this report.

LAB EXERCISE 21

Nerve Tissue

This exercise is the first of 11 that challenge you to investigate the human **nervous system.** Before going any further, it is best to lay a foundation by discussing the overall organization of this system.

The nervous system is composed of two major divisions: the **central nervous system (CNS)** and the **peripheral nervous system (PNS).** The CNS includes the brain and spinal cord; the PNS includes all the **nerves** that conduct impulses to and from the CNS. Often the nervous system is instead subdivided into the **afferent division** and the **efferent division.** The afferent division includes nerves and tracts leading *toward* the CNS—the *sensory nerves* and *sensory tracts.* The efferent division includes nerves and tracts leading *away from* the CNS—the *motor nerves* and *motor tracts.*

The nervous system can be instead subdivided into the **somatic nervous system (SNS)** and the **autonomic nervous system (ANS).** The SNS is concerned mainly with pathways that monitor somatic sensors (general senses) and regulate somatic effectors (skeletal muscles). The ANS, on the other hand, mainly monitors and regulates subconscious visceral activities that involve cardiac muscle, smooth muscle, glands, and adipose tissue.

This exercise is an investigation of the cells of the nervous system. Exercise 22 will continue the study of the organization of the nervous system with an exploration of concepts of the *reflex arc.*

BEFORE YOU BEGIN

☐ Read the appropriate chapter in your textbook and Exercise 9 in this Lab Manual.
☐ Set your learning goals. When you finish this exercise, you should be able to:
  ☐ describe the structural components of a typical neuron and identify them on a model or chart
  ☐ name the three structural categories of neurons and identify their principal locations
  ☐ identify specimens of *multipolar* and *bipolar* neurons
  ☐ identify a figure illustrating *unipolar* neurons
  ☐ name the major categories of neuroglia and identify their principal locations
  ☐ identify specimens of figures illustrating neuroglia
  ☐ describe the structure of a typical peripheral nerve
☐ Prepare your materials:
  ☐ models or charts:
    ☐ multipolar neuron
    ☐ unipolar neuron
    ☐ nerve c.s.
  ☐ microscope

☐ prepared microslides:
  ☐ spinal cord smear (multipolar neurons)
  ☐ retina c.s. (bipolar neurons)
  ☐ peripheral nerve (myelinated) c.s.
  ☐ spinal cord c.s.
☐ Read the directions and safety tips for this exercise *carefully* before starting any procedure.

safety first
Observe the usual safety precautions when using the microscope. •

Study TIPS

Before beginning this lab, review Lab Exercise 9 (Nervous Tissue). It will also be helpful if you have your textbook, the *A&P Survival Guide,* or images of neurons and each type of glial cell.

A. THE NEURON

As you already know from your study of nervous tissue histology (Exercise 9), the **neuron (Figure 21-1)** is the cell type that conducts impulses, or **action potentials.** The **neuroglia,** on the other hand, support the neurons in any number of ways. Neurons can be *unipolar,* having a single projection from the cell body; bipolar, having two projections from the cell body; or *multipolar,* having many projections (see Activity B). In this activity, you will find as many of the listed neuron structures as possible on a multipolar neuron model (or chart) and in a slide of multipolar neurons (spinal cord smear).

☐ **1** Locate the cell body, or **soma.** It is a large region made up of the nucleus and surrounding cytoplasm. Packets of rough endoplasmic reticulum (ER) in the soma produce neurotransmitters. These packets are still sometimes called **Nissl bodies** or *Nissl substance* after their discoverer, Franz Nissl.
☐ **2** The soma forms a cone-shaped projection, or **axon hillock,** as it projects to become the **axon.** The axon is one of two types of neuron projections (fibers). The axon usually conducts action potentials away from the cell body.
☐ **3** The axon may be wrapped with a series of neuroglial cells called **Schwann cells.** Schwann cells wrap like tape around

the axons of some peripheral nerves, each spiraling around a fiber to form a multilayered coating. The inner layers of the Schwann cell are filled with the fatty white substance called **myelin.** Because the Schwann cells are found in series, they form a segmented *sheath of Schwann*, or **myelin sheath.** The gaps between the Schwann cells are termed **nodes of Ranvier.** The outer wrapping of each Schwann cell is normal cytoplasm, with organelles and a nucleus. In the case described, the axon is called a **white fiber,** or myelinated fiber. A group of white fibers together is called **white matter.** Schwann cells occur only in the PNS. Within the CNS, myelinated axons are wrapped with extensions of **oligodendrocytes,** another type of neuroglial cell.

☐ **4** Schwann cells (neurilemmocytes) or oligodendrocytes are also associated with **unmyelinated axons,** which together with cell bodies and dendrites form **gray matter.** However, in this case, the neuroglia do not form multiple wrappings and are not partially filled with myelin.

☐ **5 Collateral axons,** or axon branches, can be observed in some cells. Also, the distal ends of axons are often branched. These smaller distal branches are termed **telodendria.**

☐ **6** Multipolar neurons have many projections from the soma called **dendrites.** Dendrites are branched extensions that are sensitive to stimuli from other cells. Other neurons form an association, or **synapse,** at a bump on the dendrite or cell body (soma). Stimulation of a dendrite or the cell body results in a local change in potential.

B. STRUCTURAL CLASSIFICATION OF NEURONS

There are three categories of neurons based on their shapes **(Figure 21-2)**:

☐ **1 Multipolar neurons**—Multipolar neurons have multiple projections from the cell body. Multipolar neurons comprise most of the neurons in the CNS. Almost all motor neurons are multipolar. Examine a multipolar neuron in a prepared spinal cord smear. Note the many projections.

☐ **2 Bipolar neurons**—Bipolar neurons have exactly two projections from the cell body. Normally, one process conducts impulses toward the cell body. Such a process is called the *dendrite.* The other process conducts impulses away from the cell body and is called the *axon.* Bipolar neurons are most commonly found in the sensory tracts of the eye (for vision) and nasal epithelium (for smell). Examine a prepared slide of the retina (the sensitive lining of the eyeball). Can you distinguish any bipolar cells? A color micrograph of a retina cross section is shown in Figure 21-2.

☐ **3 Unipolar neurons**—Unipolar neurons, also called **pseudounipolar neurons,** have one extension from the cell body; however, the single process splits near the body to become two long branches. One branch has dendrite-like endings that receive stimulation for an impulse. The remainder of that branch and all of the other branches then conduct the impulse along. The two branches together function as a single axon. Most sensory neurons are unipolar. Examine a figure or model of a unipolar neuron.

Coloring Exercises: Multipolar Neuron

Use colored pens or pencils to shade in both the figure and the labels. Each red numeral in the figure corresponds to a matching red numeral following the appropriate label.

SOMA₁
NUCLEUS₂
NUCLEOLUS₃
MITOCHONDRION₄
GOLGI APPARATUS₅
NISSL BODIES₆
AXON HILLOCK₇
DENDRITE₈
AXON₉
SCHWANN CELLS₁₀

Myelin sheath of Schwann cells

Node of Ranvier

Myelin sheath

Nucleus of Schwann cell

Synaptic knobs

Telodendria

FIGURE 21-1 Structure of a typical neuron.

FIGURE 21-2 Structural classification of neurons. **A,** Multipolar neuron. **B,** Bipolar neuron. **C,** Unipolar (pseudounipolar) neuron. **D,** Cross section of human retina bipolar cells. **E,** Multipolar neurons.

C. TYPES OF GLIA

Neuroglia, or simply **glia**, are the most numerous kinds of cells in nerve tissue. The conducting cells are called **neurons**. Glia are often associated with particular neurons and support the structure or function of the neurons. A brief exploration of glia in the human nervous system is outlined in this activity.

☐ 1 **Astrocytes**—Astrocytes look like tiny stars in many preparations. They have a cell body with many elongated projections. Astrocyte projections have broad "feet" that cover blood vessels in the brain. Together with the vessel wall itself, the layer formed by the astrocyte feet forms the **blood-brain barrier.** Substances that pass in and out of the blood vessel wall must also move across the wall formed by astrocyte projections. Locate astrocytes in **Figure 21-3**.

☐ 2 **Microglia**—Microglia are small glial cells that develop from different tissue than other nervous tissue cells. Because of their location, they are considered along with other glial cells. Microglia are able to move to sites of damage or infection to phagocytize harmful substances. Locate microglia in Figure 21-3.

☐ 3 **Oligodendrocytes**—Like astrocytes, oligodendrocytes have many processes. Oligodendrocyte processes form a layer over axons in the CNS. This layer, called a **myelin sheath,** affects the speed of conduction in an axon. Locate oligodendrocytes in Figure 21-3.

☐ 4 **Schwann cells**—Schwann cells form myelin sheaths around axons in the PNS. Each Schwann cell wraps entirely around a single axon, rather than projecting extensions to several axons. Locate Schwann cells in Figure 21-3. Examine a prepared slide of a peripheral nerve cross section. Locate the myelin that surrounds each nerve fiber. **Figure 21-4** shows a cross section of a peripheral nerve, with the myelin surrounding each nerve fiber clearly visible.

☐ 5 **Ependymal cells**—Ependymal cells are found lining the fluid spaces of the brain and spinal cord. Some form *cerebrospinal fluid* (CSF), and some are ciliated and assist the movement of CSF through the fluid spaces. Locate ependymal cells in Figure 21-3. Examine a prepared slide of a spinal cord cross section. Locate small ciliated ependymal cells that form the lining of the central canal. Figure 21-4 shows such a cross section, but at too low a magnification to see ependymal cells clearly.

Study TIPS

Use a mnemonic device to help you remember the different types of glial cells. An example of this would be:

Amy	Astrocytes
Makes	Microglia
Omelets	Oligodendrocytes
Seem	Schwann cells
Easy	Ependymal cells

D. NERVE STRUCTURE

The **nerve** is a bundle of axons that lies in the PNS. The coloring exercise in **Figure 21-5** and the steps outlined in the following checklist describe the essential structure of the peripheral nerve. Locate these features in a model, diagram, and/or a prepared microslide of a peripheral nerve cross section (see Figure 21-4).

☐ 1 **Epineurium**—The epineurium is a fibrous membrane that forms a sheath around the entire bundle of structures that make up the nerve.

☐ 2 **Perineurium**—The perineurium is a fibrous structure that is essentially an inward continuation of the epineurium. Acting as a sort of "inner wrapping" or "packing material," the perineurium segregates the nerve fibers (axons) within the nerve into groupings called **fascicles.**

☐ 3 **Endoneurium**—Just as the perineurium is an inward extension of the epineurium, the endoneurium is an inward extension of the perineurium. The endoneurium is a fibrous membrane that covers each individual axon (and its sheath of Schwann) within each fascicle.

CENTRAL NERVOUS SYSTEM NEUROGLIA

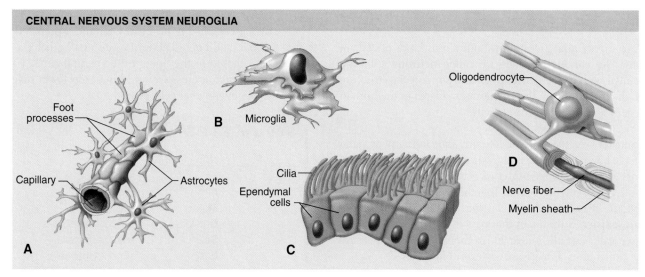

PERIPHERAL NERVOUS SYSTEM NEUROGLIA

FIGURE 21-3 Types of glia. **A,** Astrocytes attached to the outside of a capillary blood vessel in the brain. **B,** A phagocytic microglial cell. **C,** Ciliated ependymal cells form a sheet of the type that usually lines fluid cavities in the brain. **D,** An oligodendrocyte with processes that wrap around nerve fibers in the CNS to form myelin sheaths. **E,** A Schwann cell supporting a bundle of nerve fibers in the PNS. **F,** Another type of Schwann cell wrapping around a peripheral nerve fiber to form a thick myelin sheath. **G,** Satellite cells, another type of Schwann cell, surround and support cell bodies of neurons in the PNS.

FIGURE 21-4 **A,** Peripheral nerve cross section. **B,** Cross section of mammalian spinal cord.

Coloring Exercises: Nerve

Use colored pens or pencils to shade in both the figure and the labels. Each red numeral in the figure corresponds to a matching red numeral following the appropriate label.

EPINEURIUM₁
PERINEURIUM₂
ENDONEURIUM₃
AXON₄
FASCICLE₅

FIGURE 21-5 Structure of the neuron.

Name: _____ Date: _____ Section: _____

LAB REPORT 21
Nerve Tissue

Fill in this table summarizing your examination of a multipolar neuron model. Check off each structure as it is identified. For functions, refer to a reference book or your textbook.

IDENTIFICATION	STRUCTURE	FUNCTION(S)
☐	Soma	
☐	Nissl bodies	
☐	Axon hillock	
☐	Axon	
☐	Schwann cells	
☐	Nodes of Ranvier	
☐	Collateral axon	
☐	Telodendria	
☐	Dendrite	

Specimen: *multipolar neurons*
Total Magnification: _____

Specimen: *unipolar neurons*
Total Magnification: _____

Specimen: *bipolar neurons*
Total Magnification: _____

Specimen: *Schwann cells*
Total Magnification: _____

Specimen: *Schwann cells*
Total Magnification: _____

Fill-in

1. _____
2. _____
3. _____
4. _____
5. _____
6. _____
7. _____
8. _____
9. _____
10. _____
11. _____
12. _____
13. _____
14. _____
15. _____
16. _____
17. _____
18. _____
19. _____
20. _____

Fill-in (complete each statement with the correct term)

1. The soma forms a cone-shaped _?_ as it projects to form an axon.

2. _?_ are small, distal branches of an axon.

3. Either Schwann cells or extensions of _?_ can form myelin sheaths.

4. The gaps between the segments of a myelin sheath are called _?_.

5. A group of myelinated fibers may form a region of nerve tissue called _?_ matter.

6. The _?_ neuron connects an afferent neuron to an efferent neuron.

7. A junction between two neurons, or between a neuron and effector, is called a(n) _?_.

8. A bundle of parallel neurons encased in fibrous connective tissue is called a(n) _?_ (in the PNS).

9. A bundle of parallel neurons in the CNS is called a(n) _?_.

10. An action potential traveling down a myelinated axon travels _?_ (faster/slower) than in an unmyelinated axon.

11. Unmyelinated nerve tissue is called _?_ matter.

12. _?_ neurons have exactly two projections from the cell body.

13. _?_ neurons have multiple dendrites and a single axon extending from the cell body.

14. In _?_ neurons, a single process from the cell body diverges to form two long branches—one acting as a dendrite and the other as an axon.

15. Schwann cells form myelin sheaths in the _?_ nervous system.

16. Oligodendrocytes form myelin sheaths in the _?_ nervous system.

17. Neuroglial cells called _?_ cells line the fluid spaces of the brain.

18. Small glial cells that phagocytize harmful matter are called _?_.

19. _?_ are ciliated neuroglia that assist the circulation of CSF.

20. Of the two major types of cells in nerve tissue, the _?_ is the most numerous.

22

Nerve Reflexes

This exercise describes the organization of the human nervous system and relates it to the concept of the *reflex arc*. The first activity describes the nature of the reflex arc and the manner in which it elicits a response called a *reflex* in an effector. The remainder of the exercise challenges you to demonstrate some simple reflexes that are often used in clinical situations to assess the condition of the nervous system.

BEFORE YOU BEGIN

☐ Read the appropriate chapter in your textbook.
☐ Set your learning goals. When you finish this exercise, you should be able to:
  ☐ outline the features of a reflex arc and be able to apply this model to specific nerve pathways
  ☐ demonstrate several nerve reflexes in a human subject
☐ Prepare your materials:
  ☐ rubber reflex mallet
  ☐ sterile cotton balls
  ☐ penlight
☐ Read the directions and safety tips for this exercise *carefully* before starting any procedure.

Study TIPS

The features of the reflex arc follow a simple pathway. To remember this pathway you might want to use a mnemonic sentence. An example would be:

Rivers	Receptor
Sometimes	Sensory neuron
Invade	Interneuron
Mountain	Motor neuron
Environments	Effector

A. ORGANIZATION OF NERVE PATHWAYS

An often-used model of nerve pathways is the **reflex arc**. A reflex arc is a way of visualizing the direction of transmission of nerve signals (action potentials). For each step that follows, find the reflex arc featured in the diagram of a simple reflex arc in **Figure 22-1**.

☐ 1 The arc begins with a **receptor,** a specialized cell or cell projection, which is stimulated by a change in its environment. For example, some receptors in the skin are sensitive to heat, while others are sensitive to pressure.

☐ 2 If stimulation of the receptor was significant enough to initiate an action potential in the **afferent neuron,** the signal is transmitted toward the central nervous system (CNS). The afferent, or sensory, neuron brings the signal into the brain or spinal cord.

☐ 3 At the peak of the arc, where the signal is "turned around," the afferent neuron may synapse directly with an **efferent neuron** (forming a **two-neuron arc**). Often an interneuron synapses with the afferent neuron and transmits the signal to an efferent neuron. This is a **three-neuron arc.**

☐ 4 The efferent, or motor, neuron then proceeds to an **effector.** An effector is a muscle or gland innervated by a motor nerve. The effector responds in some way to nerve signals, perhaps by contracting or secreting a chemical.

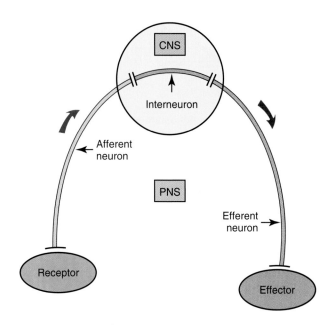

FIGURE 22-1 A simple three-neuron reflex arc. *Red arrows* indicate direction of nerve transmission.

Synthesizing the component parts of the reflex arc, we see that a stimulus at the receptor results in a reaction by an effector. A simple example is a pinprick that causes a reflexive withdrawal of the pricked limb. Reflexes may be more complex, with sensory information being relayed to several different points in the CNS before triggering a motor response. Also, more than one sensory neuron may converge on a single association neuron, or multiple motor neurons may diverge from a single association neuron. Autonomic reflexes typically involve two efferent neurons, whereas somatomotor reflexes involve only one efferent neuron.

Figure 22-2 shows that reflex arcs can become quite complicated. Carefully study this figure (and the description beneath it), noting the different pathways that efferent and afferent neurons may take in the human nervous system.

Afferent and efferent neurons generally form bundles of parallel fibers called **nerves** (in the peripheral nervous system [PNS]) or **tracts** (in the CNS). Nerves are supported by fibrous connective tissue membranes similar to those found in skeletal muscle organs **(Figure 22-3)**. See Lab Exercise 21 for more details of nerve structure.

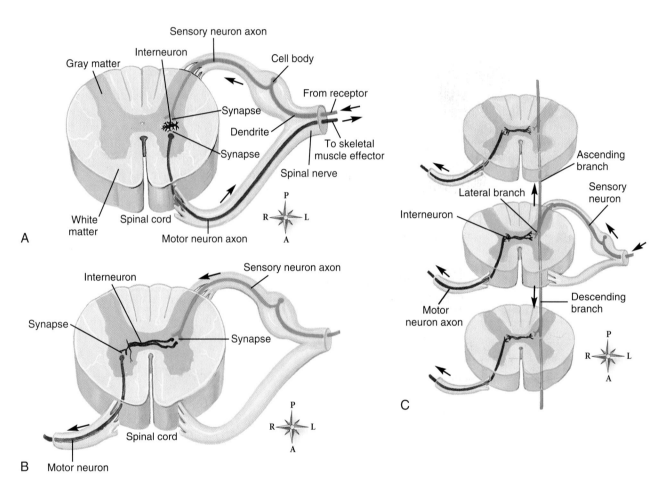

FIGURE 22-2 Examples of reflex arcs. **A,** Three-neuron ipsilateral reflex arc. Sensory information enters and motor information leaves on the same side of the CNS. **B,** Three-neuron contralateral reflex arc. Sensory information enters on the side of the CNS opposite the side from which motor information exits. **C,** Intersegmental contralateral reflex arc. Divergent branches of a sensory neuron bring information to several segments of the CNS at the same time. Motor information leaves each segment on the opposite side of the CNS.

Coloring Exercises: **Reflex Arc and Spinal Cord**

Use colored pens or pencils to shade in both the figure and the labels. Each red numeral in the figure corresponds to a matching red numeral following the appropriate label.

Reflex Arc

RECEPTOR₁
AFFERENT NEURON₂
INTERNEURON₃
EFFERENT NEURON₄
EFFECTOR₅
DORSAL SPINAL NERVE
   ROOT₆
DORSAL ROOT GANGLION₇

VENTRAL SPINAL NERVE
   ROOT₈
SPINAL NERVE₉
BRANCH OF SPINAL
   NERVE₁₀

Spinal Cord

WHITE MATTER₁₁
GRAY MATTER₁₂

FIGURE 22-3 Example of a spinal reflex arc.

B. STRETCH REFLEX DEMONSTRATIONS

Examples of reflexes can be seen in clinical tests performed in patients suspected of having some type of nerve damage. If the reflex shows an abnormal reaction or no reaction at all, damage to some component of the reflex arc is suspected. This activity demonstrates several reflexes that are categorized as *stretch* reflexes. Other types of simple reflexes are demonstrated in later activities.

☐ 1 The **patellar reflex**, or *knee-jerk reflex*, is mediated by a two-neuron arc centered in the spinal cord. Have the subject sit on a table with the legs dangling above the floor. Tap the knee sharply with a reflex mallet at the ligament just inferior to the patella (kneecap). The tap stretches a quadriceps muscle in the anterior thigh, stimulating *stretch receptors* located in the muscle. In response to the increased stretch, which normally would only occur when the muscle load has suddenly increased, the muscle contracts and extends the lower leg. In this demonstration, such a reaction seems strange, but in normal circumstances the patellar reflex allows the quadriceps muscle to reflexively increase its strength of contraction in response to increased load **(Figure 22-4, A)**.

 Possible abnormal spinal reflex results:

- **hyperreflexia** (exaggerated response) results from damaged or diseased motor areas in the CNS
- **hyporeflexia** (inhibited response) results from degeneration of nerve pathways, voluntary motor control, and other factors

   Be aware of the clinical significance of understanding appropriate reflexes. Look up Babinski sign in a baby and an adult. Look up Hoffman's sign. Which one is large bundle and which one is small tract? You will study the Babinski sign under "Cutaneous Reflexes" below. •

☐ 2 The **biceps reflex** is a spinal reflex that involves nerves C5 and C6. Have the subject sit with the elbow flexed at about 90 degrees and palm facing downward. Put your thumb on the biceps (brachii) tendon at the inside angle of the elbow and press gently. Tap your thumb with a reflex mallet. Flexion of the elbow is the normal response.

☐ 3 The **Achilles reflex** is a spinal reflex that results in plantar flexion of the foot. Have the subject kneel on a chair, facing away from you, with the toes pointing toward the floor. Tap the middle of the Achilles (calcaneal) tendon with a reflex mallet. Is the response normal?

☐ 4 The **triceps reflex** is another stretch reflex. Have the subject lie on a table, with an arm across the abdomen. Supporting the subject's arm with the elbow flexed at a 90-degree angle, sharply tap the posterior surface of the upper arm just proximal to the olecranon (Figure 22-4, B). The lower arm should extend as the triceps brachii muscle reflexively contracts. How do you explain this response?

FIGURE 22-4 A, The patellar reflex arc. *Arrow* indicates tapping point. **B,** Tapping point for triceps reflex. **C,** Demonstrating plantar reflex.

C. CUTANEOUS REFLEXES

Cutaneous reflexes are those that result from the stimulation of cutaneous (skin) receptors.

- ☐ 1 The **plantar reflex** involves cutaneous receptors rather than deep receptors in muscles or tendons. Position the subject's bare foot with the lateral surface resting on a table or chair. Demonstrate this reflex by firmly sweeping the handle of the mallet along the lateral region of the sole (Figure 22-4, C). In a normal adult, the toes flex. In a **Babinski response,** the toes extend and move apart. The Babinski response is normal in infants in whom the nerves have not fully myelinated, but the response is abnormal in adults.

- ☐ 2 Another cutaneous reflex is the **abdominal reflex.** Begin the abdominal reflex demonstration by having the subject lie on a clean, flat surface. Expose the skin of the abdomen. Use the handle of the reflex mallet to sweep gently along the anterior, lateral aspect of the skin. Move in a superior-to-inferior direction. What is the response of the abdominal muscles?

D. CRANIAL REFLEXES

Another type of reflex is mediated by the brain. For example, the *pupillary reflexes*, demonstrated in Step 1, involve cranial nerves and autonomic reflex centers.

- ☐ 1 In a dimly lit area, demonstrate the **pupillary reflexes,** which are centered in the brainstem. Have the subject stare straight ahead, with a hand held vertically between the eyes. Shine a penlight in the subject's left eye (from 5 to 7 cm away). Normally, the light receptors in the eye receive the bright light and trigger a reflexive response by the muscles in the iris. Does the pupil increase or decrease in diameter? What is the advantage of this response? The right pupil may also exhibit a reflexive response, even though light is not shown on it. Does the right pupil increase or decrease in diameter? What advantage is gained by this *consensual* reflex?

- ☐ 2 Demonstrate the **corneal reflex,** which involves the fifth cranial nerve. Begin the corneal reflex demonstration by having the subject stand facing at a 90-degree angle to you. While the subject stares straight ahead, quickly move a clean, sterile cotton ball toward the surface of one eye. *Do not actually touch the eye, however.* What is the reaction? What survival advantage does this reflex have?

Name: _____ Date: _____ Section: _____

LAB REPORT 22
Nerve Reflexes

Record your data and interpretations of the reflex tests. Be sure to indicate the function each may have.

REFLEX	RESULTS		EXPLANATION/DISCUSSION
	LEFT	RIGHT	
Patellar	☐ normal ☐ hyperreflexia ☐ hyporeflexia ☐ no response	☐ normal ☐ hyperreflexia ☐ hyporeflexia ☐ no response	
Biceps	☐ normal ☐ hyperreflexia ☐ hyporeflexia ☐ no response	☐ normal ☐ hyperreflexia ☐ hyporeflexia ☐ no response	
Achilles	☐ normal ☐ hyperreflexia ☐ hyporeflexia ☐ no response	☐ normal ☐ hyperreflexia ☐ hyporeflexia ☐ no response	
Triceps	☐ normal ☐ hyperreflexia ☐ hyporeflexia ☐ no response	☐ normal ☐ hyperreflexia ☐ hyporeflexia ☐ no response	
Plantar	☐ normal ☐ Babinski response ☐ no response	☐ normal ☐ Babinski response ☐ no response	
Abdominal	☐ normal ☐ hyperreflexia ☐ hyporeflexia ☐ no response	☐ normal ☐ hyperreflexia ☐ hyporeflexia ☐ no response	
Pupillary	☐ dilation ☐ constriction ☐ no response	☐ dilation ☐ constriction ☐ no response	
Corneal	☐ response ☐ no response	☐ response ☐ no response	

Put in Order

1. _____
2. _____
3. _____
4. _____
5. _____

Fill-in

1. _____
2. _____
3. _____
4. _____
5. _____
6. _____
7. _____
8. _____
9. _____
10. _____

Put in Order (rearrange these components of the reflex arc in the order in which nerve signals pass through them)

interneuron
effector
motor neuron
receptor
sensory neuron

Fill-in (complete each statement with the correct term)

1. In infants, the _?_ response is normal when testing the plantar reflex.

2. When testing the plantar reflex in an adult, extension of the toes may indicate damage to the _?_ somewhere along the reflex arc.

3. In the _?_ reflex, a muscle contracts when the load increases.

4. The center of the patellar reflex is in the _?_.

5. A stretch reflex involving the biceps brachii muscle causes _?_ of the elbow if the biceps muscle is stretched.

6. In the triceps reflex demonstration, the triceps muscle was the effector, and one or more _?_ were the receptors.

7. If the Achilles (calcaneal) tendon is tapped, one would expect the ankle to _?_.

8. When suddenly illuminated with a penlight, the pupil of the eye normally _?_ (dilates/constricts).

9. _?_ reflexes result from the stimulation of sensory receptors in the skin.

10. _?_ reflexes are centered in the brain and involve cranial nerves.

The Spinal Cord and Spinal Nerves

As you know, the spinal cord is one of two principal organs of the central nervous system (CNS). The brain is the other. This exercise presents the spinal cord and its accessory structures on the gross level and on the microscopic level. This exercise also includes a peek into the peripheral nervous system (PNS) by means of an introduction to the **spinal nerves.**

BEFORE YOU BEGIN

☐ Read the appropriate chapter in your textbook.
☐ Set your learning goals. When you finish this exercise, you should be able to:
    ☐ name and describe the coverings of the spinal cord
    ☐ identify principal structures of the spinal cord in figures and specimens
    ☐ define *spinal nerve, nerve root,* and *plexus*
    ☐ name the spinal nerves and locate them in a model or figure
☐ Prepare your materials:
    ☐ preserved specimen: ox spinal cord segment
    ☐ dissection tools and tray
    ☐ model or chart of the human spinal cord
    ☐ microscope
    ☐ prepared microslide: *mammalian spinal cord c.s.*
    ☐ computer setup with a program to simulate dissection of a human body (optional)
☐ Read the directions and safety tips for this exercise *carefully* before starting any procedure.

Study TIPS

As you complete this dissection, refer to an illustration or atlas of the human body. Use the illustration or atlas to locate and compare the various structures of the spinal cord with your preserved specimen. Because the vertebrate body plan among species is very similar, this may help you to understand the structure of the human spinal cord. Refer to the *A&P Survival Guide* for reference to the spinal nerves and peripheral branches.

A. SPINAL CORD DISSECTION

Use both the preserved spinal cord specimen and a model or chart to explore the features described in this activity.

> **! *safety first***
> Heed the precautions that accompany the chemical preservative used with your specimen, especially those regarding ventilation and skin protection. Use your dissection tools carefully. Use safety goggles to avoid injury during dissections. •

The spinal cord is nerve tissue continuous with that of the brain, extending inferiorly from the brain at the level of the foramen magnum. The spinal cord is covered by several layers of protective or nourishing tissue:

☐ 1 The *bony covering* of the spinal cord is formed by the vertebral column. The spinal cord lies within the spinal cavity formed by the vertebral foramina of the stacked vertebrae. What is the bony covering of the brain?

☐ 2 The outermost of three *membranous coverings,* or **meninges** (singular, *meninx*), of the spinal cord is the tough, skinlike **dura mater.** The spinal meninges are continuous with the meninges surrounding the brain.

☐ 3 Deep to the dura mater is a much thinner meninx, the spidery **arachnoid.** The space deep to the arachnoid, the **subarachnoid space,** is filled with circulating **cerebrospinal fluid (CSF)** in life. The CSF has been drained from your specimen.

☐ 4 The deepest meninx, the delicate **pia mater,** is a thin, vascular membrane adhering to the surface of the spinal cord.

☐ 5 The **anterior median fissure** is a deep groove on the anterior surface of the human spinal cord (along the midline). This fissure is analogous to that on the ventral surface of the ox spinal cord.

☐ 6 The **posterior median sulcus** is a somewhat shallower groove along the dorsal surface of the spinal cord.

☐ 7 A **cervical enlargement** is seen in the cervical region of the spinal cord, and a similar **lumbar enlargement** is found in the lower thoracic region. The lumbar enlargement tapers to a cone-shaped end called the **medullary cone.**

☐ 8 The spinal cord proper does not extend below vertebra L1. Instead, separate nerves trail inferiorly until each pair has exited the spinal cavity. This group of nerves, resembling a horse's tail, is called the **cauda equina.**

☐ 9 **Ventral** and **dorsal spinal nerve roots** may be intact in your specimen. These structures are discussed more fully in a later activity.

Hint   The following structures may or may not be easily seen in the preserved specimen, depending on the specimen's condition. A freshly cut, even cross section usually gives the best results.   •

☐ **10** A cross-sectional view of the spinal cord shows a distinct H-shaped area of gray matter surrounded by areas of white matter. The two lateral sections of gray matter are joined by a transverse **gray commissure.** In the center of the gray commissure, you may see the **central canal (Figure 23-1).** This canal contains CSF in life but contains preservative in prepared specimens.

☐ **11** Each lateral mass of the gray matter exhibits extensions termed the **anterior gray horn** and the **posterior gray horn.** The thoracic and lumbar regions have additional lateral extensions called **lateral gray horns.**

☐ **12** Columns of white matter surround the central gray matter area. These include the **anterior white column, lateral white column,** and **posterior white column.** Columns are sometimes called **funiculi.**

> ❗ *safety first*
> Observe the usual precautions when using the microscope and slides.   •

B. MICROSCOPIC EXPLORATION

☐ **1** Obtain a stained cross section preparation of a mammalian spinal cord and observe it at a low total magnification.

☐ **2** Try to find as many features of the spinal cord (as described in Activity A) as you can. White matter and gray matter are often distinguished by differential staining (contrasting colors), as in Figure 21-4.

C. SPINAL NERVES

Afferent neurons extending through the spinal cord enter as part of a **spinal nerve.** Efferent neurons in the spinal cord exit in spinal nerves. Although not really part of the spinal cord proper (they are in the PNS rather than the CNS), we will consider them in this exercise. As each structure is presented, try to locate it on a model or chart of the human nervous system and in **Figure 23-2.**

☐ **1** There are 31 pairs of spinal nerves communicating with the spinal cord by way of the intervertebral foramina formed as the vertebrae stack on one another. The spinal nerves are named for the vertebral region with which they are associated:
  ☐ **Cervical spinal nerves**—C1 through C8 (one pair between the skull and vertebra C1 and one pair inferior to each of seven cervical vertebrae)
  ☐ **Thoracic spinal nerves**—T1 through T12
  ☐ **Lumbar spinal nerves**—L1 through L5
  ☐ **Sacral spinal nerves**—S1 through S5 (branches of these nerves communicate via the dorsal and pelvic foramina of the sacrum)
  ☐ **Coccygeal spinal nerves**—C or Cx

☐ **2** Each spinal nerve communicates with the cord by means of two separate **spinal nerve roots,** each formed by the combination of six to eight tiny *rootlets.* The **ventral (anterior) spinal nerve root** includes efferent fibers (somatomotor and autonomic axons). The **dorsal (posterior) spinal nerve root** contains afferent fibers. Nuclei of afferent neurons form an area of gray matter in the dorsal root called the **dorsal root ganglion.** The spinal nerve roots are found within the spinal cavity. The spinal nerve proper passes through the intervertebral foramina.

☐ **3** Outside the spinal cavity, each spinal nerve branches to form a **ventral ramus** and a **dorsal ramus.** In most of the thoracic and lumbar nerves, the ventral ramus branches into autonomic and somatic pathways. In other segments, the fibers of the ventral rami branch to form **plexi.** Plexi are complex nerve networks in which fibers from several different spinal nerves are reorganized to form specific peripheral nerves. Identify each plexus on a model or chart:
  ☐ **Cervical plexus**
  ☐ **Brachial plexus**
  ☐ **Lumbosacral plexus**

Coloring Exercises: Spinal Cord

Use colored pens or pencils to shade in both the figure and the labels. Each red numeral in the figure corresponds to a matching red numeral following the appropriate label.

Meninges
DURA MATER₁
ARACHNOID₂
SUBARACHNOID SPACE₃
PIA MATER₄

Spinal Cord
CENTRAL CANAL₅
GRAY COMMISSURE₆
ANTERIOR GRAY HORN₇
POSTERIOR GRAY HORN₈
ANTERIOR WHITE COLUMN₉

POSTERIOR WHITE
    COLUMN₁₀
LATERAL WHITE COLUMN₁₁

Spinal Nerve
VENTRAL NERVE ROOT₁₂
DORSAL NERVE ROOT₁₃
DORSAL ROOT GANGLION₁₄
SPINAL NERVE PROPER₁₅
VENTRAL RAMUS₁₆
DORSAL RAMUS₁₇

FIGURE 23-1 Structure of the spinal cord.

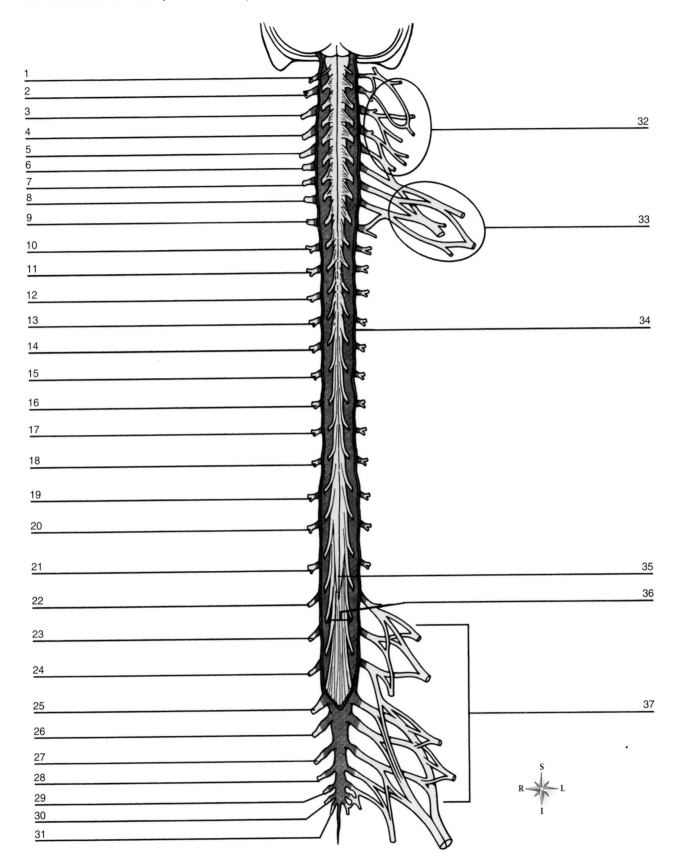

FIGURE 23-2 In the blanks numbered 1 through 31, write the correct spinal nerve abbreviation. In blanks 32 through 37, write the name of the nerve feature indicated. Also, write the abbreviations and nerve features on the corresponding blanks on the Lab Report.

Name: _____ Date: _____ Section: _____

LAB REPORT 23
The Spinal Cord and Spinal Nerves

Figure 23-2 (from p. 250)

1. _____
2. _____
3. _____
4. _____
5. _____
6. _____
7. _____
8. _____
9. _____
10. _____
11. _____
12. _____
13. _____
14. _____
15. _____
16. _____
17. _____
18. _____
19. _____
20. _____
21. _____
22. _____
23. _____
24. _____
25. _____
26. _____
27. _____
28. _____
29. _____
30. _____
31. _____
32. _____
33. _____
34. _____
35. _____
36. _____
37. _____

Summarize your exploration of the spinal cord and spinal nerves by using this checklist.

STRUCTURE	NOTES
☐ dura mater	
☐ arachnoid	
☐ subarachnoid space	
☐ pia mater	
☐ anterior median fissure	
☐ posterior median sulcus	
☐ cervical enlargement	
☐ lumbar enlargement	
☐ medullary cone	
☐ cauda equina	
☐ ventral spinal nerve root	
☐ dorsal spinal nerve root	
☐ dorsal root ganglion	
☐ gray commissure	
☐ central canal	
☐ gray horns: ☐ anterior ☐ lateral ☐ posterior	
white columns: ☐ anterior ☐ lateral ☐ posterior	
spinal nerves: ☐ cervical ☐ thoracic ☐ lumbar ☐ sacral ☐ coccygeal	
☐ ventral ramus of spinal nerve	
☐ dorsal ramus of spinal nerve	

Put in Order I

1. _____
2. _____
3. _____
4. _____
5. _____
6. _____
7. _____

Put in Order II

1. _____
2. _____
3. _____
4. _____
5. _____
6. _____
7. _____

Multiple Choice

1. _____
2. _____
3. _____
4. _____
5. _____

Put in Order I (rearrange these structures in the order in which a sensory signal might pass)

cervical plexus
dorsal root ganglion
posterior gray horn
receptor
sensory area of the brain
spinal nerve C2
ventral ramus

Put in Order II (rearrange these structures in the order in which a motor signal might pass)

anterior gray horn
effector
lateral gray horn
motor area of the brain
spinal nerve T6
ventral ramus
ventral nerve root

Multiple Choice (only one response is correct in each item that follows)

1. The medial deep groove on the ventral surface of the spinal cord is called the
   a. posterior median sulcus
   b. medial enlargement
   c. anterior lateral sulcus
   d. anterior median fissure
   e. ventral lateral column
2. The correct order for the meninges of the brain (from superficial to deep) is
   a. pia mater, dura mater, arachnoid
   b. dura mater, arachnoid, pia mater
   c. dura mater, pia mater, arachnoid
   d. dura mater, subarachnoid, pia mater
   e. the brain does not have meninges
3. The cauda equina is
   a. not present in humans
   b. a cone-shaped end of the spinal cord proper
   c. a bundle of separate nerves
   d. a bundle of cranial nerves
   e. an enlargement of the spinal cord proper
4. Spinal nerve branches from several spinal segments (vertical levels) may exchange fibers. Such a network of nerve fibers is called a
   a. braid
   b. ramus
   c. plexus
   d. ganglion
   e. spinal nerve root
5. Large groups of neuron cell bodies are likely to be found in
   a. the lateral gray horn
   b. the gray commissure
   c. a dorsal root ganglion
   d. the central canal
   e. a, b, and c are correct

24
The Brain and Cranial Nerves

Having explored the spinal cord in the previous exercise, it is time to move on to an exploration of the other major organ of the central nervous system: the **brain.** The brain occupies most of the cranial cavity within the skull. This rather large, complex organ has been partitioned, for convenience of study, into numerous divisions and subdivisions. Nerves that enter and exit the brain directly are called **cranial nerves.** In this exercise, you are challenged to explore the organization of the brain and the structure and function of the cranial nerves.

BEFORE YOU BEGIN

☐ Read the appropriate chapter in your textbook.
☐ Set your learning goals. When you finish this exercise, you should be able to:
  ☐ list and describe the principal structures of the brain
  ☐ identify structures of the human brain in a chart, model, or preserved specimen
☐ Prepare your materials:
  ☐ chart, model, or preserved specimen of a human brain
  ☐ computer setup with a program to simulate dissection of a human body (optional)
☐ Read the directions and safety tips for this exercise *carefully* before starting any procedure.

Study TIPS

Obtain an unlabeled copy of the external brain. You may want to use your cell phone and take a picture. Print this picture. As you complete this lab, use the unlabeled illustration/photo and label the external aspects of the brain.

> **Hint** Your textbook has descriptions and figures that will help you identify structures of the brain. You may wish to use your textbook as a supplemental resource for this and the following activities. •

A. EXTERNAL ASPECT OF THE BRAIN

Using a model or preserved specimen of the human brain, locate the structures of the brain listed in the following steps.

☐ 1 Determine whether any of the **meninges,** or membranous coverings of the brain, are intact **(Figure 24-1)**. If they are present, locate the following:
  ☐ **Dura mater**
  ☐ **Sagittal sinus**
  ☐ **Subdural space**
  ☐ **Arachnoid**
  ☐ **Subarachnoid space**
  ☐ **Pia mater**

☐ 2 Locate the largest part of the brain, the **cerebrum.** The cerebrum is divided into nearly symmetrical left and right **cerebral hemispheres** by a deep **longitudinal fissure.** Joining the left and right cerebral hemisphere is a band of white matter called the **corpus callosum,** which may be seen at the bottom of the longitudinal fissure. The surface of the cerebrum, or **cerebral cortex,** is characterized by large convoluted folds of gray matter called **gyri.** The grooves between the gyri are called **sulci** if they are shallow and **fissures** if they are deep. Some fissures serve as landmarks to divide the cerebrum into regions called **lobes** that correspond to the overlying skull bones:
  ☐ **Frontal lobe** (left and right)
  ☐ **Parietal lobe**
  ☐ **Occipital lobe**
  ☐ **Temporal lobe**
  ☐ **Insula** (also called the *island of Reil,* a region hidden within a fissure that separates the temporal lobe from the parietal lobe)

In addition to using lobes as a means of identifying different regions of the cerebral cortex, neurobiologists often prefer to identify **functional regions** of the cortex. **Figure 24-2** is a coloring exercise that illustrates some of the major functional areas of the cerebral cortex. How many of these areas can you identify on a specimen or model of the human brain?

Text continued on p. 258

Coloring Exercises: Coverings of the Brain

Use colored pens or pencils to shade in both the figure and the labels. Each red numeral in the figure corresponds to a matching red numeral following the appropriate label.

SKULL₁
SUPERIOR SAGITTAL
   SINUS₂
PERIOSTEUM₃
DURA MATER₄

SUBDURAL SPACE₅
ARACHNOID₆
SUBARACHNOID SPACE₇
PIA MATER₈
BRAIN₉

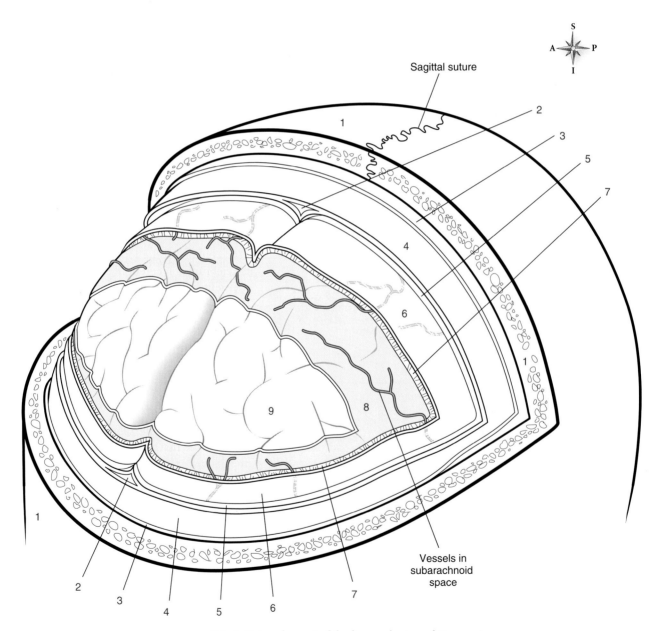

FIGURE 24-1 External aspect of the human brain and its coverings.

Coloring Exercises: Cerebral Cortex

Use colored pens or pencils to shade in both the figure and the labels. Each red numeral in the figure corresponds to a matching red numeral following the appropriate label.

Lobes

FRONTAL LOBE₁
PARIETAL LOBE₂
OCCIPITAL LOBE₃
TEMPORAL LOBE₄
INSULA₅

Functional Areas

PREFRONTAL AREA₆
PREMOTOR AREA₇
MOTOR SPEECH AREA₈
PRIMARY SOMATIC
  MOTOR AREA₉

PRIMARY SOMATIC
  SENSORY AREA₁₀
PRIMARY TASTE AREA₁₁
SOMATIC SENSORY
  ASSOCIATION AREA₁₂
SENSORY SPEECH AREA₁₃
VISUAL ASSOCIATION
  AREA₁₄
VISUAL CORTEX₁₅
PRIMARY AUDITORY AREA₁₆
AUDITORY ASSOCIATION
  AREA₁₇

FIGURE 24-2 Lobes and functional areas of the human brain.

Coloring Exercises: Cranial Nerves

Use colored pens or pencils to shade in both the figure and the labels. Each red numeral in the figure corresponds to a matching red numeral following the appropriate label.

OLFACTORY NERVE (I)₁

OPTIC NERVE (II)₂

OCULOMOTOR NERVE (III)₃

TROCHLEAR NERVE (IV)₄

TRIGEMINAL NERVE (V)₅

ABDUCENS NERVE (VI)₆

FACIAL NERVE (VII)₇

VESTIBULOCOCHLEAR
  NERVE (VIII)₈

GLOSSOPHARYNGEAL
  NERVE (IX)₉

VAGUS NERVE (X)₁₀

ACCESSORY NERVE (XI)₁₁

HYPOGLOSSAL NERVE
  (XII)₁₂

FIGURE 24-3 Ventral surface of the brain showing attachment of the cranial nerves.

☐ **3** The smaller, rounded structure under the posterior portion of the cerebrum that possesses somewhat parallel gyri is the **cerebellum.**

☐ **4** The **diencephalon** is the brain region just under the central portion of the cerebrum, superior and somewhat anterior to the brainstem. One major region of the diencephalon, the **thalamus,** is internal and cannot be seen from the outside of the brain. From the external aspect one can see some of these features of the **hypothalamus** of the diencephalon:

☐ **Optic chiasma**
☐ **Optic tracts**
☐ **Mammillary bodies**
☐ **Infundibulum**

One can also see the **pituitary,** or *hypophysis,* which is not part of the diencephalon proper but is attached to its ventral surface by the stalklike infundibulum.

☐ **5** The **brainstem** is the roughly cylindrical region of the brain that projects inferiorly from the diencephalon, anterior to the cerebellum. Locate these features if you can:

☐ **Midbrain** (upper portion, may not be visible in some models or specimens)
☐ **Pons** (bulging middle portion)
☐ **Medulla,** or *medulla oblongata* (cylindrical, inferior portion)

B. CRANIAL NERVES

The cranial nerves are bundles of nerve fibers and their coverings that project from the brain, mostly from the brainstem. There are 12 pairs, each known by both name and number (usually expressed as a Roman numeral). The term CN in front of a numeral indicates "cranial nerve." Cranial nerves are numbered in the sequence of their origin from the ventral brain surface, from anterior to posterior. *Sensory nerves* contain only sensory (afferent) fibers. *Motor nerves* contain primarily motor (efferent fibers) but also have a few sensory fibers that carry feedback proprioceptive information. *Mixed nerves* have significant numbers of both sensory and motor fibers. Locate each of the 12 pairs of cranial nerves listed here in your model. **Table 24-1** will help you identify their types and functions. **Figure 24-3** will help you find them.

Study TIPS

Use a mnemonic sentence to learn the names, in order, of the 12 pairs of cranial nerves. Refer to Table 24-1. An example would be:

On	Olfactory
Old	Optic
Olympus's	Oculomotor
Tiny	Trochlear
Tops	Trigeminal
A	Abducens
Friendly	Facial
Viking	Vestibulocochlear
Grew	Glossopharyngeal
Vines	Vagus
And	Accessory
Hops	Hypoglossal

The functional type of each cranial nerve can be remembered by this sentence: *Some Say "Marry Money," But My Brothers Say "Bad Business, Marry Money."* In this sentence, *S* indicates *sensory,* *M* indicates *motor,* and *B* indicates *both* sensory and motor (mixed). The *A&P Survival Guide* has a reference to these cranial nerves.

C. INTERNAL ASPECT OF THE BRAIN

If your brain specimen is dissectible, separate the halves of the model along the midsagittal plane to reveal the inner structures of the brain. If you are using a preserved or mounted specimen, you will need to use one that is cut in a midsagittal section to see the structures described in the following steps. Locate each structure listed **(Figure 24-4)**.

☐ 1 The **corpus callosum** that had connected the two cerebral hemispheres can now be clearly seen in the midsagittal section. The **fornix,** part of the diencephalon, is ventral to the corpus callosum and is also composed of white fibers. You may be able to see a hollow cavity just ventral to the corpus callosum in each brain half. These cavities are the right and left lateral ventricles. In the whole brain, they are separated by a thin membrane, the **septum pellucidum.** In some models and specimens, the septum may be visible as a drumlike covering to one ventricle or may partially cover both ventricles. The **choroid plexus,** a tiny mass of capillaries within each ventricle, produces the *cerebrospinal fluid (CSF)* that fills each ventricle.

☐ 2 The lateral ventricles can also be seen in a frontal section. If your model can be dissected along a frontal plane, do so. If you are using preserved specimens, you will need one that is cut in a frontal section. Locate the lateral ventricle(s). Just lateral to each lateral ventricle is a small circle of gray matter called the *caudate nucleus,* part of the cerebrum's basal ganglia. Separated from the caudate nucleus by a band of white matter called the *internal capsule* is another part of the basal ganglia. This portion of the basal ganglia, inferior and lateral to the caudate nucleus, is called the **lentiform nucleus.** The lentiform nucleus comprises a lateral *putamen* and a medial *globus pallidus,* both made of gray matter. Just

inferior to the lateral ventricles, along the midline, is a single third ventricle. Connecting each lateral ventricle to the third ventricle is an *interventricular foramen (of Monro),* which is often not visible in any of the brain sections. The lateral walls of the third ventricle are formed by a mass of gray matter called the **thalamus,** a region of the diencephalon. The two *lateral masses* of the thalamus are joined by the *intermediate mass* that passes through the third ventricle. Note the distribution of gray and white matter in the frontal section. What do you notice about its pattern?

☐ 3 Return your attention to the midsagittal section. Identify the white matter pattern, or **arbor vitae,** of the cerebellum. Ventral to the cerebellum is the fourth ventricle, which is connected to the third ventricle by the **cerebral aqueduct** (aqueduct of Sylvius).

☐ 4 Many features of the diencephalon already seen on the external aspect or in the frontal section can be seen in the midsagittal section. Locate the **optic chiasma, mammillary bodies,** and **infundibulum.** A small, rounded body on the midline, nearest the cerebrum, is the **pineal body** (or *pineal gland*) of the diencephalon. In the midsagittal section, only the intermediate mass of the thalamus is visible. It appears as a circle of gray matter surrounded by the shallow section of the third ventricle.

☐ 5 The **corpora quadrigemina** is easily seen in the midsagittal section, along the dorsal surface of the midbrain, just posterior to the pineal body. The corpora quadrigemina comprises four rounded bumps, arranged as two pairs. The larger pair is called the **superior colliculi,** and the slightly smaller pair is called the **inferior colliculi.** The white matter tracts in the ventral portion of the midbrain constitute the **cerebral peduncles.**

☐ 6 Identify the pons and medulla in the midsagittal section.

TABLE 24-1 **Cranial Nerves**

NAME	NUMBER	TYPE	GENERAL FUNCTION(S)
Olfactory	I	Sensory	Olfaction (sense of smell)
Optic	II	Sensory	Vision
Oculomotor	III	Motor	Controls upper eyelid muscles; controls superior rectus, medial rectus, inferior rectus, and inferior oblique muscles of the eye; controls ciliary muscle of the eye and sphincter in the iris
Trochlear	IV	Motor	Controls superior oblique muscle of the eye
Trigeminal	V	Mixed	Controls chewing movements *Ophthalmic branch*: sensation around the eye *Maxillary branch*: sensation from eye to upper jaw and throat *Mandibular branch*: sensation in mandibular region
Abducens	VI	Motor	Controls lateral rectus muscle of the eye
Facial	VII	Mixed	Controls facial muscles; controls secretion of tears and saliva; taste (anterior two-thirds of tongue)
Vestibulocochlear	VIII	Sensory	*Vestibular branch*: senses of equilibrium *Cochlear branch*: hearing
Glossopharyngeal	IX	Mixed	Controls salivation; controls swallowing muscles; taste (posterior third of tongue); blood pressure sensation
Vagus	X	Mixed	Controls swallowing muscles; control and sensation in various visceral effectors
Accessory	XI	Motor	Controls some head, neck, and shoulder movements
Hypoglossal	XII	Motor	Controls tongue muscles (swallowing and speech)

FIGURE 24-4 Label structures of the brain (frontal section) indicated on the lines provided and also on the blanks in the Lab Report at the end of this exercise.

Coloring Exercises: Human Brain

Use colored pens or pencils to shade in both **Figure 24-5** and the labels. Each red numeral in the figure corresponds to a matching red numeral following the appropriate label.

Cerebrum
CORPUS CALLOSUM₁
LATERAL VENTRICLE₂

Cerebellum
GRAY MATTER₃
ARBOR VITAE₄
FOURTH VENTRICLE₅

Diencephalon
OPTIC CHIASMA₆
INFUNDIBULUM₇
MAMMILLARY BODIES₈
THALAMUS₉

PINEAL BODY₁₀
FORNIX₁₁
THIRD VENTRICLE₁₂

Brainstem
Midbrain
   CEREBRAL PEDUNCLES₁₃
   CEREBRAL AQUEDUCT₁₄
   CORPORA
      QUADRIGEMINA₁₅
PONS₁₆
MEDULLA₁₇

FIGURE 24-5 Anatomy of the human brain.

clinical application: magnetic resonance imaging

As you recall, traditional radiographic imaging relies on x-rays that pass through soft tissues easily but cast shadows when they try to pass through dense tissues. Thus, soft tissues can only be seen when they are coated or filled either with a substance that blocks radiation or with a substance that emits its own radiation.

A more refined technology that produces finely detailed images of soft tissue without relying on x-rays is **nuclear magnetic resonance (NMR)**. Called **magnetic resonance imaging (MRI)** in many clinical settings, this technique relies on the magnetic (charge) properties of the nuclei of hydrogen molecules in human tissues.

When placed in a strong magnetic field, the hydrogen nuclei in a living tissue all orient themselves in one direction. At different intervals, depending on the type of tissue, the nuclei spin back to their original position and give off a burst of radio frequency (RF) energy. A computer with sensors can detect the relative position and rate of energy bursts, then construct a three-dimensional image of the tissues. Thus, a subject is placed in a magnetic field, and the MRI monitor displays sections similar to, but with better resolution than, CT (computed tomography) images.

The brain is a particularly interesting subject for MRI because it is composed entirely of soft tissue. Soft tissue contains a higher percentage of water and therefore more hydrogen atoms. Although CT scanning technology can produce images of brain structure, MRI pictures are often much more detailed. That patients scanned with MRI receive no harmful radiation makes this technology even more attractive.

FIGURE 24-6 MRI of the brain. Label the brain parts indicated on the lines provided and also on the blanks in the Lab Report at the end of this exercise.

Name: _____ Date: _____ Section: _____

LAB REPORT 24
The Brain and Cranial Nerves

Identify

1. _____
2. _____
3. _____
4. _____
5. _____
6. _____
7. _____
8. _____
9. _____
10. _____
11. _____
12. _____
13. _____
14. _____
15. _____
16. _____
17. _____

Put in Order

1. _____
2. _____
3. _____
4. _____
5. _____

Identify (write the names of the structures described as follows)

1. A mass of white fibers connecting the left and right cerebral hemispheres

2. A cerebral lobe not visible in an ordinary external inspection

3. A fold of cortical gray matter on the surface of the cerebrum

4. A deep sulcus

5. A vein in the dura mater roughly parallel to the longitudinal fissure

6. A rounded structure consisting of parallel gyri and dorsal to the brainstem

7. A distinct, branched pattern of white matter in the cerebellum

8. The middle of three divisions of the brainstem

9. A vascular structure that produces CSF and is present in all the fluid ventricles

10. The fluid ventricle associated with the cerebellum

11. The membrane that separates the left and right lateral ventricles

12. The portion of the thalamus that passes through the third ventricle

13. This structure is composed of four colliculi

14. The gland is not technically a part of the brain but is attached to the brain via the infundibulum

15. The gray matter on the surface of the cerebrum

16. A roughly cylindrical region of the brain that projects inferiorly from the diencephalon and anterior to the cerebellum

17. The most caudal structure of the brain

Put in Order (rearrange these in the order in which CSF passes through them, beginning with the place in which CSF could first be formed)

cerebral aqueduct
interventricular foramen (of Monro)
fourth ventricle
lateral ventricle
third ventricle

Figure 24-4 (from p. 260)

1. _____
2. _____
3. _____
4. _____
5. _____
6. _____
7. _____
8. _____
9. _____
10. _____

Figure 24-6 (from p. 262)

1. _____
2. _____
3. _____
4. _____
5. _____
6. _____
7. _____
8. _____
9. _____

LAB EXERCISE 25

Dissection: The Brain

In this exercise, you are challenged to dissect a mammalian brain (the sheep brain or cat brain). This activity will strengthen your understanding of the structure of the human brain, which is very similar.

BEFORE YOU BEGIN

☐ Read the appropriate chapter in your textbook.
☐ Set your learning goals. When you finish this exercise, you should be able to:
  ☐ list and describe the principal structures of the mammalian brain
  ☐ identify important parts of the mammalian brain in a preserved specimen
☐ Prepare your materials:
  ☐ dissection tools and trays
  ☐ preserved specimen: sheep brain (whole) or cat brain
☐ Read the directions and safety tips for this exercise *carefully* before starting any procedure.

> **!** ***safety first***
> Heed the safety instructions that accompany the preservative used with your specimen(s). Avoid cuts and other injuries when using the dissection tools. Use safety goggles to avoid injury during dissections. •

Study TIPS

As you complete this dissection, refer to an illustration or atlas of the human body. Use the illustration or atlas to locate and compare the various external and internal structures of the brain with your preserved specimen. Since the vertebrate body plan among species is very similar, this may help you to understand the structure of the human brain. Refer to the *A&P Survival Guide* for reference to the major regions of the brain.

Obtain an unlabeled copy of the brain, or use your cell phone to take a picture of the brain. As you complete this lab, use these illustrations/photos and label them.

A. THE MAMMALIAN BRAIN: EXTERNAL

The sheep or cat brain is remarkably similar to the human brain. One major difference is in proportion. For example, the sheep or cat has a proportionally smaller cerebrum. Another difference is in orientation. The sheep or cat brain is oriented anterior to posterior, as in any four-legged animal. The human brain is oriented superior to inferior. Examine the external features of the sheep or cat brain

as outlined in the following steps and **Figures 25-1** and **25-2** (sheep) or **Figure 25-3** (cat).

☐ 1 Determine whether the **meninges** of your specimen are still intact. If so, find the following:
  ☐ **Dura mater**—A tough, leathery outer covering (the dura forms a large cavity for blood along the top of the brain called the **sagittal sinus**)
  ☐ **Arachnoid**—The thin, translucent middle meninx (recall that the *subarachnoid space* contains cerebrospinal fluid [CSF] in living specimens)
  ☐ **Pia mater**—Thin, vascular membrane covering the brain (preserved blood in the vessels may give it a dark brown appearance)

> **Hint** If you are dissecting a cat brain, you must first remove it from the cranium. To do this, remove the muscles of the side and back of the head. Use bone-cutting shears or wire snips to cut away the back (thickest) area of the skull. Then use forceps to chip away the rest of the cranial roof. Then carefully remove the brain, cutting nerves as far away from the brain as possible. •

☐ 2 The most prominent feature of the brain is the **cerebrum.** This region is divided into nearly symmetrical left and right **hemispheres** by a deep **longitudinal fissure.** It is along this fissure that the sagittal sinus of the dura lies. Bend the two hemispheres away from each other and observe the **corpus callosum,** a mass of white fibers that connects the two hemispheres. The surface of the cerebrum is covered with large folds of tissue called **gyri.** The grooves between the gyri are **sulci.** The deeper sulci are often termed **fissures.** The fissures are used by anatomists as landmarks to divide the surface of the cerebrum (the **cerebral cortex**) into regions that roughly correspond to the overlying skull bones:
  ☐ **Frontal lobes**
  ☐ **Parietal lobes**
  ☐ **Occipital lobes**
  ☐ **Temporal lobes**
  ☐ **Insula** (buried within a fissure between the temporal and parietal lobes)

☐ 3 The smaller, rounded structure caudal to the cerebrum (and dorsal to the brainstem) but still possessing gyri is the **cerebellum.** The cerebellum has smaller gyri that are roughly parallel to one another, unlike the convoluted gyri of the cerebrum.

☐ 4 The **diencephalon** is the brain region ventral to the cerebrum and cranial to the brainstem. One can see some of its features in a ventral view of the mammalian brain. The **hypothalamus** includes the **optic chiasma**, an X-shaped junction of fibers at the bases of the **optic nerves**. The legs of the chiasma attached to the brain are the beginnings of the **optic tracts**. The **mammillary bodies**, also part of the hypothalamus, are just posterior to the optic chiasma. The stalklike **infundibulum** projects ventrally from between the chiasma and the mammillary bodies. The infundibulum connects the hypothalamus to the **pituitary gland,** or *hypophysis.* Another major part of the diencephalon is the **thalamus,** which is not visible in an external examination.

> **Hint** If your specimen has an intact pituitary (not all do), it will be in a mass of tissue on the ventral aspect. To see the infundibulum and adjacent structures, it is necessary to pull the pituitary away from the ventral surface of the brain. You may be able to keep the infundibulum in place as you do the separation, as if it were a hinge on a flap of tissue. Some cranial nerves may be pulled away from the brain, so cut them in a way that leaves as much of the nerve attached to the brain as possible. •

- ☐ 5 Holding the specimen in gloved hands, dorsal aspect toward you, carefully bend it to expose the tissue between the cerebrum and cerebellum. You may have to tease some connecting tissue apart with a probe. You now see the dorsal surface of the **midbrain.** A small, rounded body on the midline, nearest the cerebrum, is the **pineal body** of the diencephalon. The four rounded bumps caudal to the pineal body constitute the **corpora quadrigemina** of the midbrain. The four bumps are distinguished as the **superior colliculi** (the slightly larger pair) and **inferior colliculi** in the human. The midbrain is part of the brain division called the **brainstem,** which is found between the diencephalon and the spinal cord.
- ☐ 6 The portion of the brainstem just caudal to the midbrain is the **pons.** The cerebellum covers the dorsal surface of the pons, but the ventral surface of the pons can be clearly seen as a large bulge.
- ☐ 7 The **medulla,** or *medulla oblongata,* is caudal to the pons. The medulla looks as if it were a swollen region of the spinal cord, to which it is cranial. Together, the midbrain, pons, and medulla constitute the brainstem.
- ☐ 8 Because of their smallness and the manner in which specimens are usually prepared, some of the **cranial nerves** may be impossible to locate on your specimen. Normally, there would be 12 pairs of nerves extending from various parts of the brain. These nerves, of course, are part of the peripheral nervous system (PNS) rather than part of the brain proper. Using Figure 25-1, *A,* as a guide, try to locate as many cranial nerves as you can.

> **Hint** Figures 25-1, *C* and *D,* and 25-2, *B,* show color photographs of the external surface of the sheep brain. The cat brain is similar in structure but much smaller. Compare Figures 25-1 and 25-2 (sheep) with Figure 25-3 (cat). •

B. THE MAMMALIAN BRAIN: INTERNAL

- ☐ 1 Use a knife to cut the specimen along a midsagittal plane. Use the longitudinal fissure as a cutting guide (see Figure 25-2).
- ☐ 2 The corpus callosum that had connected the two cerebral hemispheres can now be clearly seen in the brain section. The **fornix,** part of the diencephalon, is ventral to the corpus callosum and is also composed of white fibers. You may be able to see a hollow cavity just ventral to the corpus callosum in each brain half. These cavities are the right and left **lateral ventricles.** In the whole brain, they are separated by a thin membrane, the **septum pellucidum.** Because of variations in the plane of sectioning, the septum may be visible as a drumlike covering to one ventricle or may partially cover both ventricles. The **choroid plexus,** a tiny mass of capillaries within each ventricle, produces the CSF that fills each ventricle.
- ☐ 3 The lateral ventricles can also be seen in a frontal section. Use one of the brain halves or a new whole brain (if available) to cut a frontal section. The infundibulum is a good landmark for the correct position of the frontal cut. Locate the lateral ventricle(s). Just lateral to each lateral ventricle is a small circle of gray matter called the **caudate nucleus,** part of the cerebrum's *basal ganglia.* Just inferior to the lateral ventricles, along the midline, is a single **third ventricle.** Connecting each lateral ventricle to the third ventricle is an **interventricular foramen (of Monro),** which is not visible in any of the brain sections. The lateral walls of the third ventricle are formed by a mass of gray matter called the **thalamus,** a region of the diencephalon. The two *lateral masses* of the thalamus are joined by the *intermediate mass* that passes through the third ventricle. Take note of the distribution of gray and white matter in the frontal section. What do you notice about its pattern?
- ☐ 4 Return your attention to the midsagittal section. Identify the white matter pattern, or **arbor vitae,** of the cerebellum. Ventral to the cerebellum is the **fourth ventricle,** which is connected to the third ventricle by the **cerebral aqueduct** (aqueduct of Sylvius).
- ☐ 5 Many features of the diencephalon already seen on the external aspect or in the frontal section can be seen in the midsagittal section. Locate the pineal body, optic chiasma, mammillary bodies, and infundibulum. In this section, only the intermediate mass of the thalamus is visible. It appears as a circle of gray matter surrounded by the shallow section of the third ventricle.
- ☐ 6 The corpora quadrigemina is easily seen in the midsagittal section, along the dorsal surface of the midbrain, just posterior to the pineal body. The white matter tracts in the ventral portion of the midbrain constitute the **cerebral peduncles.**
- ☐ 7 Identify the pons and medulla in the midsagittal section.

> **Hint** Figure 25-2, *B,* shows a color photograph of some of the internal features of the sheep brain. •

A

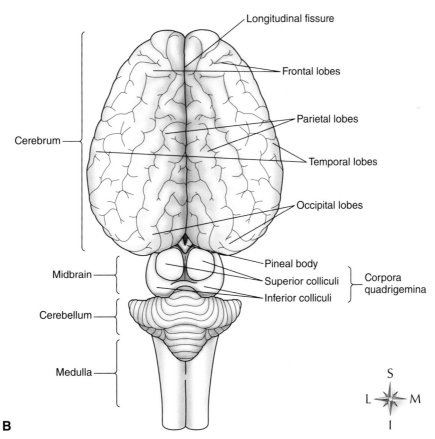

B

FIGURE 25-1 External view of sheep brain. **A,** Ventral aspect. **B,** Dorsal aspect.

Continued

FIGURE 25-1, cont'd C, Ventral view photograph. **D,** Dorsal view photograph.

FIGURE 25-2 Sheep brain. **A,** Midsagittal section. **B,** Midsagittal view photograph. **C,** Lateral view photograph.

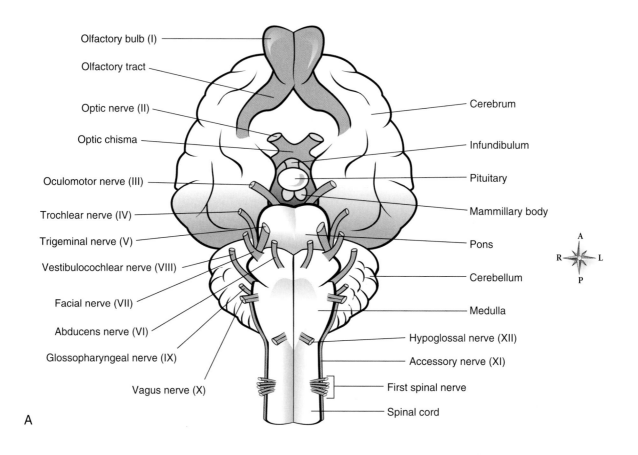

Olfactory bulb (I)
Olfactory tract
Optic nerve (II)
Optic chisma
Oculomotor nerve (III)
Trochlear nerve (IV)
Trigeminal nerve (V)
Vestibulocochlear nerve (VIII)
Facial nerve (VII)
Abducens nerve (VI)
Glossopharyngeal nerve (IX)
Vagus nerve (X)

Cerebrum
Infundibulum
Pituitary
Mammillary body
Pons
Cerebellum
Medulla
Hypoglossal nerve (XII)
Accessory nerve (XI)
First spinal nerve
Spinal cord

A

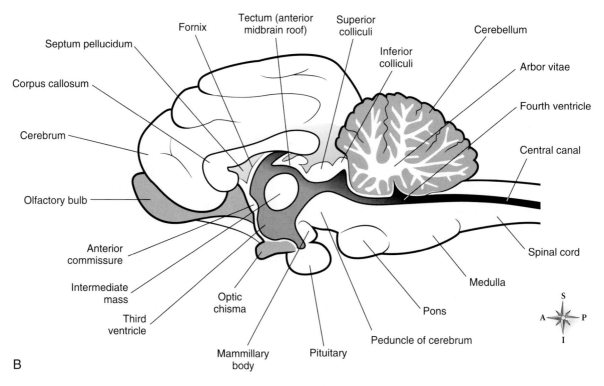

Septum pellucidum
Fornix
Tectum (anterior midbrain roof)
Superior colliculi
Inferior colliculi
Cerebellum
Corpus callosum
Arbor vitae
Cerebrum
Fourth ventricle
Central canal
Olfactory bulb
Anterior commissure
Intermediate mass
Third ventricle
Optic chisma
Mammillary body
Pituitary
Peduncle of cerebrum
Pons
Medulla
Spinal cord

B

FIGURE 25-3 Cat brain. **A,** External view of ventral aspect. **B,** Midsagittal section.

Name: _____   Date: _____   Section: _____

Dissection: The Brain

Use this table as a checklist to keep track of your study of the mammalian brain specimen.

BRAIN REGION	STRUCTURE	SPECIMEN	NOTES
Meninges	Dura mater	☐	
	Arachnoid	☐	
	Pia mater	☐	
Cerebrum	Hemispheres	☐	
	Longitudinal fissure	☐	
	Corpus callosum	☐	
	Frontal lobe	☐	
	Parietal lobe	☐	
	Occipital lobe	☐	
	Temporal lobe	☐	
	Insula	☐	
	Lateral ventricle	☐	
	Septum pellucidum	☐	
	Caudate nucleus	☐	
Cerebellum	Gray matter	☐	
	Arbor vitae	☐	
	Fourth ventricle	☐	
Diencephalon	Optic chiasma	☐	
	Infundibulum	☐	
	Mammillary bodies	☐	
	Thalamus	☐	
	Pineal body	☐	
	Fornix	☐	
	Third ventricle	☐	
Midbrain	Cerebral peduncles	☐	
	Cerebral aqueduct	☐	
	Corpora quadrigemina	☐	
Pons	Pons	☐	
Medulla	Medulla	☐	

26
Somatic Senses

Sensations occur in the central nervous system (CNS) after sensory stimuli in the internal or external environment generate nerve impulses, which in turn convey information regarding the environmental change to the CNS. Sensory receptors can be classified in a number of ways. They can be classified by **mode** (e.g., *photoreceptors* are sensitive to light, *chemoreceptors* are sensitive to certain chemicals, and *mechanoreceptors* are sensitive to mechanical changes). Sensory receptors can also be classified according to their **location** (e.g., *exteroceptors* are located in the skin, *proprioceptors* are located in the muscles, and *visceroceptors* are located in deeper tissues [the viscera]). Senses mediated by the sensory receptors of the body can be categorized into two major groups: the **somatic senses** and the **special senses**. The special senses involve elaborate sensory organs such as the eye or ear. Somatic senses involve less elaborate sensory mechanisms, often just single receptors embedded in skin or muscle tissue. This exercise briefly explores some of the somatic senses. Later exercises discuss the special senses.

BEFORE YOU BEGIN

☐ Read the appropriate chapter in your textbook.
☐ Set your learning goals. When you finish this exercise, you should be able to:
  ☐ explain the distinction between *somatic senses* and *special senses*
  ☐ demonstrate that exteroceptors are not evenly distributed in the skin
  ☐ demonstrate the use of the proprioceptive sense in controlling body movement
☐ Prepare your materials:
  ☐ compass
  ☐ metric ruler (millimeter)
  ☐ nontoxic, washable marking pen
  ☐ horse hair
  ☐ blunt metal probe
  ☐ hot water tap
  ☐ ice water
  ☐ chalkboard and chalk
☐ Read the directions and safety tips for this exercise *carefully* before starting any procedure.

Study TIPS

To help you understand the classification of the sensory receptors, develop a concept map. For reference, use your textbook or the *A&P Survival Guide*. Develop the map to include the mode and location of these sensory receptors.

A. CUTANEOUS SENSES

Cutaneous senses are somatic senses that are mediated by exteroceptors—sensory receptors in the skin. Cutaneous senses include sensitivity to touch, pressure, heat, cold, vibration, and any other stimulus felt through the skin. In this activity, you will explore the distribution pattern of some of the cutaneous senses.

☐ 1 Perform the two-point discrimination test **(Figure 26-1)** on your lab partner by following these directions:
  ☐ Adjust so that two points are touching.
  ☐ With your partner's eyes closed and hand placed palm upward on the lab table, gently place the points on the surface of your partner's index finger.
  ☐ Move the points apart by about 1 mm and touch the finger again.
  ☐ Repeat this sequence, each time increasing the distance slightly, until your partner tells you that two distinct points are felt. Record the distance between points in the lab report.
  ☐ Repeat the test on the back of the arm and compare the density of cutaneous touch receptors in these two external body regions.

! *safety first*
Do not press hard with the compass. Pressing hard ruins the results of the test and may cause injury to the subject.   •

☐ 2 Measure the density of touch receptors on the back of the hand using a different method:
  ☐ Draw a 2.5-cm (1-inch) square on the back of your lab partner's hand with a nontoxic, washable marker or rubber stamp. Divide the square into 16 blocks by drawing a grid within the box (use a ruler).
  ☐ With your partner's eyes closed, touch the tip of a horse hair to a point on the grid just hard enough to bend it slightly.
  ☐ Mark the position on the matching grid in the Lab Report. Record "0" if the subject does not feel the touch; record "+" if the subject does feel the touch. Repeat this for about 25 to 35 different points within the grid.

Hint   Touch your partner at random intervals—not with a noticeable rhythm—to avoid anticipation that might alter your results. Also, do not move from block to block in an orderly pattern. This might also cause the subject to anticipate your next move and indicate that he or she felt the hair even though he or she did not really feel it. •

☐   **3** Cold receptors are thought to outnumber heat receptors. These two types of *thermoreceptors*, or "temperature receptors," are also thought to have different distribution patterns. Determine the density of these two types of somatic receptors by performing the following:

   ☐ Draw a 2.5-cm (1-inch) square on the palmar surface of your lab partner's wrist with a nontoxic, washable marker or rubber stamp. Divide the square into 16 blocks by drawing a grid within the box (use a ruler).

   ☐ With your partner's eyes closed, gently but firmly touch the tip of a blunt metal probe that has been cooled in ice water to a point on the grid.

   ☐ Mark the position on the matching grid in the Lab Report. Record "0" if the subject does not feel the coolness; record "+" if the subject does feel the coolness. Repeat this for about 25 to 35 different points within the grid.

   ☐ Repeat the test using a probe that has been warmed in hot tap water.

safety first

Do not heat the probe in a flame. Make sure the probe is neither dangerously hot nor dangerously cold. •

Hint   Make sure the probe is kept dry. Make sure that only sensations of *heat* and *cold* are reported—not merely the sensation of touch. This is a test for thermoreceptors, not touch receptors. •

B. PROPRIOCEPTION

Also known as "muscle sense," **proprioception** is the ability to sense the contraction or tension of a muscle organ. Receptors for proprioception include stretch receptors called *muscle spindles* and *Golgi tendon organs*. Can you think of any advantages to survival that this sense gives us? Demonstrate the use of the proprioceptive sense:

☐   **1** On the first signature line in the Lab Report, write your name—with your eyes open, as you normally would. On the second signature line in the Lab Report, write your name again—only this time keep your eyes closed. You are using mainly the proprioceptive sense this time. Is your signature significantly different the second time? Can you explain your result?

☐   **2** With your eyes open, draw a cross or addition symbol on a chalkboard or whiteboard at about eye level. Now close your eyes, extend your hand out to the side, and bring it back to touch the center of the cross with the chalk or dry erase marker. Make a small mark at that spot. Now open your eyes and measure the distance from your spot to the center of the cross. Can you relate your result to the operation of the proprioceptive sense?

FIGURE 26-1 Two-point discrimination test. When two points can be distinguished, two separate receptors are being stimulated.

Name: _____ Date: _____ Section: _____

Somatic Senses

Two-point discrimination test

Location	Result
Finger	
Arm	

Density of touch receptors

Finger   Arm

Density of temperature receptors

Cold   Heat

Proprioception
Signature (eyes open) _____

Signature (eyes closed) _____

Distance from center: ____ cm

Multiple Choice

1. _____
2. _____
3. _____
4. _____
5. _____
6. _____
7. _____
8. _____
9. _____
10. _____

Multiple Choice (only one response is correct)

1. Somatic senses may include
   a. proprioception
   b. sense of touch
   c. sense of vision
   d. sense of hearing
   e. a and b are correct
   f. all of the above are correct
2. Mechanoreceptors are sensitive to changes in
   a. chemistry
   b. position, pressure, shape
   c. light intensity
   d. temperature
   e. all of the above are correct
3. Exteroceptors may be sensitive to changes in
   a. temperature
   b. pressure
   c. sound
   d. visual images
   e. a and b are correct
4. The two-point discrimination test determines the density of
   a. cutaneous touch receptors
   b. cutaneous thermoreceptors
   c. proprioceptors
   d. chemoreceptors
   e. a and b are correct
5. Thermoreceptors are sensitive to
   a. heat
   b. cold
   c. changes in temperature
   d. external stimuli
   e. any of the above may be correct
6. The sense of vision is an example of a
   a. special sense
   b. somatic sense
   c. neither type of sense
7. Cold receptors and heat receptors are probably distributed evenly over the skin of the body.
   a. true
   b. false
8. Touch receptors are probably distributed evenly over the skin's surface.
   a. true
   b. false
9. Proprioceptors may include
   a. thermoreceptors
   b. Golgi tendon organs
   c. muscle spindles
   d. a and b are correct
   e. b and c are correct
10. The proprioceptive sense involves exteroceptors.
    a. true
    b. false

27
Senses of Taste and Smell

Sensations of smell and taste are "chemical senses" because both use **chemoreceptors** to detect specific molecules, or types of molecules, in the external environment. Being able to determine the chemical nature of the atmosphere, and of various substances in our external environment, better equips us to find nutritious food and essential minerals, avoid poisonous substances, and otherwise make decisions that affect our overall survival. In this exercise, we briefly explore the sense of **olfaction** (smell) and the **gustatory sense** (taste).

BEFORE YOU BEGIN

☐ Read the appropriate chapter in your textbook.
☐ Set your learning goals. When you finish this exercise, you should be able to:
  ☐ briefly describe the sense of smell, identifying the modality, the location of receptors, and the physiological role of smell
  ☐ explain the term *adaptation* as it relates to the physiology of sensory reception
  ☐ briefly describe the sense of taste, identifying the modality, the location and structure of taste buds, and the physiological role of taste
☐ Prepare your materials:
  ☐ model of the human head (midsagittal section)
  ☐ six small vials, each containing a different recognizable scent
  ☐ stopwatch or timer
  ☐ microscope
  ☐ prepared slide: *human tongue surface c.s.*
  ☐ sterile, disposable cotton swabs
  ☐ waste container for used swabs
  ☐ small paper cup containing *fresh* salt solution
  ☐ small paper cup containing *fresh* sugar solution
  ☐ small paper cup containing *fresh* lemon juice
  ☐ small paper cup containing *fresh* bitter almond solution
  ☐ small paper cup containing *fresh* glutamate (monosodium glutamate [MSG]) solution
☐ Read the directions and safety tips for this exercise *carefully* before starting any procedure.

Study TIPS

Use your textbook to review the relationship of olfactory and gustatory pathways. You might want to examine the figures in your textbook that illustrate the structure of the nose, tongue, and taste receptors.

A. SENSE OF SMELL

The olfactory sense, or the sense of smell, is a sense mediated by chemoreceptors in the patch of mucous membrane called the **olfactory epithelium (Figure 27-1)**. The olfactory epithelium is located along the lining of the upper third of the nasal cavity. Sensory olfactory cells possess hairlike cilia that detect the presence of specific molecules when those molecules react with specialized receptor molecules in the plasma membrane covering the cilia. Because air is continually being drawn into the nasal cavity through the nostrils (and sometimes through the mouth), the olfactory epithelium can analyze the chemical content of the atmosphere. This allows us to find nutritious foods, avoid dangerous situations (e.g., fire), and otherwise maintain the stability of our internal environment.

☐ 1 In a model of the head, locate the *olfactory epithelium* in the nasal cavity. Next, locate the *olfactory bulb*. The olfactory bulb has branches of cranial nerve I (the *olfactory nerve*) that project through the *cribriform plate* of the ethmoid bone.

> **Hint** Use Figure 27-1 to help you find the olfactory epithelium and the olfactory bulb. In many models, a midsagittal section reveals these structures, but they may not be highlighted or labeled in any special way. •

☐ 2 The olfactory sense can detect many different kinds of odors, many of which are instantly recognizable to the conscious mind. Demonstrate this fact by opening each of six vials (marked A, B, C, D, E, and F) in front of your partner. Record whether your partner can detect the odor and what he or she thinks the substance in the vial is. Can you identify the odors? Check your results with the lab instructor's key.

> **⚠ safety first**
> Smell the substances in the vials by waving your hand over the top of each vial, driving the air toward your nose. Do not hold your nose directly over the vial and sniff! •

☐ **3** Adaptation can occur in many types of sensory receptors, including olfactory receptors. In adaptation, prolonged exposure to a particular stimulus causes a receptor to fatigue and thus cease sending information to the central nervous system. Olfactory adaptation is common (e.g., when we put on cologne or use a scented soap and soon cannot smell it on ourselves). Demonstrate the concept of sensory adaptation by performing the following activity:

   ☐ Hold one of the vials used in Step 2 near your nose, breathing normally, but still able to smell the substance.

   ☐ Have your partner begin timing (using a stopwatch or timer) as soon as you begin smelling the substance.

   ☐ Continue to hold the vial in place for several minutes, indicating to your partner the moment you can no longer smell the odor distinctly.

   ☐ Record your adaptation time in the Lab Report.

B. SENSE OF TASTE

The sense of taste includes at least five modalities of chemical sensation: *salt, sweet, sour, bitter,* and *umami (glutamate).* The receptor organs that mediate these sensations are the **taste buds,** found primarily along the sides of the papillae of the tongue. **Gustatory hairs** projecting from sensory cells possess receptors that can be triggered by the molecules detected by the sense of taste.

> **Hint**   Color micrographs of the tongue papillae and taste buds can be found in **Figures 27-2** and **27-3**. •

☐ **1** Locate taste buds embedded within the papillae of a prepared microscopic specimen of the human tongue. Sketch your observations in Lab Report 27.

You are already familiar with the idea of tastes such as salty, sweet, sour, and bitter. You may not be aware of the word *umami,* but you surely have tasted it. Umami is a Japanese word that describes the taste of glutamate, an amino acid found in many foods. Flavor enhancers such as MSG (e.g., Accent) add umami flavors to food. Meats and tomato products such as ketchup have a strong umami taste.

☐ **2** Determine the sensitivity of the various types of taste buds (salt, sweet, sour, bitter, and umami) by following this procedure:

   ☐ Blot the saliva from the surface of your tongue with a *clean* paper towel.

   ☐ Dip a sterile, disposable cotton swab in one of the five taste solutions provided in a clean vial and place it on various areas of the tongue. Record whether you can perceive the taste by checking the list provided in Lab Report 27.

   ☐ Repeat this procedure for the remaining four taste solutions:

   ☐ *salt:* salt (NaCl) solution

   ☐ *sweet:* sugar solution

   ☐ *sour:* lemon juice

   ☐ *bitter:* bitter almond solution

   ☐ *glutamate (umami):* MSG solution

> **! safety first**
>
> Use only *fresh,* uncontaminated solutions. Do not reuse the cotton swabs, even with the same person. Never dip a used swab into a solution. Dispose of used swabs properly. Check the contents of each solution, and avoid contact with substances that your physician has advised you to avoid or to which you think you might be overly sensitive. •

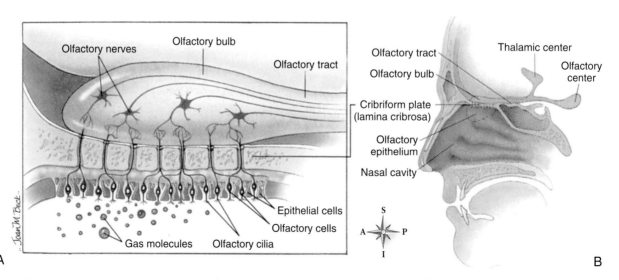

FIGURE 27-1 Olfactory epithelium. **A,** Enlarged view of cross section of olfactory epithelium and olfactory bulb that supplies sensory fibers to it. **B,** Location of olfactory epithelium in nasal cavity.

Stratified squamous epithelium

Vallate
papillae

Taste buds

Moat

FIGURE 27-2 Vallate papillae on tongue.

Papilla   Taste bud

FIGURE 27-3 Taste buds.

Name: _____ Date: _____ Section: _____

Senses of Taste and Smell

Olfactory Recognition

VIAL	UNRECOGNIZED	RECOGNIZED	SUBSTANCE
A	☐	☐	
B	☐	☐	
C	☐	☐	
D	☐	☐	
E	☐	☐	
F	☐	☐	

Olfactory Recognition

TRIAL	SUBSTANCE	ADAPTATION TIME
1		
2		

Specimen: *human tongue surface c.s.*
Total Magnification: _____

Taste bud modality
☐ salt
☐ sweet
☐ sour
☐ bitter
☐ umami

Essay: Write a few brief paragraphs outlining how the senses of smell and taste operate in ways that help the body maintain a homeostatic balance. Include at least two examples of how each might be involved in a homeostatic feedback loop. Use another sheet of paper if you need more room.

28

The Ear

The **ears** are complex sensory organs located on each side of the skull, mostly buried within each temporal bone. The ear serves as a receptor organ for at least three special senses: *hearing, static equilibrium,* and *dynamic equilibrium.* This exercise challenges you to learn the basic divisions and structures of the human ear. Once you are familiar with the structure of the ear, you will be ready to explore the functional aspects of hearing and equilibrium in Exercise 29.

BEFORE YOU BEGIN

☐ Read the appropriate chapter in your textbook.
☐ Set your learning goals. When you finish this exercise, you should be able to:
 ☐ distinguish the three main divisions of the ear
 ☐ identify the principal structures of the human ear in models and figures
 ☐ locate features of the cochlea in a prepared microscopic specimen
☐ Prepare your materials:
 ☐ model or chart of the human ear
 ☐ microscope
 ☐ prepared microslide: *cochlea c.s.*
☐ Read the directions and safety tips for this exercise *carefully* before starting any procedure.

Study TIPS

Develop a chart that summarizes the different structures of the ear. It would be helpful if you also categorize them according to the division of the ear in which they are located (external, middle, or inner). You may also want to develop a concept map that illustrates the order of these structures in which sound waves pass through them. For reference, use your textbook or the *A&P Survival Guide.*

 Hint Use a chart or model of the human ear to locate and study the ear structures listed in the three activities of this exercise. •

 safety first
Observe the usual precautions when using the microscope and prepared slides. •

A. EXTERNAL EAR

You may want to use your textbook as an additional aid in this activity. The **external (outer) ear** is the ear division comprised of the elements described in the following:

☐ 1 **Auricle (pinna)**—This external ear flap protects the auditory opening and directs sound waves toward it. It also functions as a "radiator" in thermoregulation.
☐ 2 **External auditory meatus**—This tubelike passage carries airborne sound waves further into the ear apparatus; it is also called the *ear canal.*
☐ 3 **Tympanic membrane**—Also called the *eardrum,* it covers the end of the external auditory meatus to form a boundary with the middle ear. It vibrates when struck by airborne sound waves, carrying the sound energy into the middle ear.

B. MIDDLE EAR

The **middle ear** begins where the external ear ends, with the tympanic membrane. The middle ear is an air-filled cavity lined with mucous membrane. Identify the important parts of the middle ear described in the following:

☐ 1 **Malleus**—It is one of the three *auditory ossicles* in each ear. Also called the *hammer,* it is a tiny, club-shaped bone attached to the eardrum. It vibrates when sound waves pass to it from the eardrum.
☐ 2 **Incus**—Also called the *anvil,* this tiny bone forms a synovial joint with the malleus. The incus vibrates when it receives energy from the malleus.
☐ 3 **Stapes**—Also called the *stirrup* because of its shape, this ossicle is joined to the incus, from which it receives vibrations. A flat portion of the stapes fits into the **oval window,** a passage into the inner ear. Because of the structural relationship of this chain of ossicles, sound waves are carried from the tympanic membrane to the oval window (that is, from the external ear to the inner ear). Along the way, the vibrations are amplified for better reception.
☐ 4 **Auditory (eustachian) tube**—This is a collapsible tube running between the middle ear and the pharynx. It allows internal air pressure to equalize with atmospheric air pressure so that high pressure on one side does not distort or muffle the eardrum.
☐ 5 The middle ear also has an opening to the mastoid air cells in the mastoid process of the temporal bone. What significance might this have if the middle ear becomes infected?

C. INNER EAR

The **inner ear** is the third division of the ear apparatus. The receptors for hearing and equilibrium are located here. The inner ear is within a hollow area in the petrous portion of the temporal bone. A mazelike **bony labyrinth** contains a similarly shaped but smaller **membranous labyrinth.** The fluid inside the membranous labyrinth is called **endolymph,** and the fluid outside the membranous labyrinth is called **perilymph.** The bony labyrinth, and the membranous labyrinth inside it, is composed of the three main regions described in the following:

☐ 1 **Cochlea**—This is a long passage coiled like a snail. A cross section reveals that the passage is divided into three chambers by a Y-shaped partition. The base of the Y is a projection of the bone called the **spiral lamina.** The two branches are pieces of membrane called the **vestibular membrane** and the **basilar membrane.** The space between the two membranes is the endolymph-filled **cochlear duct.** The space outside the vestibular membrane is the **scala vestibuli,** whereas the **scala tympani** is the space outside the basilar membrane. Sound waves move into the perilymph of the scala vestibuli as the stapes vibrates in the oval window. The vestibular membrane vibrates, causing the endolymph in the cochlear duct to vibrate. This, in turn, causes the flaplike **tectorial membrane** to vibrate and bend the hairs projecting from the **organ of Corti** (spiral organ) on the basilar membrane (which also vibrates). The bending of hairs induces receptor potentials in the sensory neurons. The energy dissipates as it moves through the scala tympani to the round window. A branch of cranial nerve VIII called the **cochlear nerve** carries information to auditory areas in the brain. Observe a cross section of a mammalian cochlea in the microscope and sketch your observations. Label as many parts as you can identify.

> **Hint** **Figure 28-3** shows a light micrograph of the mammalian cochlea and features a good view of the organ of Corti in cross section. •

☐ 2 **Vestibule**—This is the central area of the inner ear. The vestibule contains saclike portions of the membranous labyrinth called the **utricle** and the **saccule.** Each has a patch of sensory hair cells called a **macula (Figure 28-2, A).** The macula's hair cells are covered by a gelatinous coating embedded with hard, tiny crystals called **otoliths.** When the head is tilted, gravity pulls on the heavy otoliths and the hairs bend. This induces a receptor potential. Sensory information regarding the effects of gravity (static equilibrium) is transmitted to the brain through the **vestibular nerve,** another branch of cranial nerve VIII.

☐ 3 **Semicircular canals**—These are three round passages, each on a different plane. The semicircular canals have bubbles at their bases called **ampullae** (Figure 28-2, B). Within each ampulla is a crest of tissue called the **crista ampullaris.** Each crista is a patch of sensory hair cells covered with a gelatinous mass (without otoliths) called the **cupula.** When the speed or direction of movement of the head changes, the inertia of the endolymph within the semicircular canals causes it to circulate. As the endolymph circulates, it pushes the cupula and generates receptor potentials in the crista's sensory cells. The vestibular nerve carries the signal to the brain, where it is interpreted as kinetic (dynamic) equilibrium **(Figure 28-1).**

Coloring Exercises: Ear

Use colored pens or pencils to shade in both the figure and the labels. Each red numeral in the figure corresponds to a matching red numeral following the appropriate label.

External Ear
AURICLE₁
EXTERNAL AUDITORY MEATUS₂
TYMPANIC MEMBRANE₃

Middle Ear
MALLEUS₄
INCUS₅
STAPES₆
AUDITORY TUBE₇

Inner Ear
COCHLEA₈
SPIRAL LAMINA₉
VESTIBULAR MEMBRANE₁₀
BASILAR MEMBRANE₁₁
COCHLEAR DUCT₁₂
SCALA VESTIBULI₁₃
SCALA TYMPANI₁₄
TECTORIAL MEMBRANE₁₅
ORGAN OF CORTI₁₆
COCHLEAR NERVE₁₇
VESTIBULE₁₈
VESTIBULAR NERVE₁₉
SEMICIRCULAR CANALS₂₀

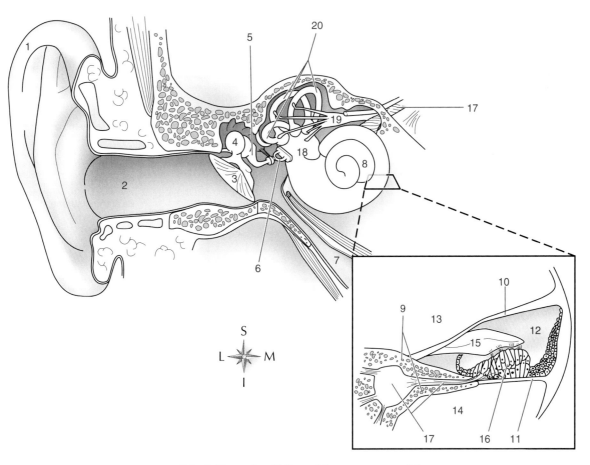

FIGURE 28-1 External, middle, and inner structures of the ear.

A

B

FIGURE 28-2 A, Sensory structures of the vestibule. **B,** Sensory structures of a semicircular canal. Identify the structures on the lines provided and also on the blanks in the Lab Report at the end of this exercise.

Tectorial membrane

Nerve fibers

Hair cells

Basilar membrane

FIGURE 28-3 Organ of Corti.

Name: _____ Date: _____ Section: _____

LAB REPORT 28
The Ear

Specimen: *cochlea c.s.*
Total Magnification: _____

Figure 28-2 (see p. 286)

1. _____
2. _____
3. _____
4. _____
5. _____

Put in Order

1. _____
2. _____
3. _____
4. _____
5. _____
6. _____
7. _____
8. _____
9. _____

Put in Order (rearrange these structures in the order in which sound waves pass through them)

auricle
endolymph
external auditory meatus
incus
malleus
perilymph
stapes
tectorial membrane/organ of Corti
tympanum

Ear Divisions

1. _____
2. _____
3. _____
4. _____
5. _____
6. _____
7. _____
8. _____
9. _____
10. _____
11. _____
12. _____
13. _____
14. _____

Fill-in

1. _____
2. _____
3. _____
4. _____
5. _____
6. _____
7. _____
8. _____
9. _____
10. _____
11. _____
12. _____
13. _____
14. _____
15. _____
16. _____

Ear Divisions (for each structure, identify whether it is part of the external ear, middle ear, or inner ear)

1. auricle
2. bony labyrinth
3. cochlea
4. external auditory meatus
5. incus
6. malleus
7. membranous labyrinth
8. organ of Corti
9. saccule
10. semicircular canal
11. stapes
12. tympanic membrane
13. utricle
14. vestibule

Fill-in (complete each statement with the correct term)

1. The _?_ are three passages, each forming a circle and each in a different plane.

2. When traveling in an automobile, you sense that you have suddenly turned a corner. The sensation you have is mainly an aspect of the sense of _?_ equilibrium.

3. In a weightless environment, as in deep space, the sense of _?_ equilibrium would not work well, if at all.

4. The vestibular membrane and basilar membrane are walls of the _?_ labyrinth.

5. The sensory patch in the utricle's lining is called the _?_.

6. The sensory patch in the utricle's lining has receptors for the sense of _?_.

7. The _?_ is a passage that allows air pressure in the middle ear to reach equilibrium with atmospheric air pressure.

8. The auditory ossicles are joined to one another with _?_ (type) joints.

9. The _?_ has a flat, pluglike portion that fits into the oval window.

10. Both the oval window and the _?_ window are on the boundary of the middle and inner ear.

11. During sound reception, the tectorial membrane vibrates and stimulates the hair cells in the _?_.

12. The _?_ is the most external portion of the external ear.

13. The _?_ amplify sound waves by as much as 20 times their original intensity.

14. The semicircular canals have sensory structures called _?_ within the ampullae.

15. The semicircular canals have sensory structures for the sense of _?_.

16. The maculae of the vestibular sensory regions are covered with gelatinous material. _?_ are embedded in this material.

29
Hearing and Equilibrium

Hearing, like vision, is considered to be one of the *special senses.* Hearing, the ability to detect a range of sound **frequencies** (pitches) and **intensities (volumes),** is only one of the senses mediated by the ear apparatus. Two types of **equilibrium** are also mediated by ear receptors. One type, **static equilibrium,** allows you to determine your position relative to a center of gravity. In other words, it tells you whether you are right side up, upside down, or something in between. Your sense of **kinetic (dynamic) equilibrium** gives information regarding the speed and direction of your body's motion.

This exercise challenges you to perform tests that demonstrate the basic functions of hearing and equilibrium.

BEFORE YOU BEGIN

☐ Read the appropriate chapter in your textbook.
☐ Set your learning goals. When you finish this exercise, you should be able to:
  ☐ demonstrate some clinical screening tests for hearing and equilibrium
☐ Prepare your materials:
  ☐ tuning fork (256 Hz)
  ☐ swimmer's earplugs (optional)
  ☐ chalkboard and chalk (whiteboard and dry erase marker)
  ☐ bright desk lamp
  ☐ metric ruler (30-100 cm)
  ☐ watch or clock
  ☐ swivel chair
☐ Read the directions and safety tips for this exercise *carefully* before starting any procedure.

Study TIPS

Develop a concept map (or use the one you may have developed in Lab 28) outlining the structures of the ear and the pathway that sound waves travel as they pass through them. For reference, use your textbook or the *A&P Survival Guide.*

A. HEARING TESTS

Conduction impairment refers to a blocking of sound waves as they are conducted through the external and middle ear to the sensory areas of the inner ear (the *conduction pathway*). **Nerve impairment** implies insensitivity to sound because of inherited or acquired nerve damage. The two hearing tests described are often used in clinical settings to screen patients with suspected hearing impairments.

☐ 1 Conduct the **Rinne test (Figure 29-1)** on a subject:
  ☐ Strike a tuning fork on the base of your palm (see Figure 29-1, *A*) and place the handle against the subject's mastoid process (see Figure 29-1, *B*).
  ☐ When the subject no longer hears the tuning fork's hum, quickly move the prongs to the opening of the external auditory meatus (but do not touch it, as in Figure 29-1, *C*).
  ☐ Normally, a hum will be heard again. If not, a conductive impairment is suspected. Repeat on the other side of the head. You may want to try simulating conductive impairment in a normal subject by using swimmer's earplugs.
☐ 2 Conduct the **Weber test** on a subject:
  ☐ Strike a tuning fork on the base of your palm and place the handle against the middle of the forehead.
  ☐ Ask the subject on which side, if any, the sound seems louder.
  ☐ A conduction problem is indicated on a side that is noticeably louder than the other. Again, you may want to simulate a conduction impairment by having the subject wear one earplug.

B. EQUILIBRIUM TESTS

☐ 1 The **Romberg test** demonstrates a subject's ability to use information sensed by the utricle and saccule alone, without any help from the sense of vision.
  ☐ Position the subject standing near a chalkboard or whiteboard, facing away from the board.
  ☐ Use a desk lamp or other light source to cast a shadow of the subject onto the chalkboard/whiteboard.
  ☐ Have the subject stand with feet together and eyes open for 2 minutes.
  ☐ Mark the farthest edges of the subject's shadow as it sways.
  ☐ After 2 minutes, measure the longest distance of sway.
  ☐ Repeat with the subject's eyes closed.
  ☐ Repeat with the subject facing perpendicular to the board.
  ☐ Results showing excessive sway, almost to the point of falling, indicate an equilibrium problem.

□ 2 The **Barany test** evaluates the function of the semicircular canals. Be sure to record your results in Lab Report 29 as you proceed.

    □ Have your lab partner sit in a rotating chair with eyes closed and head tilted 30 degrees forward.

    □ Rotate the chair in one direction for about 10 seconds.

    □ When you stop the rotation, look into your lab partner's eyes. The side-to-side movement that should be apparent is called *nystagmus*. Side-to-side nystagmus is evidence that the lateral semicircular canals are being stimulated by the rotation.

    □ Allowing time for rest, repeat the demonstration with your lab partner's head tilted toward one side about 90 degrees. This stimulates the superior canals, causing up-and-down nystagmus.

    □ Allowing time for rest, repeat the demonstration with your lab partner's head tilted as far forward as possible. This arrangement stimulates the posterior canals maximally, producing rotary nystagmus.

> **!** **safety first**
> If an equilibrium impairment exists, the Romberg test may result in the subject toppling over! One or two people should stand ready to catch the subject if necessary. •

> **!** **safety first**
> Hold onto the chair tightly and surround the subject so that no one topples over and becomes injured. Students prone to motion sickness or related problems should not participate in this activity. •

A

B

C

FIGURE 29-1 Using a tuning fork for the Rinne test. **A,** Strike the tuning fork. **B,** Hold the tuning fork on the subject's mastoid process. **C,** When the subject no longer hears the tone through the mastoid process, move the tuning fork just outside the ear.

Name: _____ Date: _____ Section: _____

LAB REPORT 29
Hearing and Equilibrium

Hearing Tests

TEST	NORMAL	IMPAIRED	NORMAL	IMPAIRED
Rinne test (normal)	☐	☐	☐	☐
Rinne test (simulated impairment)	☐	☐	☐	☐
Weber test (normal)	☐	☐	☐	☐
Weber test (simulated impairment)	☐	☐	☐	☐

Explain the difference in results between the normal hearing tests and the hearing tests performed with a simulated impairment.

Romberg Test

Observations:

Result: ☐ normal ☐ impaired

Barany Test

POSITION	OBSERVATIONS	EXPLANATION
Head forward 30 degrees		
Head to side 90 degrees		
Head full forward		

Explain how the results of the Barany test relate to the function of the semicircular canals.

30

The Eye

Vision, one of the *special senses*, relies on a very complex receptor apparatus: the **eye.** Vision depends on a variety of positioning and focusing mechanisms to form an image in the correct spot on the light-sensitive receptor cells inside the eye. These mechanisms involve muscles, lenses, and other structures that are all a part of the visual apparatus. The complexity of structure allows for complexity of function. The visual image perceived by humans has the qualities of **resolution, brightness, color,** and **depth.** These and other aspects of visual structure and function are presented in this exercise and in Lab Exercise 31.

BEFORE YOU BEGIN

- ☐ Read the appropriate chapter in your textbook.
- ☐ Set your learning goals. When you finish this exercise, you should be able to:
  - ☐ describe the major features of the eye and identify them in specimens, models, and figures
  - ☐ explain the basic function of the eye and its structures
- ☐ Prepare your materials:
  - ☐ sheep or cow eye (fresh or preserved)
  - ☐ dissection tools and trays
  - ☐ chart or dissectible model of the eye
  - ☐ microscope
  - ☐ prepared microslide: *retina c.s.*
  - ☐ computer setup with a program to simulate dissection of a human body (optional)
- ☐ Read the directions and safety tips for this exercise *carefully* before starting any procedure.

Study TIPS

As you progress through this dissection, use Figure 30-4 in the Lab Manual, your textbook, or the *A&P Survival Guide.* Obtain an unlabeled illustration of the eye and label it after you complete this lab.

A. THE HUMAN EYE

The human eye and its accessory structures provide the structural apparatus required for processing and receiving visual images. Using charts or dissectible models of the human eye and its accessories, locate each of the parts listed and describe its function in Lab Report 30.

- ☐ 1 Locate these features of the **lacrimal apparatus (Figure 30-1):**
  - ☐ **Lacrimal gland**—Exocrine "tear" gland in the superior lateral corner of the orbit
  - ☐ **Nasolacrimal duct**—Duct in the inferior medial corner of the orbit, drains tears from **lacrimal canals** toward the nasal cavity
- ☐ 2 Locate these *extrinsic eye muscles*, which are skeletal muscles that control eye movement:
  - ☐ **Rectus muscles** (four)—*Superior, inferior, medial, lateral*
  - ☐ **Oblique muscles** (two)—*Superior, inferior*
    - ☐ What is the action of each of these muscles?
- ☐ 3 Identify these additional accessory structures:
  - ☐ **Eyelids**
  - ☐ **Conjunctiva**—Thin, transparent mucous membrane adhering to the anterior surface of the eye and lining the eyelids
  - ☐ **Eyebrows**
- ☐ 4 Distinguish the three *layers* of the eyeball:
  - ☐ **Fibrous layer** *(outer coat)*—The **cornea** is the anterior, transparent portion. The **sclera** is the white, fibrous portion.
  - ☐ **Vascular layer** *(middle coat)*—The posterior portion is the thin, heavily pigmented **choroid.** The anterior portions include the circular **ciliary body,** in which are incorporated the **ciliary muscles** *(intrinsic eye muscles).* The ciliary muscles are attached to the rim of the **lens** by means of **suspensory ligaments.** Attached to the anterior edge of the ciliary body is the colored **iris,** which has an opening called the **pupil.**

safety first
Do not forget the rules for safe use of the microscope. •

- ☐ **Inner layer** *(inner coat)*—The **retina** is divided into two layers: the outer *pigmented retina* and the inner *sensory retina.* The sensory retina contains photoreceptor cells of two main types—**rods** and **cones**—as well as association neurons. In the posterior retina is a small, yellow **macula lutea** with a pit called the **fovea centralis.** The fovea is normally the center of the visual field and contains many cones. Rods become more dominant farther away from the fovea. Medial to the macula lutea is the white **optic disk.** Here, blood vessels, as well as the nerve fibers that exit as the **optic nerve,** pass out of the eyeball.

☐ Observe a cross section of the retina in a prepared microscopic specimen. Can you identify the features of the retina shown in **Figure 30-2**? Are either of the other two coats of the eyeball visible in your specimen?

> **Hint** Figure 30-2, *C*, shows a light micrograph of the retina. •

☐ **5** Identify these cavities and chambers of the eye:

☐ **Anterior cavity**—Filled with **aqueous humor,** a watery filtrate produced by the ciliary body. Aqueous humor circulates from the **posterior chamber** behind the iris, through the pupil, and to the **anterior chamber,** where it is reabsorbed.

☐ **Posterior cavity**—Filled with transparent, jellylike **vitreous body.** This cavity is posterior to the lens.

B. EYE DISSECTION

Apply your knowledge of mammalian eye anatomy by carefully dissecting a cow or sheep eye.

> **!** **safety first**
> Observe the usual precautions while dissecting the preserved or fresh tissue of the eye specimen. Use safety goggles to avoid injury during dissections. •

☐ **1** Trim away any excess adipose tissue, leaving the stub of the optic nerve and extrinsic eye muscles intact.

☐ **2** Locate these structures on the external aspect:

☐ **Optic nerve**—The nerve bundle projecting from the posterior of the eyeball

☐ **Extrinsic eye muscles** (six)—These may have been cut from your specimen during preparation **(Figures 30-3 and 30-4)**

☐ **Sclera**—The white portion of the vascular layer

☐ **Cornea**—The clear, anterior portion of the vascular layer

☐ **Iris**—The pigmented region under the cornea

☐ **Pupil**—The iris's hole (it may be oblong in your specimen rather than round as in the human)

☐ **Conjunctiva**—The thin mucous membrane over the anterior portion of the eye, extending to line the inner eyelid

☐ Any other accessory structures that may be present in your specimen

☐ **3** Puncture the sclera with the tip of your scissors (or a scalpel) about 1 cm posterior to the edge of the cornea. Use the scissors to cut a circle around the eye, staying 1 cm from the cornea's margin. Pull the anterior portion away from the posterior portion.

☐ **4** Identify these features:

☐ **Vitreous body**—The thick jellylike substance of the posterior cavity

☐ **Aqueous humor**—A watery liquid in the anterior cavity

☐ **Lens**—A plastic-like ball of translucent tissue (in fresh specimens it is very clear; hold it up and try to look through it)

☐ **Ciliary body**—A ring of ridges around the outside of the iris's margin (the ridges are formed by the ciliary muscles within)

☐ **Retina**—A thin film of gray matter loosely associated with the inside posterior wall of the eyeball (it may have fallen away, appearing as a crumpled mass still attached at the **optic disk**)

☐ **Choroid**—The pigmented region of the vascular layer in the posterior region of the eyeball's wall, deep to the sclera, superficial to the retina. In some mammals, but not in humans, an iridescent **tapetum lucidum** can be seen in the choroid.

FIGURE 30-1 Label these parts of the lacrimal apparatus on the lines provided and on the blanks in the Lab Report at the end of this exercise.

FIGURE 30-2 Cell layers of the retina. **A,** Pigmented and sensor layers of the retina. **B,** Rod and cone cells. Note their variation in the general structure of a neuron. **C,** Photomicrograph of the retina.

Coloring Exercises: Eye

Use colored pens or pencils to shade in both the figure and the labels. Each red numeral in the figure corresponds to a matching red numeral following the appropriate label.

FIBROUS LAYER1
  CORNEA2
  SCLERA3
VASCULAR LAYER4
  CHOROID5
  CILIARY BODY6
  IRIS7
  LENS8
INNER LAYER9
  RETINA10
  AQUEOUS HUMOR11
  VITREOUS BODY12
  CONJUNCTIVA13

Extrinsic Muscles
SUPERIOR RECTUS14
INFERIOR RECTUS15
LATERAL RECTUS16
SUPERIOR OBLIQUE17
INFERIOR OBLIQUE18

FIGURE 30-3 Structures of the eye.

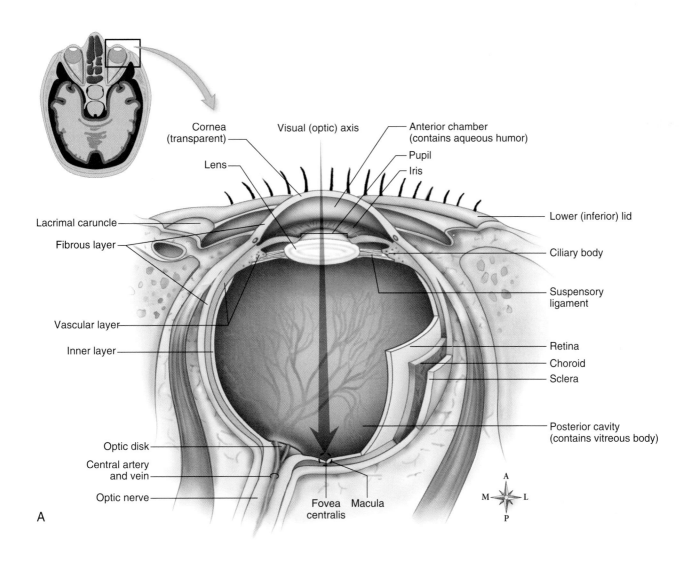

Cornea (transparent)

Visual (optic) axis

Anterior chamber (contains aqueous humor)

Lens

Pupil

Iris

Lacrimal caruncle

Lower (inferior) lid

Fibrous layer

Ciliary body

Suspensory ligament

Vascular layer

Inner layer

Retina

Choroid

Sclera

Posterior cavity (contains vitreous body)

Optic disk

Central artery and vein

Optic nerve

Fovea centralis   Macula

A
P
M   L

A

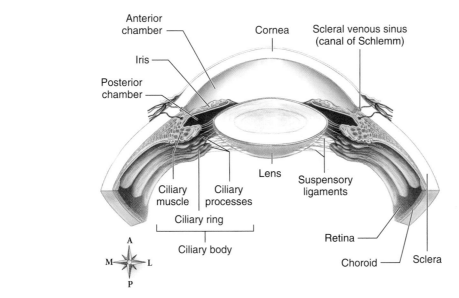

Anterior chamber

Cornea

Scleral venous sinus (canal of Schlemm)

Iris

Posterior chamber

Ciliary muscle

Ciliary processes

Lens

Suspensory ligaments

Ciliary ring

Retina

Ciliary body

Choroid   Sclera

A
P
M   L

B

FIGURE 30-4 Mammalian eye dissection. **A,** Horizontal section through the eyeball. The eye is viewed from above. **B,** Lens, cornea, iris, and ciliary body. Note the suspensory ligaments that attach the lens to the ciliary body.

Name: _____   Date: _____   Section: _____

The Eye

Use this table as a checklist for your study of the human and sheep (or cow) eye. Do not forget to fill in the function column.

TUNIC OR REGION	STRUCTURE	SHEEP	HUMAN	FUNCTION(S)
Lacrimal apparatus	Lacrimal gland	☐	☐	
	Nasolacrimal duct	☐	☐	
Extrinsic eye muscles	Rectus: superior, inferior, lateral, medial	☐	☐	
	Oblique: superior, inferior	☐	☐	
External accessories	Conjunctiva	☐	☐	
	Eyelids, eyebrows	☐	☐	
Fibrous layer	Cornea	☐	☐	
	Sclera	☐	☐	
Vascular layer	Choroid	☐	☐	
	Ciliary body	☐	☐	
	Lens	☐	☐	
	Suspensory ligaments	☐	☐	
	Iris	☐	☐	
	Pupil	☐	☐	
	Tapetum lucidum	☐	☐	
Inner layer	Retina	☐	☐	
	Macula lutea	☐	☐	
	Fovea	☐	☐	
	Optic disk	☐	☐	
Anterior cavity	Aqueous humor	☐	☐	
Posterior cavity	Vitreous body	☐	☐	
	Optic nerve	☐	☐	

Figure 30-1 (from p. 294)

1. _____
2. _____
3. _____

Fill-in

1. _____
2. _____
3. _____
4. _____
5. _____
6. _____

Put in Order

1. _____
2. _____
3. _____
4. _____
5. _____
6. _____

Fill-in (complete each statement with the correct term)

1. _?_ is a type of photoreceptor specialized for vision in dimly lit environments.

2. Tears are produced by the _?_ glands.

3. When you try to keep your eyes focused on a rocket as it ascends, you contract the _?_ muscle attached to your eyeballs.

4. Muscles in the _?_ relax or contract to alter the diameter of the pupil.

5. The redness seen in one's eyes in a smoke-filled environment is a result of temporary inflammation of the _?_.

6. On a hot day, sweat collects on your forehead. It is prevented from dripping directly toward your eye by the _?_.

Put in Order (rearrange these in the order in which light passes through them to form an image inside the eye)

conjunctiva
cornea
lens
pupil
retina
vitreous body

Specimen: *retina c.s.*
Total Magnification: _____

Visual Function

Human vision is a complex function involving **image formation, reception** by photoreceptors, **transmission** of sensory information to appropriate brain centers, and **perception** of the image in the mind. The activities described in this exercise challenge you to demonstrate just a few of the many functional characteristics of the human sense of vision.

BEFORE YOU BEGIN

☐ Read the appropriate chapter in your textbook.
☐ Set your learning goals. When you finish this exercise, you should be able to:
  ☐ demonstrate visual function by means of standard tests and demonstrations
☐ Prepare your materials:
  ☐ meter stick
  ☐ wall chart: astigmatism test
  ☐ wall chart: Snellen eye test
  ☐ pack of assorted brightly colored papers
  ☐ color blindness test plates (Ichikawa Test Book or similar)
☐ Read the directions and safety tips for this exercise *carefully* before starting any procedure.

Study TIPS

Develop a concept map that includes the structure of the eye and the pathway of light as it passes through these structures. Or you might want to take a labeled diagram of the eye and illustrate the pathway of light through the eye. For reference, use your Lab Manual, textbook, or the *A&P Survival Guide*.

A. ACUITY

Acuity is the sharpness of the visual image and is often tested in clinics with the *Snellen eye test*.

☐ **1** Place a Snellen chart **(Figure 31-1)** on the wall, and have the subject stand 20 feet (6.1 m) away, facing the chart.
☐ **2** Have the subject cover one eye and read the letters on the chart as you point to them. Begin at the top line and work your way down.
☐ **3** Note the lowest row of letters that can be read accurately. Record the number printed next to that row in Lab Report 31. (In Figure 31-1, use the bottom number of the ratio printed to the left of the row of letters.) That number is the farthest distance (in feet) that a person with normal acuity can see the letters in that row. For example, if the number is 20, the subject has 20-20 vision (meaning the subject can see at 20 feet what a person with normal vision can see at 20 feet). If the number is 100, the subject has 20-100 vision (meaning that the subject sees at 20 feet what a person with normal vision can see at 100 feet). Test both eyes; if the subject wears eyeglasses, try the test corrected (with glasses) and uncorrected (without glasses).

FIGURE 31-1 Snellen chart for testing visual acuity (for use at 1 foot from subject).

B. ASTIGMATISM

Astigmatism is abnormal curvature of the cornea or lens.

> **Hint** If you don't have a wall chart, you can use **Figure 31-2** at about 1 foot away. •

☐ 1 Test for a curvature flaw by facing the subject toward an *astigmatism test chart* 20 feet (6.1 m) away.

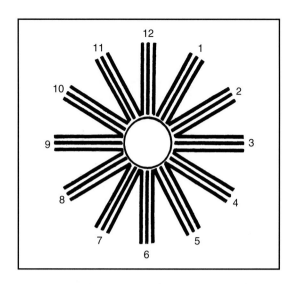

FIGURE 31-2 Example of astigmatism chart.

TEST

FIGURE 31-3 Near-point accommodation test figure.

☐ 2 Cover one of the subject's eyes, and ask him or her to stare at the circle in the center of the chart.

☐ 3 If all the lines radiating from the center appear to the subject to be straight and of equal darkness, no astigmatism is present. If the lines appear wavy, curved, or of unequal darkness, astigmatism is suspected. Test the other eye.

C. ACCOMMODATION

Accommodation is the ability to adjust the focusing apparatus to account for changes in distance from the viewed object. Your lens changes shape to accommodate near vision. Likewise, your pupil changes diameter to help accommodation.

☐ 1 Position the subject's chin on the lab table and put a meter stick on the table perpendicular to the subject's face (with 0 cm at the chin).

☐ 2 Have the subject cover one eye, and ask him or her to focus on the word TEST in **Figure 31-3** as you hold it 1 meter from the face.

☐ 3 Slowly move the figure closer and record the nearest point at which the subject can focus. Does the diameter of the pupil change as you approach the subject's *near point?* Repeat with the other eye.

FIGURE 31-4 Blind spot test objects.

D. BLIND SPOT

The **blind spot** is actually the optic disk, a point where there are no photoreceptors in the retina. The part of the *visual field* focused on the blind spot cannot be seen. We normally do not notice it because the brain "fills in" the blank area for us.

Demonstrate the location of the blind spot in your visual field by covering one eye and looking at **Figure 31-4**. Stare at the object (square or circle) medial to the other object in the figure. Starting at about 35 cm, slowly bring the figure closer to your eye. At one point, the *lateral* object will seem to disappear because its image has fallen on the blind spot.

E. PERIPHERAL MONOCHROME VISION

Rods are photoreceptors adapted to reception of dim light of a broad color range (that is, *dim-light black-and-white vision*). Cones are adapted for *bright-light color vision* because they require higher light intensity, but different cones can perceive different wavelengths (colors) of light. The cones are densest at the fovea, and the rods are densest in the peripheral portion of the visual field. You can demonstrate the *monochrome* nature of the peripheral field by means of this demonstration:

☐ **1** While the subject stares forward, slowly bring a brightly colored piece of paper into the visual field from behind the subject's head.

☐ **2** Stop when the subject indicates that the object has just entered the visual field.

☐ **3** Ask what color the object is. If you did the test properly and the subject isn't cheating, the color is difficult or impossible to determine. Why?

F. COLOR VISION

Color blindness, or color vision deficiency, can be the result of brain or nerve damage, but it is usually an inherited condition. In the more common forms, called *red-green deficiency*, red- or green-sensitive cones are missing or defective. Individuals with no green-sensitive cones have *deuteranopia*; those with no red-sensitive cones have *protanopia*. Test for red-green deficiency in your subject by following these steps (for the Ichikawa Test Book) or the steps with your test kit.

☐ **1** Hold the book of plates about 75 cm from the subject in bright, natural light, avoiding glare.

☐ **2** Without touching the figures, ask the subject to name the numeral seen in each mosaic. If more than one numeral can be seen, ask for the one that appears most distinct. Record the numeral for each plate on the form provided with the test kit.

☐ **3** Add up the marks in the two columns of the form's first section. Using the formula given there, determine whether the subject is normal or color deficient.

☐ **4** Only if the subject is color deficient, complete the second section of the form. Determine whether the subject has protanopia or deuteranopia.

Name: _____ Date: _____ Section: _____

LAB REPORT 31
Visual Function

TEST OR DEMONSTRATION	RESULT		REMARKS
	LEFT EYE	RIGHT EYE	
Snellen (acuity) test	corrected: 20-____	corrected: 20-____	
	uncorrected: 20-____	uncorrected: 20-____	
Astigmatism	corrected: ☐ normal ☐ not normal	corrected: ☐ normal ☐ not normal	
	uncorrected: ☐ normal ☐ not normal	uncorrected: ☐ normal ☐ not normal	
Accommodation (near point)	corrected: ____ cm	corrected: ____ cm	
	uncorrected: ____ cm	uncorrected: ____ cm	
Blind spot	☐ found	☐ found	
Peripheral vision test	☐ correct color identification ☐ incorrect color identification	☐ correct color identification ☐ incorrect color identification	
Color blindness screening	☐ normal ☐ protanopia ☐ deuteranopia	☐ normal ☐ protanopia ☐ deuteranopia	

Fill-in

1. _____
2. _____
3. _____
4. _____
5. _____
6. _____
7. _____
8. _____
9. _____
10. _____
11. _____
12. _____
13. _____
14. _____
15. _____

Fill-in (complete each statement with the correct term)

1-2. _?_ is the sharpness of the perceived visual image and is often evaluated in clinical situations with the _?_ eye test.

3. A person with 20-100 vision has (normal/abnormal) vision.

4. Abnormal curvature of the cornea or lens is called _?_.

5. The ability to adjust the focusing apparatus of the eye to account for changes in distance from the viewed object is called _?_.

6. When accommodating, the pupil and the _?_ may change shape.

7. The blind spot is actually the _?_.

8. Black-and-white vision is also called _?_ vision.

9. Rods are involved in (bright-light/dim-light) vision.

10. Cones are involved in (bright-light/dim-light) vision.

11. Rods are involved in (black-and-white/color) vision.

12. Cones are involved in (black-and-white/color) vision.

13. Individuals with a lack of green-sensitive cones are said to have _?_, a form of red-green color blindness.

14. Individuals with a lack of red-sensitive cones are said to have _?_, a different form of red-green color blindness.

15. Color blindness usually results from _?_.

LAB EXERCISE 32
Endocrine Glands

The **endocrine system** includes a number of glands that secrete regulatory chemicals called **hormones** into the blood for distribution throughout the body. The hormones interact only with their **target cells,** cells with receptors for those particular hormones. Endocrinology, the study of endocrine glands and hormones, is advancing rapidly as research continues. Biologists now realize that practically every tissue in the body produces at least one hormone. However, only a handful of glands are large and specialized enough and secrete enough hormone to be considered here as part of the endocrine system. The gross and microscopic structure of some of the major endocrine glands is presented in this exercise. The next exercise presents topics related to endocrine hormones.

BEFORE YOU BEGIN

☐ Read the appropriate chapter in your textbook.
☐ Set your learning goals. When you finish this exercise, you should be able to:
  ☐ describe the principal endocrine glands and locate each in a model and in figures
  ☐ identify histological features of some of the important endocrine glands
☐ Prepare your materials:
  ☐ dissectible model of the human torso and head
  ☐ microscope
  ☐ prepared microslides:
    ☐ pituitary gland
    ☐ thyroid/parathyroid glands
    ☐ adrenal gland
    ☐ pancreas
    ☐ thymus
    ☐ pineal gland
☐ Read the directions and safety tips for this exercise *carefully* before starting any procedure.

A. GROSS ANATOMY

Using a dissectible model of the human body, locate each endocrine organ described **(Figure 32-1)**. As you identify each gland, investigate its gross structure.

☐ 1 **Pituitary**—This tiny, pea-shaped gland is located on the inferior aspect of the brain. It is cradled in the sella turcica of the sphenoid bone. The pituitary, or *hypophysis cerebri*, is actually two glands that are fused together: the **anterior pituitary (adenohypophysis)** and the **posterior pituitary (neurohypophysis).**

☐ 2 **Thyroid**—This single gland is located on the anterior aspect of the trachea (windpipe), near the larynx (voice box). It resembles a bow tie in that it has two **lateral lobes** and a narrow medial **isthmus** that joins them in the middle.

☐ 3 **Parathyroids**—The parathyroids are tiny masses of tissue embedded in the posterior surface of the thyroid. There are usually two superior and two inferior parathyroid glands. (Many models do not represent these glands.)

☐ 4 **Adrenals**—The adrenals are a pair of glands, each on the superior surface of a kidney. Each adrenal resembles a cone-shaped hat on top of a kidney. Many models distinguish between the outer *adrenal cortex* and the inner *adrenal medulla*.

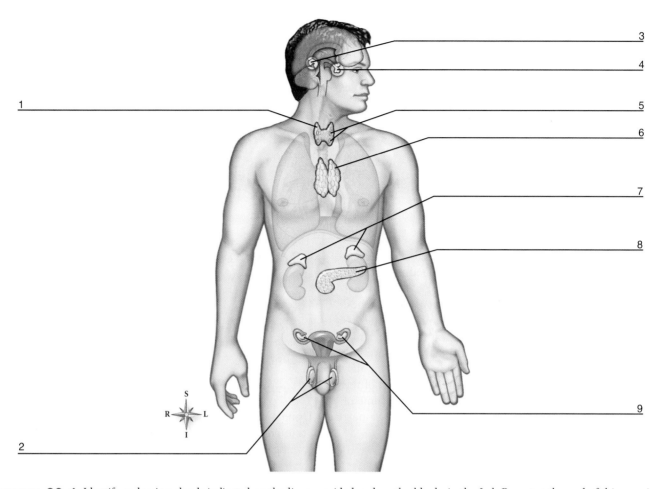

FIGURE 32-1 Identify endocrine glands indicated on the lines provided and on the blanks in the Lab Report at the end of this exercise.

□ **5 Pancreas**—Both an endocrine and exocrine gland, the pancreas is a long, narrow mass of glandular tissue. Resembling a fish, the pancreas is cradled in the bend of the C-shaped duodenum (first part of the small intestine, just inferior to the stomach).

□ **6 Thymus**—This two-lobed gland is located in the anterior mediastinum. The thymus grows until puberty, then degenerates through adulthood. It is not shown in models of the adult human body.

□ **7 Pineal**—The tiny pineal body has already been identified as a nervous structure in the diencephalon of the brain. Because it secretes several hormones, it is also considered an endocrine gland.

□ **8 Testes**—The testes, the pair of male *gonads* (primary sex organs), are ovoid organs in the saclike *scrotum* external to the lower anterior trunk.

□ **9 Ovaries**—The pair of female gonads called the *ovaries* are ovoid organs within the pelvic cavity. Each is located at the distal end of a tube leading to the uterus (womb) called a **uterine (fallopian) tube.**

□ **10 Other**—Many other organs secrete endocrine hormones and so are considered by some biologists to be components of the endocrine system. For example, the digestive tract, the placenta, the kidneys, and the skin all produce endocrine hormones.

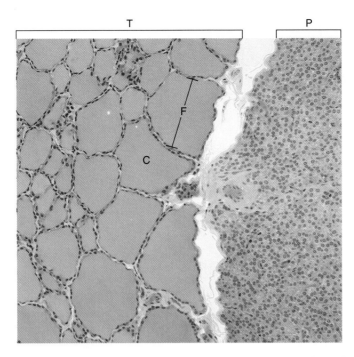

FIGURE 32-2 Thyroid colloid (*C*), thyroid follicle (*f*), thyroid tissue (*T*), and parathyroid tissue (*P*).

B. ENDOCRINE HISTOLOGY

In this activity, you are asked to identify some of the histological characteristics of endocrine glands. For each, locate the structures described in a prepared specimen and sketch your observations in Lab Report 32.

safety first

Do not forget to be cautious when using the microscope and when handling prepared slides. •

☐ **1 Pituitary**—As already stated, the pituitary (hypophysis cerebri) is actually two glands in one. The anterior pituitary (adenohypophysis) is modified epithelium, which is typical for endocrine glands (Figure 32-3, *D*). The posterior pituitary (neurohypophysis) is composed of **neurosecretory tissue,** nerve tissue whose neurons secrete hormones rather than neurotransmitters.

landmark characteristics

The anterior pituitary is usually more darkly stained than the posterior pituitary. Remember that you should be able to find both in a single cross section of the pituitary. The anterior pituitary has two regions: the *pars distalis* and the *pars intermedia*. Of the two, the pars intermedia is more lightly stained. The posterior pituitary has many dark, nonsecreting cells and only a few secretory cells (which are normally not distinguishable). •

☐ **2 Thyroid**—In thyroid tissue, the glandular epithelium forms **thyroid follicles,** which contain **thyroid colloid** (the stored form of thyroid hormones) **(Figure 32-2)**. The **follicular cells,** which form the walls of each follicle, secrete the colloid. The cells between the follicles, called **parafollicular cells,** also secrete a hormone.

landmark characteristics

One of the easiest specimens, thyroid tissue has circles of cuboidal cells with uniformly stained centers. These are cross-sectional views of follicles filled with colloid. Some parafollicular cells should be visible between the circles. •

☐ **3 Parathyroid**—Parathyroid tissue can often be found in the thyroid tissue specimen because of the close association of these two gland types (see Figure 32-2). Parathyroid tissue does not have any follicles, but rather a dense packing of glandular cells. **Chief cells** form cords, or rows, and are thought to be primary producers of hormone. **Oxyphil cells** are scattered among the chief cells and are considered by some to be backup hormone producers.

landmark characteristics

Chief cells are smaller, more densely packed cells than oxyphil cells. Oxyphil cells have more cytoplasm per cell, giving them a lighter overall appearance. As is typical in prepared histology specimens, the nuclei are darkly stained, and the cytoplasm is lightly stained. •

FIGURE 32-3 **A,** Adrenal tissue. **B,** Pancreatic tissue. **C,** Thymic tissue. **D,** Adenohypophysis. (Nonstaining chromophobes are indicated by *arrowheads.* Examples of hormone-secreting cells are labeled *a* [acidophil] and *b* [basophil].)

□ **4 Adrenals**—Each adrenal gland is composed of an inner **medulla** and an outer **cortex.** The neurosecretory **chromaffin cells** form the medullary tissue. Cortical tissue is composed of three distinct regions of glandular epithelium **(Figure 32-3, A)**:

□ **Zona glomerulosa**—The outermost region, it is just deep to the *capsule* of the organ. Here, cells are arranged in balls and loops.

□ **Zona fasciculata**—This is the middle, and thickest, region of the cortex. The cells in this zone form rather straight rows that are perpendicular to the gland's surface.

□ **Zona reticularis**—This is the innermost zone. Cells in this region form branched rows (see Figure 32-3, A).

---

landmark characteristics

With low-power magnification, you may be able to see at least part of the medulla and all the cortical zones. The medullary chromaffin cells stain more darkly than cells in the adrenal cortex. Switching to high-power magnification, you may be able to distinguish the arrangements of cells in the three zones of the cortex. The cortex appears lighter in color than the medulla because the cortical cells do not accept the stain well. •

□ **5 Pancreas**—The pancreas can be thought of as an exocrine gland with bits of endocrine tissue scattered throughout. The exocrine **acinar cells** secrete digestive *pancreatic juice.* The endocrine **pancreatic islets (of Langerhans)** are spherical masses of cells that secrete pancreatic hormones (Figure 32-3, B).

---

landmark characteristics

Pancreatic islets are usually easy to locate because their endocrine cells are more lightly stained than the surrounding acinar cells. Often several islets are visible in a single low-power field. •

□ **6 Thymus**—The thymus has a dual role in that it functions as both a lymphatic organ and an endocrine gland. It serves as a site for the development of T lymphocytes (immune cells) and secretes a hormone that influences lymphocyte development. The gland is surrounded by a *capsule* that extends inward, forming *trabeculae* that divide the thymus into **lobules.** Each lobule has a **cortex** largely filled with lymphocytes and a **medulla** with few lymphocytes. In the medulla can be found small spheres called **thymic (Hassall) corpuscles,** whose function is unclear (Figure 32-3, C).

---

landmark characteristics

The capsule and its inward extensions (trabeculae) are normally pale, easily found structures. Near these walls, the cortex can be seen as a region of darkly stained lymphocytes. Farther away from the walls, the more lightly stained medullary region can be seen. Occasional thymic corpuscles (circles with a nonuniform interior) can sometimes be seen. •

□ **7 Pineal gland**—The pineal gland is composed of neuroglia and cells sometimes called *pinealocytes,* which are thought to secrete a number of different hormones. Around puberty, calcifications called **pineal (brain) sand** may begin developing. Although several hypotheses have been proposed, the significance of brain sand is still unknown.

Study TIPS

There are many hormonal interactions that can be very cumbersome to learn. Carefully chart this information while you study. You might want to develop a chart for each gland. List the hormone(s) secreted by each gland. Include how the gland is stimulated or inhibited and what effects it has on the target. For example, the anterior pituitary secretes follicle-stimulating hormone (FSH). It is stimulated by gonadotropin-releasing hormone (GRH) and is inhibited by gonadal hormone feedback. Its target is the testes and ovaries.

---

landmark characteristics

Pineal tissue appears as a rather random hodgepodge of different cells but may have several distinct dark spots that represent calcifications ("brain sand"). •

Coloring Exercises: Adenohypophysis, Neurohypophysis, and Related Structures

Use colored pens or pencils to shade in both the figure and the labels. Each red numeral in the figure corresponds to a matching red numeral following the appropriate label.

Adenohypophysis (Anterior Pituitary)

PARS DISTALIS[1]
SECRETORY CELLS[2]
PARS INTERMEDIA[3]
HYPOPHYSEAL PORTAL
    CIRCULATION[4]

Hormones (& Targets) of Adenohypophysis

PROLACTIN (PRL)[5]
MAMMARY GLANDS[6]
FOLLICLE-STIMULATING
    HORMONE (FSH)[7]
TESTIS[8] & OVARY[9]/
    ESTROGENS[10]
LUTEINIZING HORMONE
    (LH)[11]
TESTIS[8]/TESTOSTERONE[12]
    & OVARY[9]/
    PROGESTERONE[13]
THYROID-STIMULATING
    HORMONE (TSH)[14]
THYROID GLAND[15]/
    THYROID HORMONE (TH)[16]
GROWTH HORMONE (GH)[17]
SKELETAL SYSTEM[18]
ADRENOCORTICO-TROPIC
    HORMONE (ACTH)[19]
ADRENAL CORTEX[20]/
ADRENOCORTICAL
    HORMONES[21]

Neurohypophysis (Posterior Pituitary)

NEUROHYPOPHYSIS
    (POSTERIOR PITUITARY)[22]
HYPOPHYSEAL
    CIRCULATION[23]

Hormones (& Targets) of the Neurohypophysis

ANTIDIURETIC HORMONE
    (ADH)[24]
KIDNEYS[25]
OXYTOCIN (OT)[26]
MAMMARY GLANDS[6]

Related Structures

INFUNDIBULUM[27]
HYPOTHALAMUS[28]
PARAVENTRICULAR
    NUCLEUS[29]
SUPRAOPTIC NUCLEUS[30]
HYPOTHALAMIC NEURONS[31]
RELEASING/INHIBITING
    HORMONES[32]

FIGURE 32-4 The hypophysis (pituitary gland) and related structures. The structures of the adenohypophysis (anterior pituitary) and neurohypophysis (posterior pituitary) are shown along with their hormones and targets (and the hormones produced by target glands). The infundibulum and hypothalamus are also shown.

Coloring Exercises: **Thyroid Gland, Parathyroid Gland, and Related Structures**

Use colored pens or pencils to shade in both the figure and the labels. Each red numeral in the figure corresponds to a matching red numeral following the appropriate label.

Thyroid Gland

LATERAL LOBES[1]
ISTHMUS[2]
THYROID FOLLICLE[3]
FOLLICULAR CELLS[4]
THYROID COLLOID[5]
PARAFOLLICULAR (C)
   CELLS[6]

Hormones/Targets

THYROID HORMONE (T_3/T_4)[7]/
   ALL TISSUES[8]
CALCITONIN[9]/
   BONE TISSUE[10]

Parathyroid Glands

PARATHYROID GLANDS[11]
CHIEF CELLS[12]
OXYPHIL CELLS[13]

Hormones/Targets

PARATHYROID HORMONE
   (PTH)[14]/
BONE &
   GASTROINTESTINAL
   TISSUE[10]

Related Structures

LARYNX[15]
HYOID BONE[16]
PHARYNX[17]
TRACHEA[18]
ESOPHAGUS[19]

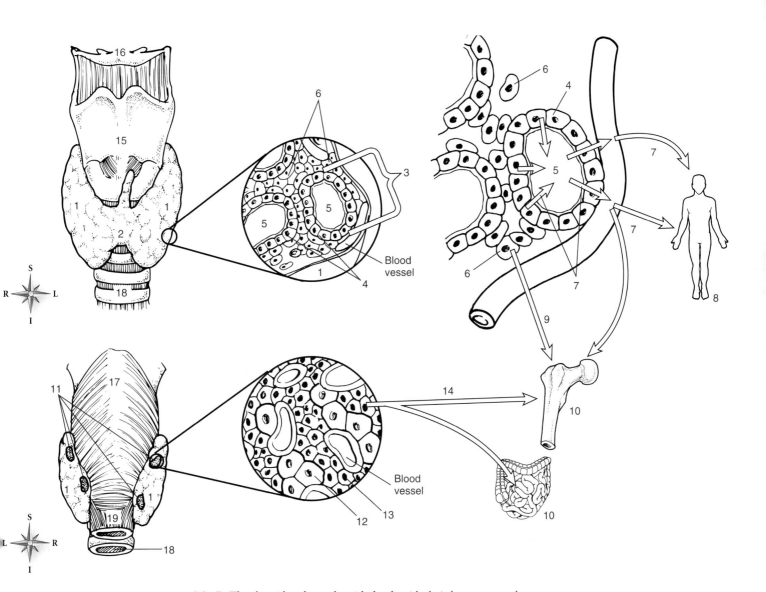

Blood vessel

Blood vessel

FIGURE 32-5 The thyroid and parathyroid glands with their hormones and target organs.

Coloring Exercises: **Adrenal Glands**

Use colored pens or pencils to shade in both the figure and the labels. Each red numeral in the figure corresponds to a matching red numeral following the appropriate label.

ADRENAL GLAND₁
CAPSULE₂
ADRENAL CORTEX₃
ZONA GLOMERULOSA₄
ALDOSTERONE₅/KIDNEYS₆
ZONA FASCICULATA₇
CORTISOL
  (HYDROCORTISONE)₈/
  ALL TISSUES₉

ZONA RETICULARIS₁₀
TESTOSTERONE &
  ESTROGEN₁₁/
  SEX ORGANS, ETC.₁₂
ADRENAL MEDULLA₁₃
EPINEPHRINE
  (ADRENALINE)₁₄
SYMPATHETIC EFFECTORS₁₅

FIGURE 32-6 The adrenal gland with its hormones and target organs.

Name: _____ Date: _____ Section: _____

LAB REPORT 32
Endocrine Glands

Figure 32-1 (from p. 308)

1. _____
2. _____
3. _____
4. _____
5. _____

6. _____
7. _____
8. _____
9. _____

Specimen: *pituitary gland*
Total Magnification: _____

Specimen: *thyroid gland*
Total Magnification: _____

Specimen: *parathyroid gland*
Total Magnification: _____

Pituitary Gland

Structure:

Location:

Thyroid Gland

Structure:

Location:

Parathyroid Gland

Structure:

Location:

Specimen: *adrenal gland*
Total Magnification: _____

Adrenal Gland

Structure:

Location:

Specimen: *pancreas*
Total Magnification: _____

Pancreas

Structure:

Location:

Specimen: *thymus*
Total Magnification: _____

Thymus

Structure:

Location:

Specimen: *pineal gland*
Total Magnification: _____

Pineal Gland

Structure:

Location:

33

Hormones

Hormones are organic molecules derived from lipids or proteins. Hormones are secreted by endocrine tissues and travel throughout the body by means of the bloodstream. Once dispersed, the hormone molecules have a regulatory effect on cells that have **receptors** for those particular hormones. The affected cells are **target** cells, affected tissues are target tissues, and affected organs are target organs.

Generally, secretion of hormones is regulated by **feedback mechanisms.** *Negative feedback* mechanisms slow or stop secretion when the metabolic changes triggered in the target cells become evident or when blood hormone concentrations get too high. Negative feedback is the most commonly observed type of regulation. For example, **insulin** tends to decrease blood glucose concentration. When the blood glucose level is high, insulin secretion increases; when the blood glucose level drops, insulin secretion decreases. *Positive feedback*, less commonly observed, results in an increased hormone secretion when the metabolic changes become evident or blood hormone levels increase. For example, high levels of labor-stimulating **oxytocin** trigger uterine contractions, which push the baby and stretch the birth canal. The stretch sensation feeds back to cause more oxytocin secretion, which then stimulates more contraction, creating a cycle of increasingly stronger (and more frequent) uterine contractions. Another mechanism of regulating hormone secretion is the **biological clock.** Endocrinologists have long observed cyclic rises and falls in the secretion of several hormones related to reproduction, but more recent evidence suggests that most, if not all, hormones may be regulated to some degree by a biological timekeeping mechanism.

This activity challenges you to learn the names, sources, targets, and actions of some of the principal endocrine hormones and presents some demonstrations of hormone detection tests.

BEFORE YOU BEGIN

- ☐ Read the appropriate chapter in your textbook.
- ☐ Set your learning goals. When you finish this exercise, you should be able to:
  - ☐ name the major hormones of the endocrine system and identify their sources, targets, and principal actions
  - ☐ appreciate the noncontinuous pattern of secretion in hormones
  - ☐ explain the hormonal basis of pregnancy testing

- ☐ Prepare your materials:
  - ☐ textbook or (hormone) reference book
  - ☐ packaged pregnancy test kit (Fact Plus *Pro* kit used in this example); two required per experiment (your instructor may use another locally available kit; please check with the instructor for appropriate instructions to be used for this lab)
  - ☐ urine samples:
    - ☐ pregnant (first trimester) female
    - ☐ nonpregnant female
  - ☐ timer, watch, or clock
  - ☐ paper lab wipes
  - ☐ urine collection cups (disposable)
- ☐ Read the directions and safety tips for this exercise *carefully* before starting any procedure.

Study TIPS

The endocrine system links closely with the reproductive system. There are many hormonal interactions that can be very difficult to learn. You may want to chart this information while you study. For reference, refer to the chart you developed in Lab 32, or use your textbook or the *A&P Survival Guide*.

A. ENDOCRINE HORMONES

Fill in the hormone table presented in Lab Report 33. If you have already studied the endocrine hormones, try to fill it in without referring to a book or your notes. If this is your first exposure to endocrine hormones, you will need to use your textbook or a reference book. As you complete the table, you will find it a helpful study technique to shade in the rows of hormones that come from the same source with the same-colored pen or pencil. A brief review of Lab Exercise 32 will be helpful.

B. HUMAN CHORIONIC GONADOTROPIN

Human chorionic gonadotropin (hCG) is not found on the list of hormones in Lab Report 33 because it is not secreted from one of the major endocrine glands. Studies suggest that tiny amounts of hCG are found in tissues throughout the adult human body. However, it seems that the only time a physiologically significant amount is secreted is from embryonic tissue in a structure called the *chorion* during the early stages of development in the womb.

As you can see in **Figure 33-1, A**, estrogen and **progesterone** levels begin to increase at **ovulation** (release of a mature *ovum*). Both hormones promote conditions necessary for successful development of the offspring. For example, the **endometrium** (uterine lining) thickens and becomes more vascular. If fertilization and implantation do not occur, estrogen and progesterone levels fall, resulting in loss (sloughing) of the vascularized endometrial lining (*menstrual flow*). However, if pregnancy does begin, a decrease in estrogen and progesterone would result in the loss of the endometrium and the developing offspring. To prevent this loss, the offspring's tissue secretes large amounts of hCG. hCG stimulates the ovary's secretion of progesterone and estrogen, preventing the decrease in hormones that would otherwise occur. As the **placenta** develops, it begins to secrete its own progesterone and estrogen. hCG secretion decreases during the later phases of pregnancy. Because the placenta is secreting high levels of progesterone and estrogen by this time, stimulation of ovarian secretion is no longer required (Figure 33-1, B).

High blood levels of many molecules are reflected in the urine. This is the case with the very high hCG levels during the first trimester of pregnancy. Because high levels of hCG are detectable in the urine almost immediately after fertilization of an ovum, hCG *urinalysis* is a common form of pregnancy testing.

One type of pregnancy test seldom used anymore requires that a urine sample be processed, then injected into a female laboratory animal. If the urine stimulates ovulation or similar physiological changes, it is concluded that it contains the high levels of hCG typical of early pregnancy.

A more convenient hCG test uses *monoclonal antibodies*, which are protein molecules from cultured immune cells that react with hCG (and only with hCG or similar molecules). Anti-hCG antibodies react with hCG to produce a visible reaction. If a reaction occurs, hCG is present in the sample (and one concludes that the subject is pregnant). If no reaction occurs, hCG must be absent or low (and the subject is not pregnant).

Over-the-counter (OTC) pregnancy test kits and most laboratory pregnancy-screening tests are based on the antibody method. Demonstrate this test by performing antibody urinalysis with the Fact Plus *Pro* pregnancy test kit. Any OTC test kit can be used, but this one has the advantage of having an *experimental control* component. Control tests help ensure that the results are valid and not the result of a side reaction or experimental error. If a different test is used, follow the directions accompanying that test kit.

☐ 1 Obtain two urine samples from a biological supply house: one from a pregnant woman (in the first trimester) and one from a nonpregnant woman.

Hint Warm the urine to room temperature before testing. Always wear gloves and goggles, and use other appropriate safety precautions when handling human body fluids. •

☐ 2 Arrange the test kit components as illustrated in **Figure 33-2, A**. Notice that the *test disk* has two round windows above the *sample well*. The larger *result window* has a pad coated with anti-hCG antibodies. The pad in the smaller *control window* does not have anti-hCG antibodies and is the basis for the control test.

☐ 3 Use the *urine dropper* to remove urine from the *urine collection cup* (see Figure 33-2, A).

☐ 4 Without touching the test disk, drop three drops (only) of the urine into the *sample well* (Figure 32-2, B). There may be a bluish color moving across the windows of the test disk; if it occurs, this is normal.

☐ 5 At exactly 3 minutes from dropping your sample into the sample well, read your result. Results may be read earlier if a red line appears in the control window. If a red line has not appeared in the control window after 3 minutes, the test is invalid and must be repeated. Do not read results after 10 minutes have passed. **Figure 33-3** shows how to interpret results.

☐ 6 Record your results in Lab Report 33 and dispose of the materials as directed by your laboratory supervisor.

Hint A positive result means the person has hCG in the urine and is, therefore, in the early stages of pregnancy. A negative result means that the person does not have hCG in the urine and therefore is not in the early stages of pregnancy. An invalid result means that the test did not work properly, and you can make no conclusions about hCG levels or pregnancy. Most OTC pregnancy tests are 99% accurate. Note that certain drugs that contain hCG (e.g., Profasi, Pregnyl, and Novarel) may give a "false-positive" result, meaning that the test result is positive but the person is not really pregnant. False-positive results may also occur if a person has recently miscarried, aborted, or given birth. •

A

B

FIGURE 33-1 **A,** Female reproductive cycle, assuming ovum is not fertilized. **B,** Changes in reproductive hormones during pregnancy.

FIGURE 33-2 A, Pregnancy test kit. **B,** Apply three drops of urine to the sample well with the urine dropper.

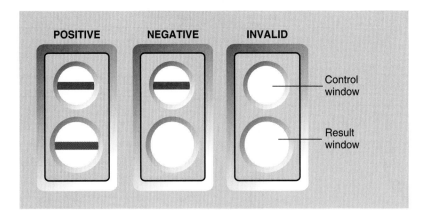

FIGURE 33-3 Interpretation of pregnancy test results. A blue line of *any* shade (light or dark) is a positive result. No line in the result window is a negative result (unless there is also no red line in the control window, which means that the test did not work and the result is invalid).

Name: _____ Date: _____ Section: _____

Hormones

Use your textbook or class notes to fill in the following tables.

HORMONE	GLAND (SOURCE)	TARGET	ACTION
Antidiuretic hormone			
Oxytocin			
Growth hormone			
Thyroid-stimulating hormone			
Adrenocorticotropic hormone			
Luteinizing hormone			
Follicle-stimulating hormone			
Prolactin			
Thyroid hormones			
Calcitonin			
Parathyroid hormones			
Epinephrine			
Aldosterone			
Cortisol			
Melatonin			
Thymosin			
Insulin			
Glucagon			
Testosterone			
Estrogen			
Progesterone			
Prostaglandin(s)			

TEST	SAMPLE	RESULT PAD	CONTROL PAD	RESULT	EXPLANATION
Pregnancy (hCG)	Pregnant			hCG present (+) not present (–)	
	Nonpregnant			hCG present (+) not present (–)	

Discussion Questions (answer these questions on a separate sheet of paper)

1. Explain how hCG secretion is regulated. Is it secreted by a pregnant woman or her offspring?
2. hCG depresses some reactions of the immune system. What adaptive advantage do you think this has?

Blood

Blood is the fluid tissue that circulates within the cardiovascular system. Typical of connective tissues, it has a dominant extracellular matrix. In this case the matrix is a liquid called **plasma.** Suspended in the plasma are blood cells or **formed elements.** **Figure 34-1** shows the major components of human blood. The characteristics of a person's blood vary according to age, sex, metabolic condition, health condition, genetics, and other factors. Clinical evaluation of blood characteristics is important in assessing the condition of patients. This exercise provides demonstrations of just a few of the more common tests. Many blood tests are done by automated machines, at least in some areas, but it is important to understand the basis of these tests to interpret them correctly.

BEFORE YOU BEGIN

☐ Read the appropriate chapter in your textbook.
☐ Set your learning goals. When you finish this exercise, you should be able to:
  ☐ name the components of human blood tissue and identify their functions
  ☐ demonstrate how common blood tests are performed
  ☐ interpret the meaning of important blood tests
  ☐ state the limitations of clinical blood testing
☐ Prepare your materials:
  ☐ blood sample (see SAFETY FIRST box) **Note:** You will be using artificial blood samples purchased for the purpose of performing these exercises. No actual blood will be used.
  ☐ paper towels, lab wipes
  ☐ clean microscope slides
  ☐ bibulous paper
  ☐ distilled water (in dropper bottle)
  ☐ Wright stain (in dropper bottle)
  ☐ wax pencil
  ☐ hemocytometer (glass)
  ☐ BMP LeukoChek (WBC) count kit
  ☐ heparinized capillary tubes
  ☐ microhematocrit centrifuge
  ☐ capillary tube sealing clay or plugs
  ☐ metric ruler (mm)
  ☐ Tallquist test paper and hemoglobin (Hb) scale (or hemoglobinometer kit)
  ☐ Toothpicks
  ☐ blood typing sera: *anti-A, anti-B, anti-D*
  ☐ slide warming box
  ☐ microscope
☐ Read the directions and safety tips for this exercise *carefully* before starting any procedure.

> **! safety first**
> This exercise calls for the use of synthetic human blood samples. These tests should be performed as a demonstration by the instructor using simulated human blood designed specifically for student demonstrations. Follow current laboratory practice by wearing a lab coat, gloves, and protective eyewear while in the lab. •

A. SAMPLING BLOOD

Blood sampling for clinical testing usually requires only tiny amounts of blood, often only a few drops. The usual method for collecting small blood samples is to draw it from a punctured finger. This activity tells you how blood can be drawn for clinical testing. **Please remember: You will *not* be collecting any blood from yourself or a classmate. You will be using only artificial blood supplied by your instructor.**

B. BLOOD SMEAR

Investigate blood tissue by looking at several prepared blood smear slides provided by your instructor. As the name implies, it is merely some blood smeared on a slide, then prepared for microscopic examination.

☐ 1 Scan prepared blood slides under low power on your microscope until you find an area where the cells are thinly spread. Switch to high power and observe the blood cells on the slide. Do all the cells look the same? Are different cells (if there are any) distributed equally? What unique characteristics do these cells have (compared with other cells you have observed)? Describe the pattern or order of the cells in the tissue observed. Write your answers to these questions, and any other observations, in Lab Report 34.

> **Hint** ▸ If your microscope has an oil-immersion objective, you may want to use it to see the blood cells more clearly. After focusing on high-dry, rotate the nosepiece *halfway* to the high-oil objective. Put a drop of immersion oil on the slide, then rotate the high-oil objective into the oil drop. You may need to increase the lighting. •

Coloring Exercises: Human Blood

Use colored pens or pencils to shade in both the figure and the labels. Each red numeral in the figure corresponds to a matching red numeral following the appropriate label.

WHOLE BLOOD₁
PLASMA₂
PROTEINS₃
ALBUMINS₄
GLOBULINS₅
FIBRINOGEN₆
WATER₇
OTHER SOLUTES₈
IONS₉
NUTRIENTS₁₀
WASTE PRODUCTS₁₁
GASES₁₂

REGULATORY
    SUBSTANCES₁₃
FORMED ELEMENTS₁₄
THROMBOCYTES₁₅
LEUKOCYTES₁₆
NEUTROPHILS₁₇
LYMPHOCYTES₁₈
MONOCYTES₁₉
EOSINOPHILS₂₀
BASOPHILS₂₁
ERYTHROCYTES₂₂

FIGURE 34-1 Components of human blood tissue. (*Note:* Do not color inside the numerals or % symbols in the figure so that you can see them easier when you study them later.)

C. DIFFERENTIAL WHITE BLOOD CELL COUNT

The larger nucleated cells that you may have observed in the previous activity are **WBCs**, or **leukocytes**. WBCs are far less numerous than **RBCs** (erythrocytes) and **platelets** (thrombocytes). **Figure 34-2** shows the different types of blood cells. WBCs have numerous protective functions in the body, so their numbers sometimes change in response to changes in health.

Different leukocytes have different functions, so the changes may be reflected in changes in the relative proportions of different types of leukocytes. Clinically, information about relative proportions of leukocyte types is very useful. A test that gives this information is the **differential WBC count**.

☐ 1 Focus on a portion of the blood smear, as in the previous activity. Look around the field for any leukocytes.

☐ 2 In Lab Report 34, mark off how many leukocytes you see of each type until you reach 100 total cells. Obviously, you'll have to move around to different fields to reach 100 cells. Move the slide in the manner shown in **Figure 34-3** so that you do not count the same portion of the slide twice.

☐ 3 Determine the total number of WBCs of each type. If the total for all types is 100, the number for each type is also the percent of that type (i.e., because 100 is the total, 1 cell is also 1% of the cells).

📌 landmark characteristics

WBCs have nuclei and are distinctly larger than **RBCs.** **Agranulocytes** *(agranular leukocytes)* have no granules (spots) visible in the cytoplasm, but **granulocytes** *(granular leukocytes)* do.

- **Monocytes** are very large, agranular leukocytes with large, variably shaped nuclei.
- **Lymphocytes** are agranular WBCs that are almost as small as RBCs. Lymphocyte nuclei are sometimes so large that a lymphocyte appears to have no cytoplasm.
- **Neutrophils** are granular WBCs with small, pinkish granules and lobed nuclei that resemble several links of sausage.
- **Eosinophils** have red granules and two-lobed, dark nuclei.
- **Basophils** have fewer granules, which are a bluish tint and of variable size. Basophils have large, two-lobed or kidney-shaped nuclei.
- See Figure 34-2.

📌 landmark characteristics

Monocytes: 3% to 8% (in chronic infections)
Lymphocytes: 20% to 25% (in antibody reactions)
Neutrophils: 60% to 70% (in acute infections)
Eosinophils: 2% to 4% (in allergic reactions)
Basophils: 0.5% to 1%

☐ 4 How do your results compare with the normal values given in the box?

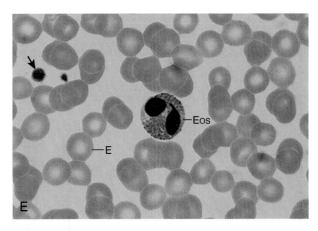

FIGURE 34-2 Representative human blood cells. **A,** Monocyte. **B,** Lymphocyte. **C,** Neutrophil. **D,** Basophil. **E,** Erythrocyte, eosinophil, platelet. (*E,* erythrocyte; *Eos,* eosinophil; *arrow,* platelet.)

FIGURE 34-3 Move the slide in this manner to prevent counting the same cells more than once.

D. WHITE BLOOD CELL COUNT

WBC counts are clinical tests that estimate the number of leukocytes present in each cubic millimeter (mm³) of blood. A known volume of a solution called the *diluent* is used to dilute a blood sample (also of a known volume) so that the cells are more spread out and therefore easier to count. The diluted sample is placed on a special glass microscope slide called a **hemocytometer.** The hemocytometer, shown in **Figures 34-4** and **34-5**, has two counting grids etched on it. When filled correctly, just the right volume is present under the coverslip and over the counting grid.

The instructions that follow are for the BMP LeukoChek test **(Figure 34-6)**. The BMP LeukoChek test is for the microscopic counting of leukocytes in whole blood. If you are using another method, follow the directions supplied by the manufacturer of the test kit or by your instructor. In any case, be sure to heed all safety advice.

> **Hint** Artificial whole blood (20 μl) will be added to the BMP LeukoChek reservoir from a well-mixed anticoagulated tube of whole blood. The manufacturer provides a capillary tube that fills via capillary action to exactly 20 μl of artificial whole blood. Each reservoir contains 1.98 ml of a 1% buffered ammonium oxalate solution. This provides for a ratio of 1 to 100, sample of total volume. •

☐ 1 Puncture the cap diaphragm with the protective shield on the pipette assembly.

☐ 2 Remove the shield and fill the tube with artificial whole blood from a sample provided by your instructor that supplies you with the artificial whole blood. Be sure that the capillary tube fills completely. When the blood reaches the end of the capillary tube, it will stop automatically, filling the tube with 20 μl of artificial whole blood. Gently wipe excess blood from the outside of the capillary tube.

☐ 3 Squeeze the reservoir slightly to expel a volume of air. Maintain pressure on the reservoir while inserting the pipette with whole blood into the reservoir. Be sure to simultaneously cover the top opening of the capillary tube holder.

☐ 4 Release pressure from the reservoir and then from the capillary tube opening. This will cause the artificial whole blood to be drawn into the diluent.

☐ 5 Gently squeeze the reservoir to rinse the capillary tube, taking care not to expel any mixture of diluent and whole blood through the top of the opening of the inserted capillary tube holder. Place your finger over the top of the opening of the capillary tube holder and gently invert the reservoir several times to ensure proper mixing.

☐ 6 Wait 10 minutes before attempting to count leukocytes.

☐ 7 Remove the pipette assembly, and invert and seat the assembly in a reverse position into the top of the cap. This changes the pipette assembly from a collection device to a dropper.

☐ 8 Discard the first 3 or 4 drops, and then expel the reservoir solution into a hemocytometer with a Neubaur grid for counting the leukocytes.

☐ 9 A leukocyte count is performed under 100× magnification. Leukocytes are counted in all nine large squares of the counting chamber. Add 10% to the total number and then multiply this value by 100 to get the total leukocyte count. For example, if 60 cells are counted, the total count would be 60 + 6 × 100, which would represent a total count of 6600 leukocytes per cubic mm.

landmark characteristics

Normal: 4500 to 11,000 WBCs/mm³

↑ in acute infections, trauma, some cancers

↓ in some forms of anemia or during chemotherapy

FIGURE 34-4 Hemocytometer slide. **A,** Viewed from top, without coverslip. **B,** Viewed from front, with coverslip.

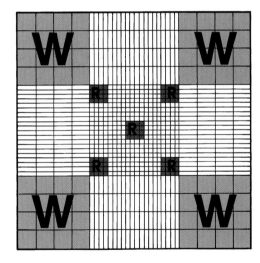

FIGURE 34-5 Detail of hemocytometer counting grid. Areas used for counting WBCs are marked W, and the areas used for counting RBCs are marked R.

FIGURE 34-6 LeukoChek test.

E. HEMATOCRIT

Blood is composed of a number of components. Plasma is the extracellular fluid matrix of blood tissue. Mostly water, it also contains ions (e.g., Na^+ and Cl^-), **plasma proteins** (e.g., *antibodies* and *albumin*), and other dissolved substances (e.g., *urea*, O_2, and glucose). The formed elements (blood cells or *blood solids*) include RBCs, WBCs, and platelets. You have already completed blood tests that look at numbers and proportions of WBCs and total numbers of RBCs. The test demonstrated in this activity explores the relative proportions of blood solids and blood plasma.

The **hematocrit** test is also called the **packed cell volume (PCV)** determination because it involves the packing of all the cells in a blood sample at one end of a tube. The sample is placed in a *centrifuge*, a machine that spins a tube of blood and allows centrifugal force to push the heavy blood cells to the bottom. Once the cells are packed, the proportion of cells to total volume can be calculated. The results are used to determine whether there is a shortage of RBCs (as in some *anemias*) or an excess of RBCs (*polycythemia*), or dehydration.

☐ 1 Fill a heparinized capillary tube about 75% full of artificial blood by touching it to the sample whole blood provided by your instructor. Heparinized tubes are red-tipped for easy identification.

☐ 2 Seal the unused end of the tube by holding it near the tip and pushing it into a tray of sealing clay at a 90-degree angle with a twisting motion. A plug of clay will then seal the tube. Remove the tube. Plastic plugs are also available for this purpose.

☐ 3 Place the tube in one of the numbered grooves of a micro-hematocrit centrifuge with the sealed end facing the perimeter of the centrifuge tray. Close the top of the centrifuge according to the manufacturer's instructions and spin the tubes for 4 minutes.

☐ 4 Remove your tube from the centrifuge and notice that the RBCs are now packed in one end of the tube. There may be a thin, lightly colored, *buffy coat* topping the RBCs. This coat is actually the WBCs, which are slightly less dense than RBCs. The rest of the tube contains the yellowish, transparent plasma.

☐ 5 Lay the tube on a paper towel next to a metric ruler and measure the total length of the sample, from the clay-RBC border to the end of the plasma. Next, measure the RBC portion only. Record your results here:

☐ _____ mm Total length
☐ _____ mm Packed cell length

☐ 6 Divide the length of the RBC section by the total sample length. Multiply your answer by 100 to arrive at the percent volume of packed RBCs. This is the hematocrit value reported with or without the percent symbol. Report your results in Lab Report 34. Use the normal values given in the Landmark Characteristics box to determine whether your results fall within the normal range.

landmark characteristics

Hematocrit: male, 40% to 54%; female, 38% to 47%
↑ in severe dehydration, shock, polycythemia
↓ in anemia, leukemia, cirrhosis, hyperthyroidism

! *safety first*

Capillary tubes are easily broken, causing injury and contamination by the blood. Have the instructor demonstrate the proper technique for sealing them before attempting it yourself. Handle capillary tubes with gloved hands. •

F. HEMOGLOBIN DETERMINATION

Hemoglobin (Hb) is the pigment inside RBCs that has an affinity for O_2 (and CO_2), so it functions to transport blood gases. Although knowing the number or proportion of RBCs in the blood may hint at the total Hb content, a *hemoglobin determination* gives a relatively accurate figure. Most methods operate on the principle that the denser the color of the sample, the higher the content of Hb pigment. Of course, the Hb has to first be liberated from the RBCs and allowed to diffuse evenly throughout the plasma. The more accurate methods use *colorimeters* or *spectrophotometers* that measure the percentage of filtered light transmitted through the sample. Some clinics use a handheld version of this type of instrument called a *hemoglobinometer*. A less accurate method, the *Tallquist method*, is used here to demonstrate Hb determination. (If you have a hemoglobinometer and wish to use it, follow the directions that follow those for the Tallquist method.)

Tallquist Method:

☐ **1** Place a drop of blood supplied by your instructor on the special paper in the Tallquist test kit. The RBCs break open in the paper.

☐ **2** Allow the drop to dry long enough to lose its glossy appearance but not long enough for it to become brown.

☐ **3** Compare the color of the blood spot to the colors in the Tallquist chart in your kit. Determine the Hb content by matching colors as closely as possible. Record your result in grams of Hb per 100 ml of blood (g/100 ml) in Lab Report 34. How does it compare with normal values?

Hemoglobinometer Method:

☐ **1** Obtain a hemoglobinometer and locate the eyepiece, sample chamber, cover plate, and clip. Also obtain some hemolysis applicators.

☐ **2** Let a drop of sample blood fall on the open sample chamber.

☐ **3** Hemolyze (break open) the blood cells in the sample chamber by agitating gently with a hemolysis applicator. When hemolysis is complete (after about 45 seconds), the blood will have changed to a clear red solution.

☐ **4** Clip the cover on the sample chamber and slide the whole assembly into the slot on the side of the hemoglobinometer.

☐ **5** Press the illuminating button on the bottom of the hemoglobinometer as you look into the eyepiece. Move the sliding knob on the side of the hemoglobinometer until both sides of the split green field match in intensity.

☐ **6** Read the hemoglobin concentration directly from the scale and record your result in Lab Report 34.

landmark characteristics

Hb: male, 14 to 16.5 g/100 ml; female, 12 to 15 g/100 ml

↑ in polycythemia, congestive heart failure, obstructive pulmonary disease, high altitudes

↓ in anemia, hyperthyroidism, liver cirrhosis, severe hemorrhage

G. BLOOD TYPING

All cells have different proteins on the surface of their cell membranes that act as identification tags. The human immune system has cells and chemicals that can recognize proteins as *non-self* proteins. In this way, immune processes can try to destroy or inhibit proteins (and cells to which they may be attached) that are foreign to a person's body. The identifying proteins on cell surfaces are determined by heredity. If a foreign tissue is transplanted into someone's body, as in blood transfusions, the immune system will destroy new blood cells that don't have the *self* type of marker proteins.

To prevent this *tissue rejection* from happening, biologists have determined which blood cell marker proteins elicit life-threatening immune reactions. Biologists have also devised tests to determine the presence of these proteins and systems of naming them. This demonstration shows you how some of these **blood typing** tests work.

Before beginning the demonstration, you must learn some new terms. The term **antigen** refers to a molecule that elicits an immune response. In the case of blood transfusions, marker proteins on the donor's RBCs can be antigens (if they are non-self relative to the recipient). The term **antibody** refers to a type of plasma protein produced by the immune system. Antibodies react with non-self markers (antigens) and try to destroy or inhibit them. One type of antigen-antibody reaction is the **agglutination reaction,** in which antigens are "glued" together with antibodies like flies on flypaper. This clumping (agglutination) is the reaction commonly seen when incompatible blood types are transfused.

In the **ABO system** of blood typing, two blood antigens are important: the **A antigen** and the **B antigen.** People with *type A* blood have the A antigen but not the B antigen. *Type B* blood has the B antigen but not the A antigen. *Type AB* blood has both A and B antigens, whereas *type O* blood has neither A nor B antigens. To type blood in the ABO system, blood is mixed with *anti-A serum* and *anti-B serum.* Serum is plasma with the clotting factors removed. Anti-A serum contains antibodies that cause agglutination when the A antigen is present. Anti-B serum contains antibodies that react with the B antigen.

> **!** **safety first**
> Handle artificial blood serum with the same caution that you would use when handling any blood sample. •

☐ **1** Place a clean microscope slide on a paper towel and write "Anti-A" near the left side and "Anti-B" near the right side. Use a wax pencil to make two 1-cm circles on the slide, one on the right and one on the left.

☐ **2** Put a drop of artificial blood supplied from the samples provided by your instructor in each circle.

☐ **3** To the drop of blood in the left circle, add a drop of anti-A serum *without touching the dropper to the blood.* Similarly, add a drop of anti-B serum to the right blood drop. Using a

different toothpick for each circle, mix the serum and the blood.

☐ **4** Check each mixture for a clumping (agglutination) reaction, in which the mixture changes from a uniform reddish color to distinct dark clumps in a transparent medium. If a reaction occurred in the left circle (anti-A), then the A antigen is present. If no reaction occurred, then the antigen is not present. According to the ABO system, what type is the blood (i.e., A, B, AB, or O)? Check your results against **Figure 34-7**.

Another commonly used blood typing system is the **Rh system,** which deals with the **Rh antigen.** Sometimes called the *D antigen,* this blood cell marker does not elicit an immune reaction in someone who does not have it until a second exposure to the antigen because the immune system doesn't make **anti-D antibodies** until it has been exposed to the D antigen. Once exposed, however, an army of antibodies (and anti-D–producing cells) stands ready to react with the D antigen. A person with the antigen is said to be *Rh positive* and a person without the antigen is termed *Rh negative.* The Rh typing test is similar to the ABO test:

☐ **1** Draw a circle on a clean glass slide and place a drop of blood within it (as described earlier).

☐ **2** Add a drop of anti-D serum and place the slide on a slide warmer. This device warms the slide to about 45° C and tilts it back and forth. Because the Rh reaction is less severe than reactions in the ABO system, such treatment is necessary to help the reaction so that it can be easily observed. Look for fine clumping. What Rh type is the sample?

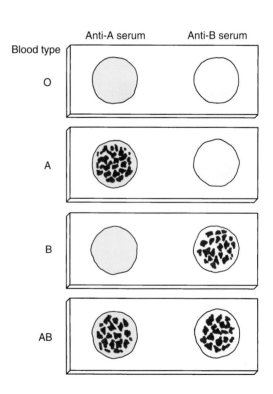

FIGURE 34-7 Possible results in the ABO test.

Name: _____ Date: _____ Section: _____

LAB REPORT 34
Blood

Specimen: *blood smear*
Total Magnification: _____

Observation: *blood smear*

Differential WBC Count Tally Grid

TYPE	MONOCYTE	LYMPHOCYTE	NEUTROPHIL	EOSINOPHIL	BASOPHIL
Tally marks					
Totals					
Percentages					
Normal value					
Interpretation					

Blood Test Results

SUBJECT:	SEX: ☐ MALE ☐ FEMALE		
TEST	NORMAL VALUE	RESULT	INTERPRETATION
WBC count			
RBC count			
Hematocrit			
Hemoglobin			
Method: _____			
ABO type			

Fill-in

1. _____
2. _____
3. _____
4. _____
5. _____
6. _____
7. _____
8. _____
9. _____
10. _____
11. _____
12. _____
13. _____
14. _____
15. _____
16. _____
17. _____
18. _____
19. _____
20. _____

Fill-in (respond with the term that completes the statement correctly)

1. A blood cell protein that elicits an immune reaction may be called a(n) _?_.

2. The _?_ scale compares the color of blood-soaked paper with a standard, allowing one to determine hemoglobin content.

3. Lab materials soiled by a blood sample should be disinfected or disposed of in a puncture-proof _?_ container.

4. _?_ stain is used to make the cells in the blood smear more easily observable.

5. Blood is often collected in _?_ capillary tubes, rather than plain capillary tubes, to prevent clotting of the blood.

6. A(n) _?_ is a machine required for the hematocrit test.

7. The PCV test determines the ratio of _?_ volume to total blood volume.

8. _?_ is an oxygen-carrying pigment in the blood.

9. A person with a high differential count of _?_ WBCs is suspected to have an acute infection.

10. A person with a high differential count of _?_ WBCs is suspected to have a chronic infection.

11. Robert's hematocrit is 53%. Is this normal?

12. Maria's hematocrit also is 53%. Is this normal?

13. On a very hot day, Hiro has been outside doing heavy work and just collapsed. If you took a blood sample right now, would you find his hematocrit to be _?_ (higher/lower) than his usual hematocrit value?

14. The hemoglobinometer is _?_ (more/less) accurate than the Tallquist method.

15. Fred has just been informed that his Rh type is negative. Is this normal?

16. Fred has AB blood. He needs a transfusion, and his wife (type AB+) is willing to donate her blood. Assuming Fred has never had any type of blood transfusion before, it is _?_ (likely/unlikely) that there will be an antigen-antibody reaction if the transfusion is done.

17. Kevin has B+ blood. His plasma is likely to contain anti-_?_ antibodies.

18. Bruce has been living in the mountains for years. The hemoglobin content of his blood is likely to have _?_ (risen/fallen) since he moved there.

19. Irma has cirrhosis of the liver. Her Hb value is likely to be _?_ (high/low).

20. Hb values are usually reported in grams of Hb per _?_ of blood.

35
Structure of the Heart

The **heart** is a four-chambered hollow organ composed primarily of cardiac muscle tissue. It contracts rhythmically, pumping blood into the **arteries**. After passing through tissues, blood returns to the heart by way of the **veins** and is pumped again. This exercise challenges you to explore the anatomy of the heart through the use of models and preserved specimens.

BEFORE YOU BEGIN

☐ Read the appropriate chapter in your textbook.
☐ Set your learning goals. When you finish this exercise, you should be able to:
  ☐ describe the structure of the heart
  ☐ locate anatomical features of the heart in models and in preserved mammalian specimens
  ☐ explain the function of major heart structures
☐ Prepare your materials:
  ☐ dissectible models of the human heart
  ☐ preserved sheep heart
  ☐ dissection tools and trays
  ☐ wooden dowels (1 cm diameter × 12 cm), pencils, or dull probes
☐ Read the directions and safety tips for this exercise *carefully* before starting any procedure.

Study TIPS

Use the following terms and develop a flowchart that illustrates the flow of blood through the heart:

Aortic arch
Aortic semilunar valve
Ascending aorta
Bicuspid valve
Descending aorta
Inferior vena cava
Left atrium
Left ventricle
Lungs
Pulmonary arteries
Pulmonary semilunar valve
Pulmonary trunk
Pulmonary veins
Right atrium
Right ventricle
Superior vena cava
Tricuspid valve

A. HUMAN HEART ANATOMY

Using dissectible models and **Figures 35-1 and 35-2**, find these features of the heart:

☐ 1 Identify these structures on the external aspect, ventral surface:
  ☐ **Interventricular sulcus**—This diagonal groove is located between the walls of the two lower heart chambers (**ventricles**). Along this groove lie the **anterior interventricular branches** of the **left coronary artery** and the **great cardiac vein.**
  ☐ **Auricles**—These are the flaplike outpouchings of the left and right **atria** (the upper heart chambers).
  ☐ **Atrioventricular sulci**—These are grooves between the walls of the atria above and the ventricles below. Locate the **small cardiac vein** and **right coronary artery** on the right and the **great cardiac vein** and its branch, the **circumflex artery,** on the left.
  ☐ **Aorta**—The largest artery of the body, it forms the **aortic arch** above the heart.
  ☐ **Pulmonary artery**—Somewhat smaller than the aorta, this vessel leaves the heart as a single **trunk** but soon branches to become the **left** and **right pulmonary arteries.**
  ☐ **Superior and inferior vena cava**—These two large veins communicate with the right atrium.
  ☐ **Apex**—The apex is the lower "point" of the heart.
☐ 2 Identify these features of the heart on the external aspect, dorsal surface:
  ☐ **Atria**—These are the upper left and right chambers. They have relatively thin walls.
  ☐ **Ventricles**—These are the lower left and right chambers. They have relatively thick walls.
  ☐ **Interventricular sulcus**—It is similar to that on the ventral surface. Locate the **middle cardiac vein** and the **posterior ventricular artery.**
  ☐ **Pulmonary veins**—These veins communicate with the atria.
☐ 3 Identify these features visible on the internal aspect:
  ☐ **Atria**—They are distinguished by their position and thin walls.
  ☐ **Ventricles**—They are thick-walled lower chambers. Note that one ventricle has thicker walls than the other. What functional adaptation does this represent?

Text continued on p. 340

Coloring Exercises: Heart

Use colored pens or pencils to shade in both the figure and the labels. Each red numeral in the figure corresponds to a matching red numeral following the appropriate label.

RIGHT ATRIUM1

LEFT ATRIUM2

RIGHT VENTRICLE3

LEFT VENTRICLE4

INTERVENTRICULAR SULCUS5

ANTERIOR INTERVENTRICULAR BRANCH (LEFT CORONARY ARTERY)6

GREAT CARDIAC VEIN7

SMALL CARDIAC VEIN8

RIGHT CORONARY ARTERY9

CIRCUMFLEX ARTERY10

LEFT CORONARY ARTERY11

AORTA12

PULMONARY ARTERY13

SUPERIOR VENA CAVA14

INFERIOR VENA CAVA15

INTERVENTRICULAR SEPTUM16

MYOCARDIUM17

EPICARDIUM18

MITRAL VALVE19

TRICUSPID VALVE20

CHORDAE TENDINEAE21

PAPILLARY MUSCLE22

AORTIC SEMILUNAR VALVE23

PULMONARY SEMILUNAR VALVE24

ANTERIOR INTERVENTRICULAR BRANCH (CARDIAC VEIN)25

FIGURE 35-1 Structures of the heart.

- ☐ **Interventricular septum**—This heart wall separates the left and right ventricles from each other.
- ☐ **Cuspid valves**—Also called **atrioventricular (AV) valves,** these valves ensure one-way flow of blood from the atria into the ventricles. The left AV valve, or **mitral (bicuspid)** valve, is composed of two cusps (flaps). The right AV valve, or **tricuspid valve,** has three cusps. Each cusp is attached to the wall of the ventricle below by means of fibrous **chordae tendineae** connected to fingerlike projections of the ventricular myocardium called **papillary muscles.**
- ☐ **Semilunar (SL) valves**—The right SL valve, or **pulmonary semilunar valve,** ensures one-way flow from the right ventricle into the pulmonary artery. The left SL valve, or **aortic semilunar valve,** is at the entrance of the aorta. SL valves are each composed of thin-walled bags that hang from the walls of the vessel.
- ☐ **Myocardium**—This is the muscular layer of the heart wall.
- ☐ **Endocardium**—The thin endothelial lining of the heart chambers, it covers the beamlike **trabeculae** on the inner face of the myocardium.
- ☐ **4** Locate these structures of the heart coverings:
  - ☐ **Serous pericardium**—The thin serous membrane that covers the outside of the heart reflects (folds) on itself to form two layers. The inner layer is the **visceral pericardium** and also serves as the outer wall of the heart or **epicardium.** The outer layer is the **parietal pericardium.** Between the two layers of the serous pericardium is the **pericardial space,** which contains lubricating **pericardial fluid.**

- ☐ **Fibrous pericardium**—The tough, fibrous outer covering of the heart and the serous pericardium, it adheres to the outer surface of the parietal pericardium and thus forms a flexible, protective pouch around the heart. The fibrous pericardium rests on the superior surface of the diaphragm.

❗ safety first

Observe the usual precautions when dissecting your specimen. Heed the safety advice accompanying the preservative used, and avoid cuts and punctures when using the dissecting tools. Use safety goggles to avoid injury during dissections. As always, dispose of your specimen as instructed. •

Study TIPS

Before you begin the dissection in Activity B of this exercise, obtain an illustration of the human heart. For reference, you can use your Lab Manual, textbook, or the *A&P Survival Guide*. To distinguish the anterior from the posterior view of the heart, use the coronary sinus as a landmark for the posterior view. As you proceed through the dissection, use your references to identify the external and internal aspects of the heart. Obtain an unlabeled diagram of the heart, or with your cell phone, photograph your specimen. After you complete the dissection, label your diagram/photo. See if you can complete this without using your references.

Coloring Exercises: Wall and Coverings of the Heart

Use colored pens or pencils to shade in both the figure and the labels. Each red numeral in the figure corresponds to a matching red numeral following the appropriate label.

Wall of the Heart

ENDOCARDIUM1
MYOCARDIUM2
EPICARDIUM3

Coverings of the Heart

SEROUS PERICARDIUM4
VISCERAL PERICARDIUM3
PERICARDIAL SPACE5
PARIETAL PERICARDIUM6
FIBROUS PERICARDIUM7
DIAPHRAGM8

FIGURE 35-2 The wall and coverings of the heart.

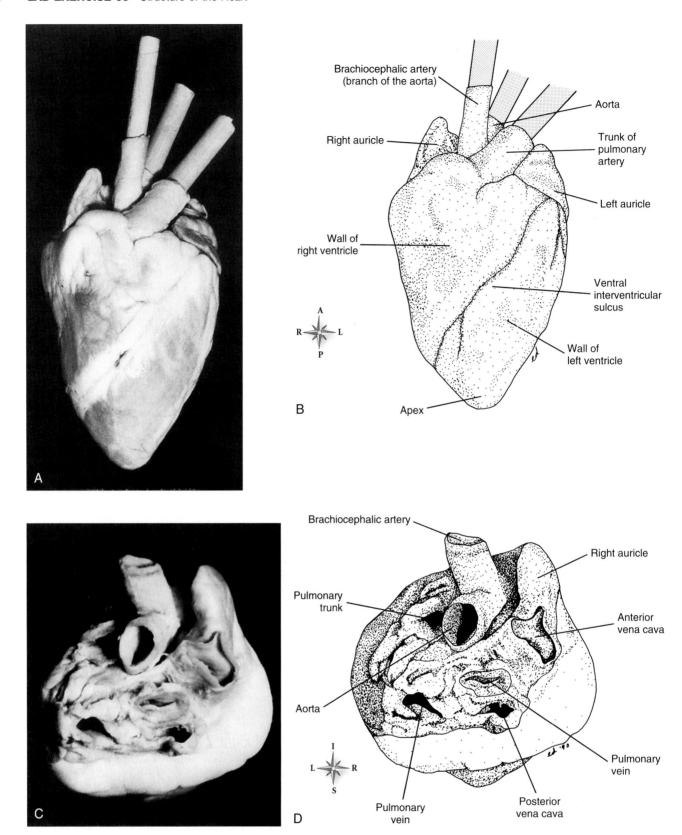

FIGURE 35-3 A and **B**, Ventral view of the sheep heart. **C** and **D**, Anterior view of the sheep heart, analogous to a superior view of the human heart.

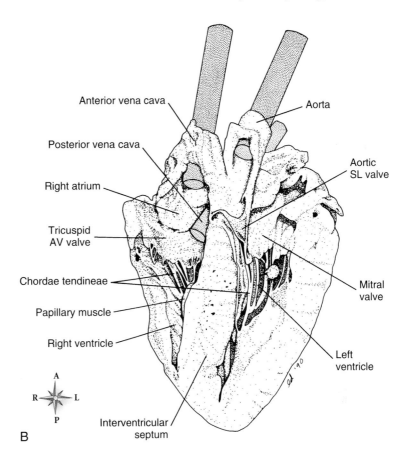

Anterior vena cava

Posterior vena cava

Right atrium

Tricuspid
AV valve

Chordae tendineae

Papillary muscle

Right ventricle

Aorta

Aortic
SL valve

Mitral
valve

Left
ventricle

Interventricular
septum

A
R ✳ L
P

A

B

FIGURE 35-4 **A** and **B**, Ventral view of the frontal section of a sheep heart.

B. SHEEP HEART DISSECTION

The sheep heart is very similar in structure to the human heart. It is nearly the same size, so it makes an ideal study specimen.

☐ 1 Orient yourself to the specimen. Using the photos as a guide, locate the dorsal and ventral surfaces. The shape of your specimen may have become distorted in shipping, so don't rely on shape as a guide. Recall that directions for the sheep heart are based on the fact that the sheep is a four-legged animal, so its heart is oriented differently than in the human.

☐ 2 Identify the structures of the external aspect of the sheep heart as you did for the human heart. Some adipose tissue may have to be removed so that you can see all the structures clearly. You may not be able to locate all the *coronary vessels* because they are buried under fat. Many of the large heart vessels may have been cut very closely to the heart wall, so they appear as holes or short stubs. Use a wooden dowel or pencil to open the vessels for better viewing **(Figure 35-3, A)**. Some identifications of external structures will be tentative until you open the heart and verify your observations.

☐ 3 Use a long knife or your scalpel and scissors to cut a frontal section in your specimen **(Figure 35-4)**. Try to identify the internal heart features as you did with the human heart model.

Name: _____ Date: _____ Section: _____

LAB REPORT 35
Structure of the Heart

Use this table as a checklist for your study of the heart. Do not forget to fill in the function column.

STRUCTURE	SHEEP	HUMAN	FUNCTION(S)
Right atrium	☐	☐	
Left atrium	☐	☐	
Right ventricle	☐	☐	
Left ventricle	☐	☐	
Interventricular sulcus	☐	☐	
Anterior interventricular branch of left coronary artery	☐	☐	
Anterior interventricular branch of great cardiac vein	☐	☐	
Great cardiac vein	☐	☐	
Small cardiac vein	☐	☐	
Right coronary artery	☐	☐	
Circumflex artery	☐	☐	
Left coronary artery	☐	☐	
Aorta	☐	☐	
Pulmonary artery	☐	☐	
Superior vena cava	☐	☐	
Inferior vena cava	☐	☐	
Interventricular septum	☐	☐	
Myocardium	☐	☐	
Epicardium	☐	☐	
Parietal pericardium	☐	☐	
Pericardial space	☐	☐	
Fibrous pericardium	☐	☐	
Mitral valve	☐	☐	
Tricuspid valve	☐	☐	
Chordae tendineae	☐	☐	
Papillary muscle	☐	☐	
Aortic semilunar valve	☐	☐	
Pulmonary semilunar valve	☐	☐	

Put in Order

1. _____
2. _____
3. _____
4. _____
5. _____
6. _____
7. _____
8. _____
9. _____
10. _____
11. _____
12. _____

Fill-in

1. _____
2. _____
3. _____
4. _____
5. _____
6. _____
7. _____
8. _____
9. _____
10. _____
11. _____
12. _____
13. _____
14. _____
15. _____

Put in Order (rearrange these structures in the order in which blood passes through them; assume that the blood is about to leave the right atrium)

aorta
aortic semilunar valve
left ventricle
left atrium
lungs
mitral valve
pulmonary semilunar valve
pulmonary artery
right ventricle
superior/inferior vena cava
tissues of the body
tricuspid valve

Fill-in (complete each statement with the correct term)

1. The flaplike lateral wall of each atrium is called the _?_.

2. The _?_ valve is also known as the mitral valve or left AV valve.

3. The right AV valve is also known as the _?_ valve.

4. The aortic semilunar valve has _?_ pocketlike flaps of tissue.

5. The _?_ are fibrous structures that prevent the cuspid valves from prolapsing (bending backward).

6. One-way flow of blood from the right ventricle is ensured by the presence of the _?_ valve.

7. Mitral valve prolapse, which is abnormal, may allow blood to enter the _?_ during contraction of the left ventricle.

8. The small cardiac vein and right coronary artery can be found along the right _?_ sulcus.

9. The anterior interventricular branches of the left coronary artery and cardiac vein are found along the anterior _?_ sulcus.

10. The _?_ is a muscular wall between the left and right ventricles.

11. The myocardium of the _?_ ventricle is thicker than the other ventricle.

12. The wall of the aorta is _?_ (thicker/thinner) than the wall of the superior vena cava.

13. The _?_ are beamlike processes of the inner face of the myocardium.

14. The "point" of the heart is called the _?_.

15. In the sheep heart, the right atrium is _?_ to the right ventricle.

Electrical Activity of the Heart

In the previous exercise, you learned some of the major anatomical features of the heart. This exercise challenges you to take a step beyond the basics and learn about the electrical nature of the heart. As part of your study, you will demonstrate one of the most commonly used clinical tools for assessing the health of the heart: electrocardiography.

This exercise calls for any of several electrocardiographs commonly available in educational laboratories (Activities A and B). A computer-based approach is presented as an alternate method in Activities C and D.

BEFORE YOU BEGIN

☐ Read the appropriate chapter in your textbook.
☐ Set your learning goals. When you finish this exercise, you should be able to:
  ☐ describe the conduction system of the heart
  ☐ demonstrate electrocardiography
  ☐ identify the features of a typical electrocardiogram (ECG) and explain their significance
☐ Prepare your materials:
  ☐ electrocardiograph apparatus or computerized ECG program
  ☐ alcohol swabs
  ☐ electrocardiographic electrodes, electrode tape, and gel
  ☐ table or cot
  ☐ metric (mm) ruler
☐ Read the directions and safety tips for this exercise *carefully* before starting any procedure.

> ## ❗ safety first
> The apparatus used in this exercise is powered by electricity, so appropriate cautions should be taken to avoid electrical hazards. Students with known heart problems may volunteer as subjects in the study of resting ECGs but should not participate in activities involving exercise or other stressful situations. •

Study TIPS

Reading and interpreting an ECG requires a lot of practice and expertise. However, there are two variations from a normal ECG that may indicate an abnormality: variation in wave height (elevated or depressed) or variation in normal time intervals between waves. Refer to the Cardiac Dysrhythmia section in this lab exercise. Your textbook also provides examples of ECG strip recordings.

A. ELECTROCARDIOGRAPHY

The **cardiac cycle** is the pattern of physiological events exhibited during each beat of the heart. One approach is to describe the cardiac cycle as atrial, then ventricular, **systole** (contraction), and **diastole** (relaxation). In other words, the atria contract and relax, and the ventricles contract and relax, producing one pumping cycle of the heart. During the cardiac cycle, a variety of physiological characteristics of the heart and pumped blood change in a way that is measurable. For example, the **blood pressure** within each chamber changes with the volume of the chamber and the strength of contraction of the myocardium. Certain **heart sounds** are heard as the valves snap shut and portions of the myocardium contract. The electrical properties of the heart change as action potentials travel through the myocardium. This electrical aspect of the cardiac cycle is of interest in this activity.

As you know, all muscle requires *excitation* of the cell membrane coupled with contraction involving filaments within the cell. This excitation, taking the form of action potentials, is an electrical event in which the polarity of electrical potential across the cell membranes changes. Because so much myocardial tissue depolarizes at more or less the same time, a great deal of current flows around the heart tissue, and the depolarization is easily detected from the outside of the body. Around the beginning of the twentieth century, a Dutch scientist named Einthoven was one of the first to use a recording voltmeter to measure this electrical activity of the heart and to describe the changes found in a typical cardiac cycle. This technique is called **electrocardiography.**

The **ECG** is a waveform graph produced by a recording voltmeter called an **electrocardiograph.** The graph is a line on a paper or monitor that rises and falls with changes in voltage (electric potential) between two points. **Figure 36-1, A**, shows the voltage changes seen in one typical cardiac cycle. For convenience, each wave is given a name:

☐ **P wave**—This wave represents depolarization of the atrial walls, which precedes atrial systole.
☐ **QRS complex**—This set of waves results from the more or less concurrent ventricular depolarization (preceding ventricular systole) and atrial repolarization (signaling the onset of atrial diastole).
☐ **T wave**—This wave represents ventricular repolarization, which precedes ventricular diastole.

The length of time during waves and between waves indicates the efficiency of conduction through the myocardium. Lengthened ECG portions are often evidence of blocked conduction. To understand the significance of conduction blockage, we must first outline the structure and function of the conduction system:

☐ **Sinoatrial (SA) node**—This specialized section of cardiac muscle in the upper lateral wall of the right atrium generates its own action potentials at a faster rate than surrounding muscle, so it acts as a **pacemaker** for the rest of the heart (Figure 36-1, *B*).

☐ **Atrioventricular (AV) node**—A pacemaker in the lower right atrium subordinate to the SA node, it normally generates action potentials in response to potentials that travel to it through the atrial walls from the SA node.

☐ **AV bundle (of His)**—This bundle of cardiac muscles in the interventricular septum is specialized to conduct action potentials rapidly. The AV bundle branches spread out as **subendocardial fibers (Purkinje fibers)** through the lateral ventricular walls.

Action potentials generated by the SA node travel across the atrial myocardium, triggering atrial systole. The AV node then picks up the signal and generates action potentials that travel rapidly through the AV bundle and its branches to stimulate the ventricular myocardium, resulting in ventricular systole.

The **PR interval** (sometimes termed the PQ interval) is the time required for a signal to pass from the SA node, through the atrial myocardium (depolarizing it), to the AV node, and through its branches. The **QT interval** represents the time needed for complete depolarization and recovery of the ventricular myocardium.

Einthoven proposed three basic arrangements, or **leads,** of the ECG electrodes. Each lead is a set of one positive voltmeter electrode and one negative voltmeter electrode. These standard leads, or appendicular leads, are:

☐ Lead I—One electrode on the left arm, one on the right arm
☐ Lead II—One electrode on the right arm, one on the left leg
☐ Lead III—One electrode on the left arm, one on the left leg

The electrode positions are shown in **Figure 36-2**.

The appendicular leads form what is called *Einthoven's triangle*, diagrammed in **Figure 36-3**. In the diagram, the heart is shown at the peak of the R wave, when the ventricles are partly depolarized. As you can see, an electric current flows from the positive area of the undepolarized region to the negative depolarized region. This difference in charge is detected by the ECG and graphed as the R wave. Because the direction of current flow is close to the angle of lead II, the R wave of lead II is larger than in lead III and lead I.

Demonstrate the resting ECG:

☐ 1 Set up an electrocardiograph apparatus as directed by the instructions that accompany it. Set PAPER SPEED or TRACE VELOCITY to 25 mm/sec (2.5 cm/sec), the standard rate for ECG recording. Calibrate the SENSITIVITY or GAIN to 1 cm = 1 mV (see the instructions for your machine).

☐ 2 Have the (rested) subject lie on a cot or table or sit comfortably in a chair. Expose both ankles and wrists and clean a small area on each with alcohol pads. Put a small drop of electrode gel on each ECG electrode and place each on a different limb. Rub each electrode around gently to evenly distribute the gel. Complete attaching the limb wires to the appropriate electrode by snapping the cap from the end of the wire over the "button" on the pad. (see Figure 36-2)
　　☐ LA to the left arm electrode
　　☐ RA to the right arm electrode
　　☐ LL to the left leg electrode
　　☐ RL to the right leg (for grounding the system)

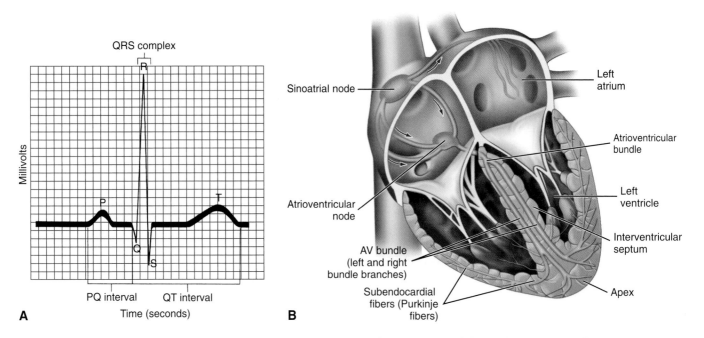

FIGURE 36-1 **A,** An idealized ECG pattern for one cardiac cycle. **B,** Anatomy of the conduction system of the heart.

FIGURE 36-2 Placement of ECG electrodes for the three standard (appendicular) leads.

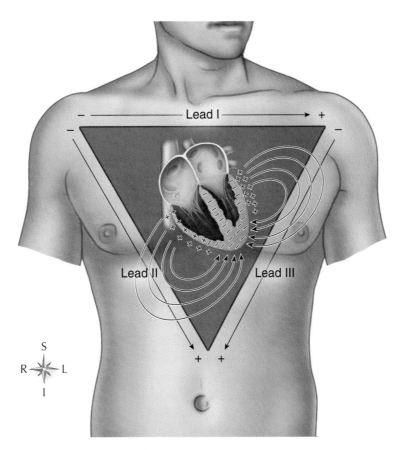

FIGURE 36-3 Einthoven's triangle.

□ **3** Record lead I for about 20 cardiac cycles, and then do likewise for leads II and III. Be sure to mark the part of the strip chart where you switched leads. If possible, record an ECG of every student in your group.

□ **4** Using your lead II results, label a P wave, QRS complex, and T wave. If the P wave is absent and the heart rate is low, **SA node block** may be indicated. This could result from ischemia (reduced myocardial circulation) or infarction (myocardial damage).

□ **5** Using lead II results, measure these values:

□ Heart rate (in beats per minute)—Remember that the paper rate is 25 mm/sec (each mm = 0.04 seconds). **Tachycardia** is the condition of a heart rate greater than 100 beats/min and may be caused by excitement (stress), high body temperature, or toxicity **(see Figure 36-5, D)**. **Bradycardia** is the condition of lowered heart rate (less than 60 beats/min). It is normal in conditioned athletes because they have a high stroke volume, or it may result from excessive vagal stimulation (see Figure 36-5, C).

□ PR (PQ) interval—If greater than 0.2 seconds, a **first-degree heart block** could be present (see Figure 36-5, B). This may result from inflammation of the AV bundle, which slows down conduction of a signal to the ventricles. If the PR interval is 0.25 to 0.45 seconds (and some P waves are not followed by QRS complexes), **second-degree heart block** may be present. This could result from AV node damage or excessive vagal stimulation. If the P wave seems independent of the QRS complex, with a P rate of about 100 per minute and a QRS of less than 40 per minute, **complete heart block** may be present.

□ Your instructor may ask you to make other measurements and consult your textbook or a reference book for guidance in interpreting your results.

B. THE AUGMENTED LEADS

Many computerized ECG programs are designed to print out results of the standard (appendicular) leads, as well as three **augmented leads.** You may recall that Einthoven's triangle diagrammatically represents the direction of electric potential measurements using the three standard electrode arrangements (leads I, II, and III; **Figure 36-4, A**). Einthoven described a number of mathematical relationships among data produced by the three leads. For example, knowing data from any two leads is sufficient to mathematically reconstruct a data line for the third lead. Information from combinations of two leads can be manipulated to produce the three augmented, or attenuated, leads. These are not bipolar leads or electrode placements but are the result of combining two negative electrodes and measuring them against one positive electrode. Thus, three more leads are produced:

□ aV$_R$—The LA and LL are combined to form the negative electrode; RA is the positive electrode.

□ aV$_L$—The RA and LL electrodes form the negative electrode; LA is the positive electrode.

□ aV$_F$—The RA and LA electrodes form the negative pole; LL is the positive pole.

Using Einthoven's triangle concept, the augmented leads are each shifted 90 degrees from the standard leads (Figure 36-5, B).

Current clinical practice calls for recording 12 leads in all. So far, we have discussed the three standard leads and the three augmented leads. The remaining six leads are the **chest,** or **precordial,** leads. The chest leads use RA, LA, and LL combined to form the negative pole and each of six chest electrodes to form the positive poles. The chest leads are named V$_1$ through V$_6$.

What is the advantage of chest leads?

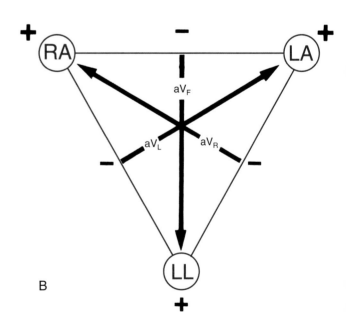

FIGURE 36-4 A, Einthoven's triangle. **B,** Einthoven's triangle superimposed with the three augmented leads.

C. DEVIATIONS FROM THE NORMAL ECG

A variety of factors may result in ECG readings far different from those expected. For example, the conditions just described may produce variations in the resting heart rate. In this activity, you are challenged to demonstrate some factors that alter the standard ECG pattern.

☐ 1 Set up the ECG demonstration as described in Activity A. Set the device to record lead II.

☐ 2 Once a normal ECG pattern is observed, have the subject breathe in and out deeply several times. What happens? What consequences might this have in a clinical setting?

☐ 3 Have the subject tense the muscles of the upper arm. What happens? What do you think causes this result? What implications does this observation have in clinical ECG applications?

☐ 4 Remove the ECG cables, leaving the electrodes in place. Have the subject exercise for 2 to 5 minutes, and then quickly reconnect the ECG cables. With the subject again in resting position, record 15 or 20 cardiac cycles. Continue to sample 15 to 20 cycles every minute for the next 10 minutes. Record the heart rate for each sample. How do you explain your results? Does exercise alter the features of each ECG cycle? Why or why not?

☐ 5 What other factors might alter the ECG of the subject? As a group, discuss your hypotheses and, under the supervision of your instructor, perform experiments to test them (as time permits). Write a report of your experiment(s) and attach it to Lab Report 36. Be sure to include a statement of your hypothesis, an outline of your experimental design (methods), your results, and your interpretation of the results.

safety first
Observe the safety precautions given earlier in this exercise and in the computerized system manual. •

D. COMPUTERIZED ELECTROCARDIOGRAPHY

Many computer-based ECG systems are available for student use. If your lab has a computerized ECG setup, set it up according to the manual that accompanies it or the instruction screen on the computer. You may also follow the steps given in Activities A and B. In any case, collect the information asked for in the Lab Report and attach printouts of your ECG data/graphs to the Lab Report.

Most computerized ECG systems allow you to measure ECG intervals on screen automatically or with very little trouble. You may usually also save your ECG data and analyze it at a later time.

clinical applications: cardiac dysrhythmia

The normal rhythmical beating of the heart (Figure 36-4, A) can be disturbed by conditions (e.g., inflammation of the endocardium [*endocarditis*] or myocardial infarction [*heart attack*]) that damage the heart's conduction system. The term **dysrhythmia** refers to an abnormality of heart rhythm.

One kind of dysrhythmia is called a **heart block.** In *AV node block*, impulses are blocked from getting through to the ventricular myocardium, resulting in the ventricles contracting at a much slower rate than normal. On an ECG, there may be a large interval between the P wave and the R peak of the QRS complex (Figure 36-4, B). *Complete heart block* occurs when the P waves do not match up at all with the QRS complexes—as in an ECG that shows two or more P waves for every QRS complex. A physician may treat heart block by implanting an *artificial pacemaker* in the heart.

Bradycardia is a slow heart rhythm—less than 50 beats/min (Figure 36-4, C). Slight bradycardia is normal during sleep and in conditioned athletes while they are awake (but at rest). Abnormal bradycardia can result from improper autonomic nervous control of the heart or from a damaged SA node. If the problem is severe, artificial pacemakers can be used to increase the heart rate by taking the place of the SA node.

Tachycardia is a very rapid heart rhythm—more than 100 beats/min (Figure 36-4, D). Tachycardia is normal during and after exercise and during the stress response. Abnormal tachycardia can result from improper autonomic control of the heart, blood loss or shock, the action of drugs and toxins, fever, and other factors.

Sinus dysrhythmia is a variation in heart rate during the breathing cycle. Typically, the rate increases during inspiration and decreases during expiration. The causes of sinus dysrhythmia are not clear. This phenomenon is common in young people and usually does not require treatment.

FIGURE 36-5 A, Normal ECG strip chart recording. B, AV node block. Very slow ventricular contraction (25-45 beats/min at rest); P waves widely separated from peaks of QRS complexes. C, Bradycardia. Slow heart rhythm (less than 60 beats/min); no disruption of normal rhythm pattern.

clinical applications: cardiac dysrhythmia—cont'd

Premature contractions, or *extrasystoles,* are contractions that occur before the next expected contraction in a series of cardiac cycles. For example, *premature atrial contractions (PACs)* may occur shortly after the ventricles contract—seen as early P waves on the ECG (Figure 36-4, *E*). Premature atrial contractions often occur with lack of sleep, too much caffeine or nicotine, alcoholism, or heart damage. Ventricular depolarizations that appear earlier than expected are called *premature ventricular contractions (PVCs).* PVCs appear on the ECG as early, wide QRS complexes without a preceding related P wave. PVCs are caused by a variety of circumstances that include stress, electrolyte imbalance, acidosis, hypoxemia, ventricular enlargement, or drug reactions. Occasional PVCs are not clinically significant in otherwise healthy individuals. However, in people with heart disease, they may reduce cardiac output.

Frequent premature contractions can lead to **fibrillation,** a condition in which cardiac muscle fibers contract out of step with each other. This event can be seen in an ECG as the absence of regular P waves or abnormal QRS and T waves (Figure 36-4, *F*). In fibrillation, the affected heart chambers do not effectively pump blood. *Atrial fibrillation* occurs commonly in mitral stenosis, rheumatic heart disease, and infarction of the atrial myocardium. This condition can be treated with drugs such as digoxin (a *digitalis* preparation) or by *defibrillation* (application of electrical shock to force cardiac muscle fibers to contract in unison). *Ventricular fibrillation* is an immediately life-threatening condition in which the lack of ventricular pumping suddenly stops the flow of blood to vital tissues (Figure 36-4, *G*). Unless ventricular fibrillation is corrected immediately by defibrillation or some other method, death may occur within minutes.

FIGURE 36-5, cont'd *D,* Tachycardia. Rapid heart rhythm (greater than 100 beats/min); no disruption of normal rhythm pattern (NSR, normal sinus rhythm; PAT, paroxysmal [sudden] atrial tachycardia). *E,* Premature atrial contraction (PAC). Unexpected, early P wave that is different from normal P waves; PR interval may be shorter or longer than normal; normal QRS complex; more than 6 PACs per minute may precede atrial fibrillation. *F,* Atrial fibrillation. Irregular, rapid atrial depolarizations; P wave rapid (greater than 300/min) with irregular QRS complexes (150-170 beats/min). *G,* Ventricular fibrillation. Complete disruption of normal heart rhythm.

Name: _____ Date: _____ Section: _____

LAB REPORT 36
Electrical Activity of the Heart

Attach reports of any additional ECG experiments that you did.

TEST CONDITION	HEART RATE	PR (PQ) INTERVAL	OTHER OBSERVATIONS	INTERPRETATION
Resting				
Deep breathing				
Arm tensed				
Postexercise:				
0 min				
1 min				
2 min				
3 min				
4 min				
5 min				
6 min				
7 min				
8 min				
9 min				
10 min				

Use this grid to graph the heart rates observed after exercise. Be sure to label your graph completely and accurately.

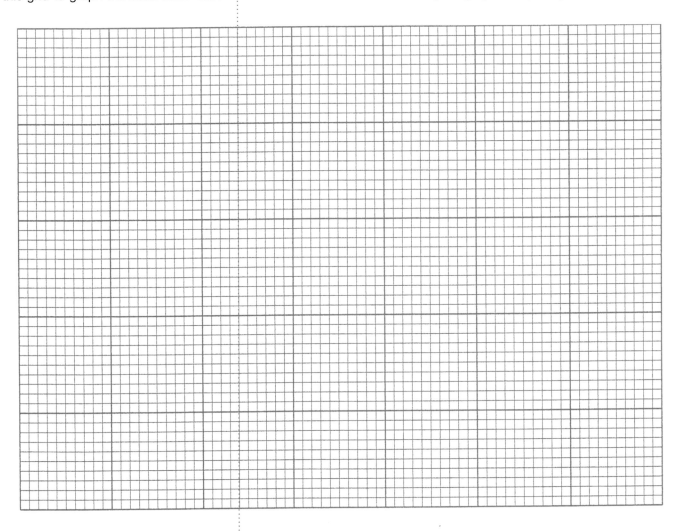

Put in Order

1. _____
2. _____
3. _____
4. _____
5. _____
6. _____
7. _____

Fill-in

1. _____
2. _____
3. _____
4. _____
5. _____

Put in Order (rearrange these heart structures in the order through which electrical signals are conducted in a single cardiac cycle)

atrial myocardium
AV bundle branches
AV bundle
AV node
Subendocardial (Purkinje) fibers
SA node
ventricular myocardium

Fill-in (complete each statement with the correct term)

1. Relaxation of a heart chamber is called _?_.

2. Contraction of a heart chamber is called _?_.

3. The portion of the ECG that represents ventricular repolarization is the _?_.

4. Leads I, II, and III together are called the _?_ leads, or appendicular leads.

5. _?_ is the condition of elevated heart rate.

LAB EXERCISE 37

The Pulse and Blood Pressure

The heart pushes blood from the left ventricle into the aorta with great force, as you already know. The wall of the aorta and its branches stretch a little with the sudden burst of blood during each ventricular ejection. Burst after burst after burst of blood ejected from the heart produce bulge after bulge after bulge in the arterial wall. These **pressure waves,** known as *pulse waves* or simply as the **pulse,** occur at more or less the same rhythm as the cardiac cycle. The pulse waves can be detected in clinical situations and are used to determine many things about cardiovascular function. The rhythm and strength of the pulse in distal arteries can indicate something about how efficiently blood is being pumped into the circulation. The pressure of the waves can be measured indirectly and used to give information about overall arterial **blood pressure.** This exercise challenges you to find and measure some characteristics of blood pressure waves and use that skill to find some factors that affect cardiovascular function.

BEFORE YOU BEGIN

☐ Read the appropriate chapter in your textbook.
☐ Set your learning goals. When you finish this exercise, you should be able to:
  ☐ explain the concept of the pressure wave, or pulse
  ☐ demonstrate detection of the pulse in a human subject
  ☐ use a sphygmomanometer to measure blood pressure
  ☐ list some factors that affect pulse and blood pressure
☐ Prepare your materials:
  ☐ sphygmomanometer
  ☐ stethoscope
  ☐ alcohol swabs
  ☐ watch or timer
☐ Read the directions and safety tips for this exercise *carefully* before starting any procedure.

Study TIPS

Review the various arteries that are positioned for pulse detection. For reference, use your lab manual or textbook. Which of these pulse points would provide a stronger pulse? A weaker pulse? Why would there be a difference in the strength of the pulse throughout the body?

A. THE PULSE

As blood is ejected from the left ventricle during each cardiac cycle, it is subjected to great pressure. Because fluids are unable to be compressed, this great pressure pushes the compliant walls of the arteries outward. Between ejections, the blood pressure is lower and the arterial walls bounce back to their original diameter. Because this occurs with each cardiac cycle, multiple waves of high pressure move into the arteries. These **pressure waves** are also called the **pulse.**

The rate and strength of the pulse can be measured easily with no special equipment. By simply pressing on the skin and pushing an artery against bone, one can feel the pressure waves. Counting the number of waves per minute gives the *pulse rate,* and the pulse strength (pressure) can be assessed by receptors in your fingertips.

Determine the pulse rate of a resting subject by placing your second and third fingers on the anterior surface of the wrist, over the point where the *radial artery* passes over the distal end of the radius. Do not use your thumb, or you may feel your own pulse waves. Using a watch, count the number of waves in 15 seconds. Multiply your result by 4 to determine the pulse rate in waves per minute. Try one or more of the other pulse points identified in **Figure 37-1**. Are the pulse waves of equal pressure at each pulse point? Why or why not?

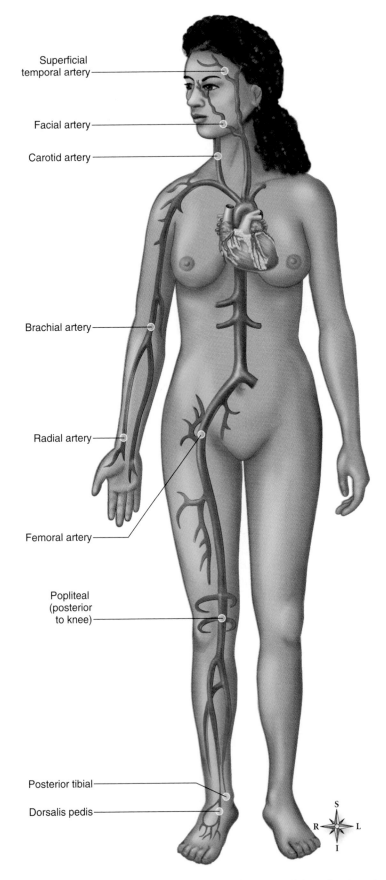

FIGURE 37-1 Locations of arteries that are well positioned for pulse detection.

Study TIPS

To help you understand blood pressure, think of the water pressure within a garden hose. Blood pressure is a type of hydrostatic pressure. The water pressure within a garden hose results from the force of water against the inside of the hose. Blood exerts similar pressure against the walls of the blood vessels.

B. BLOOD PRESSURE

Biologists often measure the pressure of body fluids in units called **millimeters of mercury (mm Hg).** This unit is based on a measuring device called a *manometer*, which is an inverted tube of liquid mercury. As something presses against the mercury reservoir at the bottom of the tube, the column of mercury in the tube rises higher. The more pressure pushing on the mercury, the higher the column rises. Thus, the millimeters the mercury rises (mm Hg) indicate the level of the pressure. A **sphygmomanometer** is a manometer with an air cuff attached to the reservoir; it is used to indirectly measure the changing blood pressures associated with the pulse. Many sphygmomanometers do not use mercury but are still calibrated to the "millimeters of mercury" scale.

> ## ❗ *safety first*
> Exposure to mercury can be extremely hazardous. If you are using a mercury-filled device, take great care not to damage it or permit leakage of mercury. If a mercury leak or spill does occur, *do not attempt to clean it yourself.* Notify the lab supervisor if you spill or come into direct contact with mercury. •

☐ 1 To measure the blood pressure of a resting subject, first clean the earpieces of a stethoscope with an alcohol swab and place them in your ears. Then wrap the sphygmomanometer air cuff around the subject's left upper arm, just above the elbow.

☐ 2 Place the stethoscope sensor in the position shown in **Figure 37-2, *B***, and listen to the pulse in the *brachial artery*. Close the valve of the sphygmomanometer's air bulb and pump the cuff to a pressure of about 175 mm Hg or so.

☐ 3 Still listening to the artery and watching the mercury column, open the valve slightly and slowly release air. As you decrease the pressure, you will suddenly notice loud, tapping **Korotkoff sounds** in the artery. Note the pressure at which they begin. Continue to decrease pressure until the Korotkoff sounds disappear, also noting that point on the pressure scale. The point at which the sounds are first heard is the **systolic pressure,** the pressure of the pulse wave's crest (Figure 37-2, A). The sounds disappear when the **diastolic pressure,** the blood pressure between pulse waves, is reached. Blood pressure is usually expressed as systolic pressure over diastolic pressure. The example given in Figure 37-2 is about "120 over 80," or 120 mm Hg/80 mm Hg. Normal ranges of resting blood pressure are shown in **Figure 37-3.**

C. VARIATIONS IN PULSE AND PRESSURE

Determine the pulse rate and blood pressure in the situations described. Compare the results to each other and to the results for a resting subject. How do you account for the variations?

☐ 1 Test a variety of body positions: lying down (immediately, then after 5 minutes) and standing (immediately, then after 5 minutes).

☐ 2 Test a subject after exercise (immediately after 2-5 minutes of exercise, then once per minute for the next 10 minutes of recovery). Compare your results with those for the postexercise electrocardiogram (Lab Exercise 36).

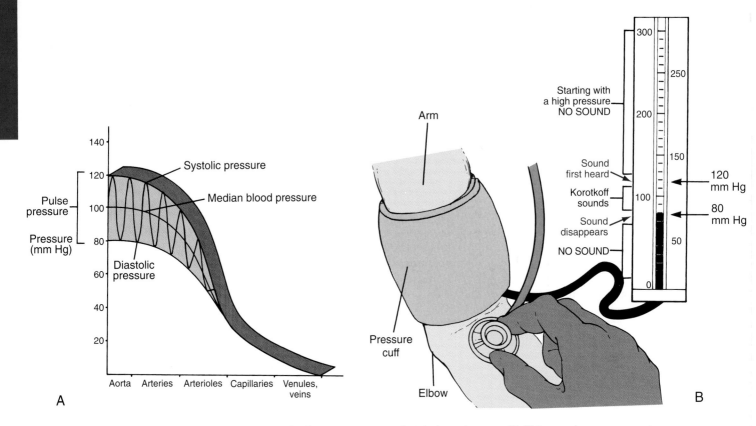

FIGURE 37-2 **A,** The changing blood pressures associated with the pulse wave. **B,** Using a sphygmomanometer.

Blood Pressure (BP) Classification

Classification	Systolic BP		Diastolic BP
Normal	<120	and	<80
Prehypertension	120-139	or	80-89
High BP			
Stage 1 hypertension	140-159	or	90-99
Stage 2 hypertension	≥160	or	≥100

FIGURE 37-3 Blood pressure ranges. This classification scheme is adapted from the National High Blood Pressure Education Program.

Name: _____ Date: _____ Section: _____

LAB REPORT 37
The Pulse and Blood Pressure

TEST CONDITION	PULSE RATE	PULSE STRENGTH	SYSTOLIC BLOOD PRESSURE	DIASTOLIC BLOOD PRESSURE	PULSE PRESSURE (SYSTOLIC MINUS DIASTOLIC)
Resting: *radial*					
Resting: _____					
Resting: _____					
Lying down:					
0 min					
5 min					
Standing:					
0 min					
5 min					
After exercise:					
0 min					
1 min					
2 min					
3 min					
4 min					
5 min					
6 min					
7 min					
8 min					
9 min					
10 min					

The next page is marked *Interpretation.* In the space provided, write your interpretation of the results reported in the preceding table. For example, tell why the strength of the resting pulse rate may have varied depending on where it was detected. Look for similarities and differences from row to row (how does pulse rate in different body positions compare?). Look for relationships from column to column (does pulse strength relate to pulse pressure?). Use the questions given in the exercise itself for further guidance.

Interpretation:

_____

_____

_____

_____

_____

_____

_____

_____

_____

_____

_____

_____

_____

_____

_____

_____

_____

_____

_____

_____

_____

_____

_____

_____

_____

_____

_____

_____

_____

_____

_____

_____

38
The Circulatory Pathway

Blood pumped from the right ventricle of the heart travels to and through the lungs before returning to the left atrium. This pathway is termed the **pulmonary circulation,** or the *pulmonary loop.* Blood pumped from the left ventricle travels to and through the other organs and tissues of the body. This pathway is termed the **systemic circulation** (*systemic loop*). These two pathways together with the heart form the basic structure of the cardiovascular system. In this exercise you are challenged to learn some of the major blood vessels that form the circulatory pathways of the human body.

BEFORE YOU BEGIN

☐ Read the appropriate chapter in your textbook.
☐ Set your learning goals. When you finish this exercise, you should be able to:
   ☐ locate major veins and arteries in models and charts
   ☐ describe the circulatory pathways to and from major body regions

   ☐ describe the fetal circulatory plan and the changes in circulation that occur around the time of birth
☐ Prepare your materials:
   ☐ model of the human body (showing major vessels)
   ☐ charts of human circulatory routes (including fetal circulation)
☐ Read the directions and safety tips for this exercise *carefully* before starting any procedure.

Study TIPS

Develop a schematic chart of the major arterial branches. Use the arteries that are mentioned in this lab activity. For reference, use your textbook or the *A&P Survival Guide*.

A. ARTERIES

Arteries are blood vessels that conduct blood away from the heart and toward tissues **(Figure 38-1)**. In the pulmonary circulation, **pulmonary arteries** conduct deoxygenated blood to the lungs. In the systemic circulation, the aorta and its branches conduct oxygenated blood toward the systemic tissues. Small arteries are usually called **arterioles**. Arterioles conduct blood into a network of even smaller vessels, or **capillaries**. On a chart, and then in a model of the human body, locate the major human arteries listed. As you do so, note how they form routes to major regions of the body.

☐ 1 Find these portions of the aorta:
   ☐ **Ascending aorta**—First portion, before the aorta bends inferiorly
   ☐ **Aortic arch**—Bend of the aorta, just superior to the heart
   ☐ **Descending aorta**—The remainder of the aorta
   ☐ **Thoracic aorta**—Portion of the descending aorta that is within the thorax
   ☐ **Abdominal aorta**—Portion of the descending aorta that is within the abdomen

☐ 2 Locate these arteries of the head and neck:
   ☐ **Brachiocephalic**—First branch from the aorta
   ☐ **Right common carotid**—Medial branch of the brachiocephalic artery
   ☐ **Right subclavian**—Lateral branch of the brachiocephalic artery
   ☐ **Left common carotid, left subclavian**—Second and third branches, respectively, of the aorta
   ☐ **Internal carotid, external carotid**—Branches of the common carotid arteries
   ☐ **Vertebral**—Branches of the subclavians
   ☐ **Basilar**—Artery formed by the fusion of vertebral arteries
   ☐ **Cerebral Arterial Circle (of Willis)**—Circular system of arteries around the brain's base, formed by branches of the basilar artery and the internal carotids

☐ 3 Identify these arteries of the upper limb:
   ☐ **Axillary artery**—Continuation of the subclavian artery inferior to the clavicle
   ☐ **Brachial**—Continuation of the axillary artery in the upper arm
   ☐ **Ulnar**—Medial branch of the brachial artery
   ☐ **Radial**—Lateral branch of the brachial artery

☐ 4 Identify these branches of the descending aorta:
   ☐ **Intercostal**—Branches from the aorta to the intercostal muscles
   ☐ **Phrenic**—Branches from the aorta to the diaphragm
   ☐ **Celiac**—Branch of the aorta to the stomach, pancreas, and liver
   ☐ **Superior mesenteric**—Branch of the aorta to the small intestine and proximal large intestine
   ☐ **Inferior mesenteric**—Branch of the aorta to the distal regions of the large intestine
   ☐ **Renal**—Branches from the aorta to the kidneys
   ☐ **Suprarenal**—Branches from the aorta to the adrenal glands
   ☐ **Testicular, ovarian**—Branches from the aorta to the gonads
   ☐ **Common iliac**—Branch from the inferior end of the descending aorta toward a leg

☐ 5 Identify these arteries of the pelvis and lower limbs:
   ☐ **Internal iliac**—Medial branch of the common iliacs
   ☐ **External iliac**—Lateral branch of the common iliac
   ☐ **Femoral**—Continuation of the external iliac artery in the thigh
   ☐ **Popliteal**—Continuation of the femoral artery in the popliteal area (posterior knee)
   ☐ **Anterior tibial**—Anterior branch of the popliteal artery
   ☐ **Posterior tibial**—Posterior branch of the popliteal artery

1 _____

2 _____

3 _____

4 _____

5 _____

6 _____

7 _____

8 _____

9 _____

10 _____

11 _____

12 _____

13 _____

14 _____

15 _____

16 _____

17 _____

18 _____

19 _____

20 _____

21 _____

22 _____

FIGURE 38-1 Major arteries of the body. Write the names of the arteries indicated on the lines provided and on the blanks in the Lab Report at the end of this exercise.

Study **TIPS**

As suggested with your study of the arteries, develop a schematic chart that illustrates the major branches of the veins throughout the body. Use the veins that are mentioned in this lab activity. For reference, use your textbook or the *A&P Survival Guide*.

B. VEINS

Veins are blood vessels that conduct blood toward the heart **(Figure 38-2)**. In the pulmonary circulation, the **pulmonary veins** return oxygenated blood from the lungs. In the systemic circulation, the **superior vena cava** returns deoxygenated blood from the head, neck, thorax, and arms. The **inferior vena cava** returns deoxygenated blood from the rest of the systemic loop. **Venules** are small veins. On a chart, and then in a model, locate the listed major veins. As with the arteries, note how they form routes from major body regions.

☐ 1 Identify these veins of the head and neck:
  ☐ **Brachiocephalic**—Medial branch into the superior vena cava
  ☐ **Subclavian**—Lateral branch into the brachiocephalic vein
  ☐ **Internal jugular**—Medial branch into the brachiocephalic vein
  ☐ **External jugular**—External vein of the neck that returns blood to the subclavian vein

☐ 2 Identify these veins of the upper limb and thorax:
  ☐ **Axillary**—Medial branch into the subclavian vein
  ☐ **Basilic**—Superficial vein that empties into the axillary vein
  ☐ **Brachial**—Upper arm vein that continues into the axillary region as the axillary vein
  ☐ **Cephalic**—Lateral, superficial branch into the subclavian vein
  ☐ **Azygos**—Unpaired branch into the posterior aspect of the superior vena cava
  ☐ **Hemiazygos, accessory hemiazygos**—Two sets of multiple veins that empty into the azygos vein
  ☐ **Intercostal**—Veins that empty into the azygos vein (right) and hemiazygos or accessory hemiazygos veins (left)

☐ 3 Identify these tributaries of the inferior vena cava:
  ☐ **Hepatic**—Vein from the liver to the inferior vena cava
  ☐ **Renal**—Vein from the kidney to the inferior vena cava
  ☐ **Testicular, ovarian**—Vein from the gonad to the inferior vena cava
  ☐ **Common iliac**—Two branches that fuse to become the inferior vena cava
  ☐ **Internal iliac**—Medial branch of the common iliac (in the pelvis)

☐ 4 A **portal circulation** is a set of vessels that begins and ends with capillary networks. In other words, blood is returned to a second set of capillaries before being returned to the heart. The **hepatic portal system** is an important part of the venous systemic circulation **(Figure 38-3)**. It returns blood from digestive organs to the liver, rather than directly to the heart. Identify these hepatic portal vessels:
  ☐ **Hepatic portal**—From the veins of abdominal organs to the liver
  ☐ **Superior mesenteric**—From the small intestine to the hepatic portal vein
  ☐ **Inferior mesenteric**—From the large intestine, joining the splenic vein to the hepatic portal vein
  ☐ **Splenic**—From the spleen to the hepatic portal vein
  ☐ **Gastroepiploic**—From the stomach, joining the splenic vein to the hepatic portal vein. What physiological purpose can be served by the presence of the hepatic portal system?

☐ 5 Identify these veins of the lower limbs:
  ☐ **External iliac**—Lateral branch into the common iliac vein (in the pelvis)
  ☐ **Femoral**—Major lateral branch into the external iliac vein
  ☐ **Great saphenous**—Major medial, superficial branch into the external iliac vein
  ☐ **Popliteal**—Posterior branch into the femoral vein, on the posterior of the knee
  ☐ **Small saphenous**—Lateral, superficial branch into the popliteal vein, lateral to the tibia
  ☐ **Anterior tibial**—Branch into the popliteal vein, on the anterior aspect of the tibia
  ☐ **Posterior tibial**—Posterior to the tibia, draining into the popliteal vein

1 _____

2 _____

3 _____

4 _____

5 _____

6 _____

7 _____

8 _____

9 _____

10 _____

11 _____

12 _____

13 _____

14 _____

15 _____

16 _____

17 _____

18 _____

19 _____

S

R — L

I

Beck

FIGURE 38-2 Major veins of the body. Write the names of the veins on the lines provided and on the blanks in the Lab Report at the end of this exercise.

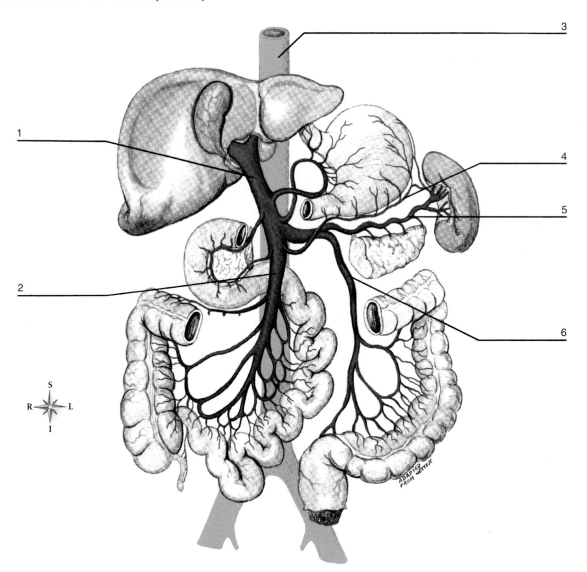

FIGURE 38-3 The hepatic portal system. Write the names of the vessels on the lines provided and on the blanks in the Lab Report at the end of this exercise.

Study TIPS

Review the plan of fetal circulation. Refer to **Figure 38-4**. Photocopy this illustration and remove the labels. After you have reviewed the plan of fetal circulation, label the illustration.

C. FETAL CIRCULATION

Among the many dramatic anatomical and physiological changes that occur at parturition are changes in the cardiovascular circulation. The fetal circulatory plan functions well in the circumstances found in utero but must change quickly if a newborn is to survive outside the uterus. Examine Figure 38-5 or a model or chart of fetal circulation, and note these special features:

☐ 1 The **placenta** has already been described. Located on the inside wall of the uterus, one function of the placenta is the exchange of nutrients and wastes between fetal and maternal blood. Most materials move by means of diffusion, crossing the membranes that separate the two blood systems.

☐ 2 The **umbilical vein** conducts oxygenated fetal blood from the placenta, through the umbilical cord, to and through the liver, and into the **ductus venosus**. The ductus venosus drains into the inferior vena cava, which returns the blood to the fetal heart (right atrium).

☐ 3 From the right atrium, oxygenated blood may flow through the **foramen ovale** into the left atrium. This effectively bypasses the entire pulmonary loop. Some right atrial blood moves into the right ventricle. Right ventricular blood exits the heart by way of the pulmonary artery. Near the branching of the pulmonary artery into left and right branches, the **ductus arteriosus** provides another bypass of the pulmonary loop. Blood tends to bypass circulation to the lungs here and at the right atrium because of the high resistance to blood flow in the developing lungs. Only a small proportion of blood reaches the lungs, just enough for their continued development.

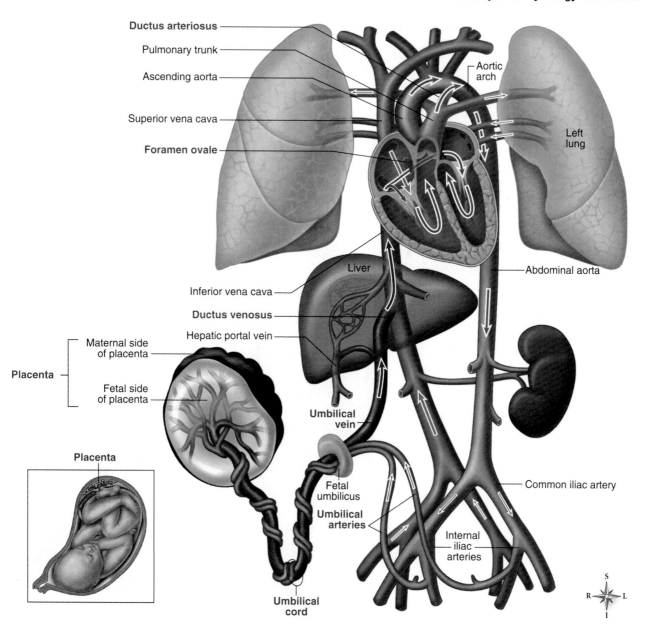

Ductus arteriosus
Pulmonary trunk
Ascending aorta
Superior vena cava
Foramen ovale
Aortic arch
Left lung
Liver
Abdominal aorta
Inferior vena cava
Ductus venosus
Hepatic portal vein
Maternal side of placenta
Fetal side of placenta
Placenta
Umbilical vein
Placenta
Fetal umbilicus
Umbilical arteries
Common iliac artery
Internal iliac arteries
Umbilical cord
S
R   L
I

FIGURE 38-4 The fetal circulatory plan.

☐ **4** Blood in the systemic circulation may enter the two **umbilical arteries** that branch from the internal iliac arteries. The umbilical arteries conduct partially deoxygenated blood through the umbilical cord to the placenta. Follow the possible circulatory paths through the fetal body several times, noting the differences between fetal and adult patterns of blood circulation.

☐ **5** Your model or chart may indicate the changes that occur at parturition to shift the fetal circulatory pattern to the adult pattern. The major changes are noted here:

☐ Flow through the umbilical arteries and vein stops when the umbilical cord is cut and tied, and the vessels degenerate. The umbilical vein and ductus venosus are replaced by ligaments.

☐ When respirations begin after birth and the lungs expand, pulmonary resistance to blood flow is reduced. Therefore, blood tends to flow through the pulmonary loop and not flow through the foramen ovale or into the ductus arteriosus. Increased left atrial pressure forces a flap of the septum over the foramen ovale, which eventually seals the opening completely. The ductus arteriosus constricts and is later replaced by a fibrous ligament.

clinical application: angiography

Angiography is a radiographic (x-ray) imaging method used to visualize blood vessels. A *radiopaque* dye, a water-soluble material that absorbs x-rays so that it casts a heavy shadow on the film, is injected near the vessels of interest. When used to visualize the heart and nearby vessels, the resulting image is called an *angiocardiogram*. When used to visualize veins, the resulting image is called a *venogram*. When angiography is used to image arteries, the result is called an *arteriogram*.

Angiography is used to visualize the structure of blood vessels to determine cardiovascular health.

Some abnormalities that may be seen in an angiogram include:

☐ blood vessel injuries
☐ *aneurysms*, abnormal local distensions of a vessel wall
☐ blockage, perhaps by *atherosclerosis* (buildup of cholesterol and other matter on the inside of a vessel wall)

Figure 38-5 is an arteriogram in which radiopaque dye has been injected into the femoral artery. Try to identify each artery labeled in the figure.

FIGURE 38-5 Arteriogram. Try to identify the arteries on the lines provided and on the blanks in the Lab Report at the end of this exercise.

Name: _____   Date: _____   Section: _____

LAB REPORT 38
The Circulatory Pathway

Figure 38-1 (from p. 365)

1. _____
2. _____
3. _____
4. _____
5. _____
6. _____
7. _____
8. _____
9. _____
10. _____
11. _____
12. _____
13. _____
14. _____
15. _____
16. _____
17. _____
18. _____
19. _____
20. _____
21. _____
22. _____

Put in Order

1. left ventricle _____
2. _____
3. _____
4. _____
5. _____
6. _____
7. _____
8. _____
9. _____
10. _____
11. _____
12. _____
13. _____
14. _____
15. _____
16. _____
17. _____
18. _____

Identify

1. _____
2. _____
3. _____
4. _____
5. _____
6. _____
7. _____
8. _____

Put in Order (rearrange these structures in the order in which blood passes through them in a circuit from the heart to the foot and back; the first one is done for you)

abdominal aorta
anterior tibial artery
anterior tibial vein
aortic arch
ascending aorta
common iliac vein
common iliac artery
external iliac artery
external iliac vein
femoral artery
femoral vein
foot
inferior vena cava
left ventricle
popliteal artery
popliteal vein
right atrium
thoracic aorta

Identify (tell what structure is described in each item)

1. Portion of the aorta in the abdomen

2. Continuation of the subclavian artery inferior to the clavicle

3. Artery that supplies the diaphragm

4. Vein that drains the liver

5. Vessel that conducts blood from digestive organs to the liver

6. Major medial tributary of the external iliac vein

7. Unpaired vein that drains into the posterior aspect of the superior vena cava

8. First major branch of the aorta

Figure 38-2 (from p. 367)

1. _____
2. _____
3. _____
4. _____
5. _____
6. _____
7. _____
8. _____
9. _____
10. _____
11. _____
12. _____
13. _____
14. _____
15. _____
16. _____
17. _____
18. _____
19. _____

Figure 38-3 (from p. 368)

1. _____
2. _____
3. _____
4. _____
5. _____
6. _____

Figure 38-4 (from p. 369)

1. _____
2. _____
3. _____
4. _____
5. _____

Concept Mapping To learn the concept of how blood flows through various circulatory routes, draw a schematic diagram (of a design of your choice) that clearly shows the structures through which blood flows in the following routes:

1. Hepatic portal circulation (include routes all the way to and from the heart in your diagram)
2. Fetal circulation
3. Systemic circulation: to and from any organ of your choice

VESSEL	TISSUES SUPPLIED OR DRAINED
Brachiocephalic artery	
Left common carotid artery	
Left subclavian artery	
Celiac artery	
Phrenic arteries	
Superior mesenteric artery	
Inferior mesenteric artery	
Renal artery	
Suprarenal artery	
External iliac artery	
Internal iliac artery	
Hepatic vein	
External iliac vein	
Internal iliac vein	
Renal vein	
Testicular vein	
Ovarian vein	
Phrenic vein	
Superior mesenteric vein	
Inferior mesenteric vein	
Gastroepiploic vein	
Cystic vein	

The Lymphatic System

The **lymphatic system** has several primary functions: it participates in maintaining extracellular fluid balance, it absorbs fats and other substances from the digestive tract, and it functions in the **immune system** defense of the body. To do this, the lymphatic system is composed of a number of vessels and other structures. This exercise presents some of the basics of lymphatic anatomy and physiology.

BEFORE YOU BEGIN

- ☐ Read the appropriate chapter in your textbook.
- ☐ Set your learning goals. When you finish this exercise, you should be able to:
  - ☐ describe the major organs of the lymphatic system and find them in a chart
  - ☐ identify the features of a lymph node
  - ☐ briefly state the function of lymph nodes
- ☐ Prepare your materials:
  - ☐ charts or models of the lymphatic system
  - ☐ microscope
  - ☐ prepared microslides:
    - ☐ lymphatic vessel l.s.
    - ☐ lymph node c.s.
    - ☐ palatine tonsil c.s.
    - ☐ spleen c.s.
    - ☐ thymus c.s.
- ☐ Read the directions and safety tips for this exercise *carefully* before starting any procedure.

Study TIPS

The best way to understand the role of the lymphatic system is to use the analogy of the system of storm drains and sewage treatment in a city. Check out the complete analogy described in the *A&P Survival Guide*.

A. OVERVIEW OF THE LYMPHATIC SYSTEM

Use a chart or model of the lymphatic system, along with **Figure 39-1**, to find these gross features:

- ☐ 1 Locate some of the **lymphatic vessels**. These vessels are similar to veins in the structure of their walls and the presence of many valves. Lymph vessels collect **lymph** from interstitial spaces in the regions served and conduct it toward the blood circulation. Lymph, or *lymphatic fluid*, is an excess of fluid from interstitial areas. The **right lymphatic** duct is a large collecting vessel that receives lymph from the superior right quadrant of the body. The **thoracic duct** similarly conducts lymph received from the rest of the body. Each duct empties into a subclavian vein.

- ☐ 2 Lymph nodes are small, round organs located at irregular intervals in the network of lymph vessels. Like all *lymphoid* organs, they contain **lymphoid tissue** composed mainly of lymphocytes (a category of white blood cell). They are distributed unevenly, with major aggregations of nodes in the neck (**cervical nodes**), armpit (**axillary nodes**), and groin (**inguinal nodes**).

- ☐ 3 The **tonsils** are *lymphoid* organs that surround the openings of the mouth, nose, and throat into the lower digestive and respiratory tracts. The **palatine tonsils** are on each lateral side of the opening of the mouth into the throat. The **pharyngeal tonsils** are at the top of the throat (*pharynx*) near the posterior of the nasal cavity. The **lingual tonsils** are on the posterior of the tongue's base **(see Figure 39-4, A)**.

- ☐ 4 The **spleen** and **thymus** should already be familiar to you. The spleen is located in the upper left abdominal cavity and the thymus is located in the anterior mediastinum.

> **Hint** A microscopic study of thymic tissue is offered in Lab Exercise 32. •

Study TIPS

Think of the lymph node as a filter. Just as an oil filter cleans the oil in a car's engine, lymph nodes clean the debris that accumulates in your lymph.

B. THE LYMPH NODE

There are numerous lymph nodes throughout the lymphatic system (see Figure 39-1, A). Lymph usually passes through one or more lymph nodes on its path toward the blood circulation. The materials in lymph may stimulate lymphocyte development (an immune response) or may be destroyed by *macrophages* in the node. Identify these structures associated with the lymph node in Figure 39-4, B, and in a chart or model:

- ☐ 1 **Afferent lymph vessels** conduct lymph into a lymph node, whereas **efferent lymph vessels** conduct lymph out of each node. The terms afferent and efferent apply to several organ systems. One way to distinguish them: **afferent–arriving** and **efferent–exiting**.

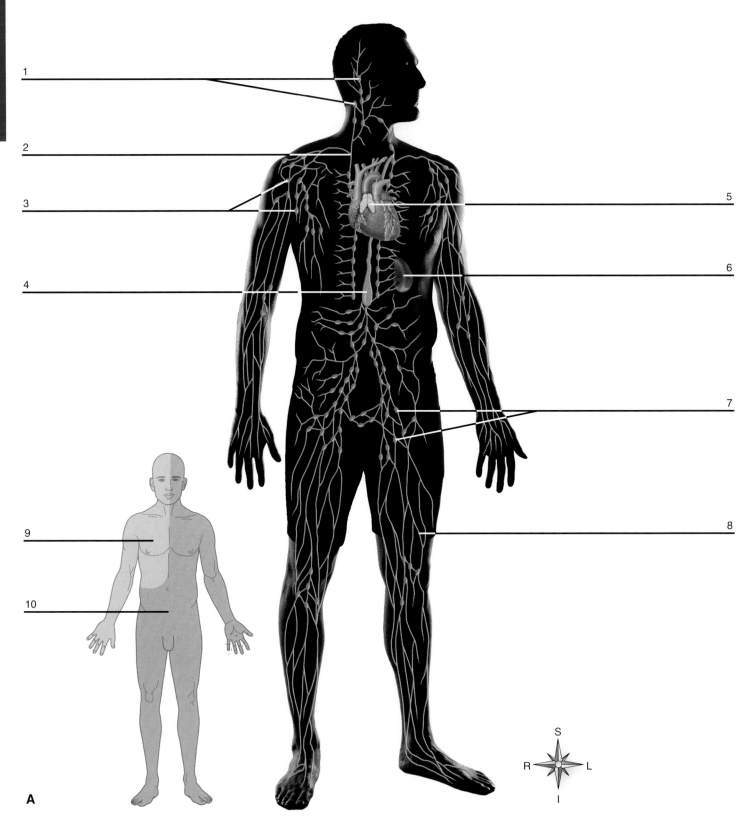

1

2

3

4

5

6

7

8

9

10

A

FIGURE 39-1 A, Label the lymphatic structures indicated on the lines provided and on the blanks in the Lab Report at the end of this exercise.

FIGURE 39-1, cont'd B, Lymphatic vessel. C, Lymph node. D, Palatine tonsil. E, Spleen tissue.

☐ **2** Within the node, lymph tissue often forms dense masses of lymphoid tissue called **lymph nodules.** Each nodule contains a **germinal center** composed of rapidly dividing lymphocytes. Surrounding each node is a space through which lymph circulates; this space is called a **lymph sinus.** The sinuses also contain macrophages.

☐ **3** The fibrous **capsule** functions as the outer boundary and support structure for each lymph node. The inner surface of the capsule has inward extensions that separate the nodules from one another (see Figure 39-4, *B*).

C. MICROSCOPIC STUDIES OF LYMPHATIC STRUCTURES

To complete our study of the lymphatic system, we will briefly explore some of the microscopic features of structures with which you are already familiar. Please refer to the figures in this exercise and in your textbook as you try to identify the structures described in this section.

> **❗ safety first**
> Do not forget the rules for safe use of the microscope. •

☐ **1** **Lymphatic vessel**—As described in Section A, lymphatic vessels are similar to veins in the structure of their walls and the presence of regulatory valves that ensure one-way flow of fluid. Scan your specimen to locate at least one of these valves (see Figure 39-1, *B*).

> *landmark characteristics*
> Compare your specimen with those in Figure 39-1, *B* to *E*. You will notice relatively thin walls compared with blood vessels of the same size, and more valves than normally seen in veins of the same size. •

☐ **2** **Lymph node and tonsil**—See Section A, Step 2, for an overview of the structure of the lymph node, and Section A, Step 3, for an overview of the structure of tonsils. Also see Figure 39-1, *C* and *D*, and Figure 39-4.

> *landmark characteristics*
> A well-prepared cross section of a lymph node should show all the features shown in Figure 39-4, *B*. Lymph nodes are often rounded with a distinct capsule that projects inward to separate the tissue of the cortex into sinuses that contain lymph nodules. Each lymph nodule will be seen to contain a pinkish, rounded germinal center, or *follicle*, surrounded by a distinct purple line. Toward the middle of the node, you may see the medulla—which is made up of cords of lymphocytes and plasma cells, with macrophages spanning the spaces between the cords. As Figure 39-1, *D*, shows, a tonsil is essentially a smaller version of a lymph node—that is, a stand-alone nodule with a single germinal center. •

☐ **3** **Spleen**—The spleen, like the lymph node, has an outer capsule that divides it into subsections **(Figure 39-2)**. Arteries that enter these compartments are surrounded by masses of developing lymphocytes, forming a whitish lymphoid tissue, here called **white pulp.** Surrounding the white pulp is a network of reticular fibers through which blood tissue is flowing. This bloody meshwork is called **red pulp** (see Figure 39-1, *E*).

> *landmark characteristics*
> The splenic capsule and its inward extensions (trabeculae) are normally pale, easy-to-find structures. Within the compartments of the spleen, try to find an area where there are one or more small arteries close together. Surrounding the arteries will be a darkly stained region of cells; this is the white pulp. The red pulp is less densely stained and surrounds the darker white pulp. You may notice some fine reticular fibers in the red pulp. •

☐ **4** **Thymus**—The thymus has a dual role in that it functions as both a lymphatic organ and an endocrine gland. It serves as a site for the development of T lymphocytes (immune cells) and secretes a hormone that influences lymphocyte development. The gland is surrounded by a *capsule* that extends inward, forming *trabeculae* that divide the thymus into lobules **(Figure 39-3, *B*)**. Each lobule has a **cortex,** largely filled with lymphocytes, and a medulla with few lymphocytes. In the medulla, small spheres called *thymic (Hassall) corpuscles*, whose function is unclear, can be found (see Figure 39-3, *B*).

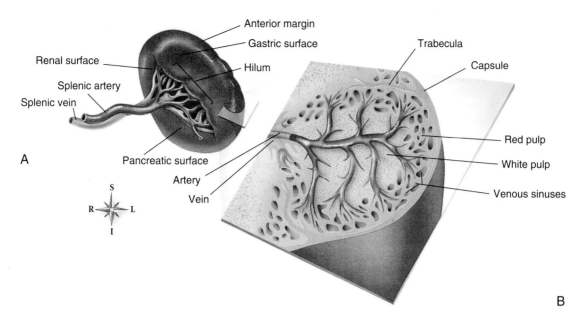

FIGURE 39-2 Spleen. **A,** Medial aspect of the spleen. Note the concave surface that fits against the stomach within the abdominopelvic cavity. **B,** Section showing the internal organization of the spleen.

FIGURE 39-3 Thymus. **A,** Location of the thymus within the mediastinum. **B,** Microscopic structure of the thymus showing several lobules, each with a cortex and a medulla.

landmark characteristics

The thymic capsule and its inward extensions (trabeculae) are normally pale, easy-to-find structures. Near these walls, the cortex can be seen as a region of darkly stained lymphocytes. Farther away from the walls, the more lightly stained medullary region can be seen. Occasional thymic corpuscles (circles with a nonuniform interior) can sometimes be seen. •

Coloring Exercises: Tonsils and Lymph Node

Use colored pens or pencils to shade in both the figure and the labels. Each red numeral in the figure corresponds to a matching red numeral following the appropriate label.

Tonsils

PALATINE TONSILS₁

PHARYNGEAL TONSILS₂

LINGUAL TONSILS₃

Lymph Node

AFFERENT VESSEL₁

EFFERENT VESSEL₂

LYMPH NODULE₃

GERMINAL CENTER₄

LYMPH SINUS₅

CAPSULE₆

ARTERY₇

VEIN₈

A

B

FIGURE 39-4 A, Location of the tonsils. B, Structure of a lymph node.

clinical application: *immune system and autoimmunity disease*

Lymphocytes may be involved in two major types of responses to the presence of potentially threatening foreign substances. In **antibody-mediated immunity,** *B lymphocytes* may produce antibodies that react with specific antigens on an invading cell or molecule. In **cell-mediated immunity,** *T lymphocytes* secrete **lymphokines** that signal other immune responses and often destroy antigen-containing cells directly.

The antibody-antigen reactions associated with immune responses have been used by clinical biologists for years. Several examples are given. Think about each example and answer the questions.

1. Biologists often use antibodies to test for the presence of certain antigens in a particular substance. In Lab Exercises 33 and 34, you witnessed demonstrations of this technique. For each antigen listed, indicate the substance tested (e.g., blood, urine) and give a brief summary of the antibody-antigen reaction involved.

hCG ANTIGEN:

A and B ANTIGENS:

D ANTIGEN:

2. *Rheumatoid arthritis* is an inflammatory disease affecting joint tissues. This disease is known to have an *autoimmune* component. Autoimmunity is an immune response inappropriately directed toward normal self-antigens. Many persons with rheumatoid arthritis have *rheumatoid factor (RF)* present in their blood. RF is an abnormal antibody. Not all persons with the disease have RF in their plasma, and RF is known to be present in conditions other than rheumatoid arthritis. Based on this information and your previous study, outline a simple test to detect the presence of RF in plasma. If your test is used to screen for rheumatoid arthritis, does a positive result (i.e., RF is present) mean that the person definitely has the disease? Why or why not?

Name: _____ Date: _____ Section: _____

LAB REPORT 39
The Lymphatic System

Figure 39-1 (from p. 374)

1. _____
2. _____
3. _____
4. _____
5. _____
6. _____
7. _____
8. _____

Ducts

9. _____
10. _____

Multiple Choice

1. _____
2. _____
3. _____
4. _____
5. _____
6. _____
7. _____

Multiple Choice (choose the best response—only one is correct)

1. Lymphatic tissue contains
   a. mainly lymphocytes
   b. mainly erythrocytes
   c. mainly monocytes

2. The large lymphatic organ found in the left hypochondriac region is the
   a. thymus
   b. palatine tonsil
   c. spleen
   d. lingual tonsil
   e. inguinal lymph node

3. The lymph from tissues of the lower limbs is conducted by the
   a. right lymphatic duct
   b. thoracic duct

4. Lymph nodes function to
   a. provide a site for lymphocyte reproduction
   b. anchor lymphatic vessels
   c. provide a site for phagocytosis of foreign cells or debris
   d. a and b are correct
   e. a and c are correct

5. Lymph vessels that conduct lymph into a lymph node are termed
   a. efferent lymphatic vessels
   b. efferent arterioles
   c. afferent arterioles
   d. afferent lymphatic vessels
   e. none of the above

6. The lymphatic system functions to
   a. maintain extracellular fluid balance
   b. collect excess fluid from the interstitial spaces
   c. defend the body against foreign cells and molecules
   d. a and c are correct
   e. a, b, and c are correct

7. Lymph drains directly into the blood at
   a. the right subclavian vein
   b. the left subclavian vein
   c. the subclavian arteries
   d. a and b are correct
   e. none of the above

LYMPHATIC STRUCTURE	LOCATION	FUNCTION(S)
Lymphatic capillaries		
Lymphatic vessels		
Right lymphatic duct		
Thoracic duct		
Lymph node		
Palatine tonsils		
Pharyngeal tonsils		
Lingual tonsils		
Spleen		
Thymus		

Sketch (draw a cross section of a lymph node and label its parts)

Specimen: *lymphatic vessel l.s.*
Total Magnification: _____

Specimen: *lymph node c.s.*
Total Magnification: _____

Specimen: *palatine tonsil c.s.*
Total Magnification: _____

Specimen: *spleen c.s.*
Total Magnification: _____

Specimen: *thymus c.s.*
Total Magnification: _____

Dissection: Cardiovascular and Lymphatic Systems

In this exercise, you continue your study of cardiovascular and lymphatic anatomy by dissecting a whole preserved specimen.

Activity A provides directions for studying the cardiovascular and lymphatic anatomy of the cat. Activity B is an alternate activity, providing directions for studying the cardiovascular and lymphatic anatomy of the fetal pig.

BEFORE YOU BEGIN

❑ Read the appropriate chapter in your textbook.
❑ Set your learning goals. When you finish this exercise, you should be able to:
  ❑ dissect the cardiovascular and lymphatic anatomy of a preserved cat or fetal pig
  ❑ identify the following in a dissected mammalian specimen:
    ❑ heart and its major features
    ❑ major arteries
    ❑ major veins
    ❑ lymph nodes
❑ Prepare your materials:
  ❑ preserved (injected) cat or fetal pig
  ❑ dissection tools and trays
  ❑ storage container (if specimen is to be reused)
❑ Read the directions and safety tips for this exercise *carefully* before starting any procedure.

safety first

Observe the usual precautions when working with a preserved specimen. Heed the safety advice accompanying preservatives used with your specimen. Use protective gloves while handling your specimen. Avoid injury with dissection tools. Use safety goggles to avoid injury during dissections. Dispose of or store your specimen as instructed. •

Study TIPS

As in previous dissections, it would be helpful to use references of the human circulatory and lymphatic systems. You may want to use your cell phone to photograph your specimens. Afterward, you can use this photo as a resource for the circulatory and lymphatic systems.

A. CARDIOVASCULAR AND LYMPHATIC ANATOMY OF THE CAT

This activity challenges you to identify the major systemic blood vessels of the cat, features of the cat's heart, and lymphoid organs inside the cat's body. To find these structures, you must cut open the cat's thoracic and abdominopelvic cavities. Assuming you have already removed the cat's skin (Exercise 10), you can simply cut through the ventral aspect of the thoracic and abdominal musculature. Do this by inserting your scissors into the ventral abdominal wall (without damaging any internal organs), lifting up the scissors, and cutting along the midline toward the head and tail. You will need to cut through the costal cartilage that connects the ribs to the sternum. Transverse cuts from this initial cut will produce "doors" to the internal body cavities that can be pulled back to expose the viscera. You may have to cut the ribs to see the thoracic viscera. Carefully move the viscera out of the way (without cutting or removing them) to see the structures indicated in this activity.

Hint In double-injected specimens, *arteries* are filled with red latex and *veins* are filled with blue latex. This makes these vessels easy to identify. In specimens that are not injected, you can often distinguish veins and arteries by the thickness of their walls—veins often have thinner walls than arteries. Veins and arteries can also be distinguished by their *locations*—systemic veins lead toward a vena cava, and systemic arteries branch from the aorta. •

□ 1 Identify the aorta extending from the heart. Distinguish these regions of the aorta:
  □ Ascending aorta
  □ Aortic arch
  □ Thoracic portion of descending aorta
  □ Abdominal portion of descending aorta

> **Hint** **Figures 40-1 through 40-4** illustrate many of the structures of the cat listed in this activity. •

□ 2 Identify these branches of the **ascending aorta** (Figure 40-1):
  □ Coronary arteries
□ 3 Identify these branches of the aortic arch:
  □ Brachiocephalic artery (on right side only)
  □ Subclavian arteries
  □ Axillary arteries
  □ Brachial arteries
  □ Vertebral arteries
  □ Costocervical arteries
  □ Common carotid arteries
□ 4 Identify these branches of the thoracic aorta:
  □ Intercostal arteries
  □ Anterior phrenic arteries
□ 5 Identify these branches of the abdominal aorta (Figure 40-2):
  □ Posterior phrenic arteries
  □ Celiac artery
  □ Splenic artery
  □ Anterior mesenteric artery
  □ Suprarenal arteries
  □ Renal arteries
  □ Gonadal (testicular or ovarian) arteries
  □ Lumbar arteries
  □ Posterior mesenteric artery

□ External iliac arteries
□ Internal iliac arteries
□ Femoral arteries

□ 6 Identify the large **anterior vena cava,** which corresponds to the *superior vena cava* in the human. Identify these tributaries of the anterior vena cava in the cat (Figure 40-3):
  □ Azygous vein
  □ Internal mammary vein
  □ Brachiocephalic vein
  □ Axillary vein
  □ Subclavian vein
  □ Subscapular vein
  □ Transverse scapular vein
  □ Brachial vein
  □ Long thoracic vein
  □ Internal jugular vein
  □ External jugular vein
  □ Transverse jugular vein
  □ Posterior facial vein
  □ Anterior facial vein
  □ Submental vein
□ 7 Identify the large **posterior vena cava,** which corresponds to the *inferior vena cava* in the human. Identify these tributaries of the posterior vena cava in the cat (Figure 40-4):
  □ Adrenolumbar vein
  □ Renal vein
  □ Common iliac vein
  □ External iliac vein
  □ Internal iliac vein
  □ Femoral vein
  □ Greater saphenous vein
□ 8 Examine the **heart** of the cat. Identify as many features as you can, using the information in Lab Exercise 35 as a guide.
□ 9 Locate the **spleen,** a lymphoid organ near the stomach. Try to find one or more **lymph nodes** or **lymphatic vessels.**

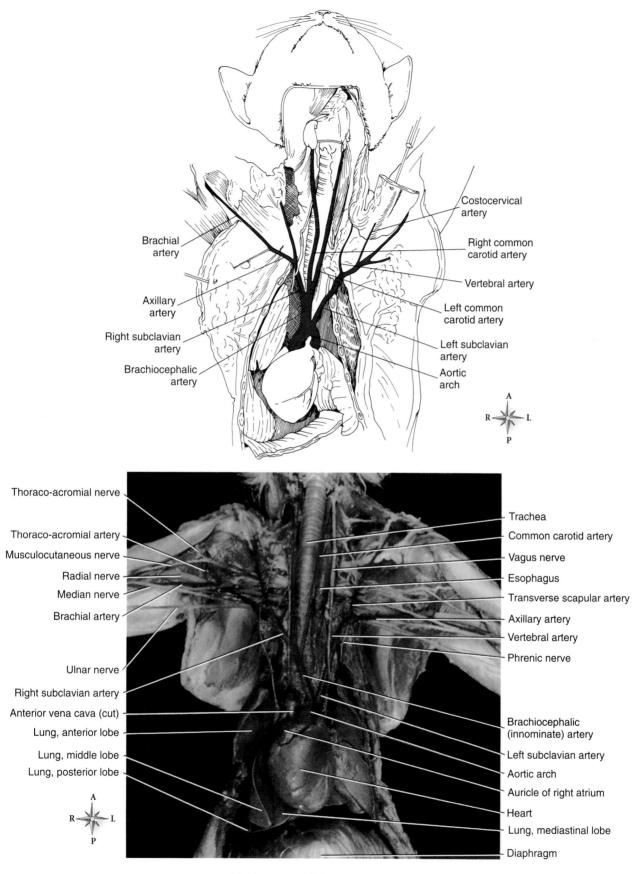

Brachial artery

Axillary artery

Right subclavian artery

Brachiocephalic artery

Costocervical artery

Right common carotid artery

Vertebral artery

Left common carotid artery

Left subclavian artery

Aortic arch

Thoraco-acromial nerve

Thoraco-acromial artery

Musculocutaneous nerve

Radial nerve

Median nerve

Brachial artery

Ulnar nerve

Right subclavian artery

Anterior vena cava (cut)

Lung, anterior lobe

Lung, middle lobe

Lung, posterior lobe

Trachea

Common carotid artery

Vagus nerve

Esophagus

Transverse scapular artery

Axillary artery

Vertebral artery

Phrenic nerve

Brachiocephalic (innominate) artery

Left subclavian artery

Aortic arch

Auricle of right atrium

Heart

Lung, mediastinal lobe

Diaphragm

FIGURE 40-1 Arteries of the cat. Thorax, ventral view.

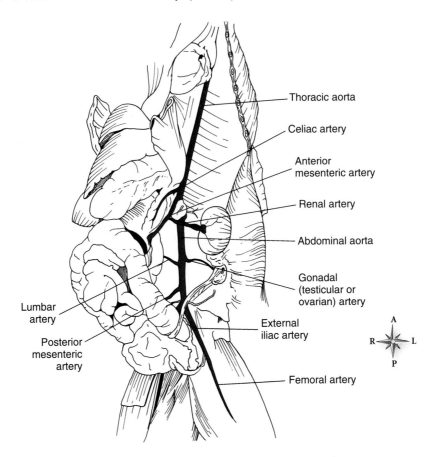

FIGURE 40-2 Arteries of the cat. Abdomen, ventral view.

FIGURE 40-3 Veins of the cat. Thorax, ventral view.

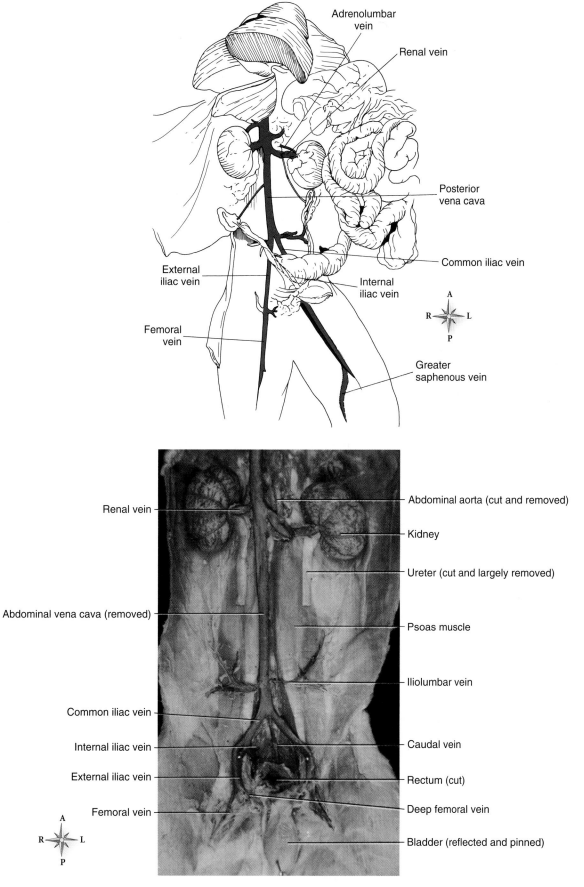

Adrenolumbar vein

Renal vein

Posterior vena cava

Common iliac vein

External iliac vein

Internal iliac vein

Femoral vein

Greater saphenous vein

Renal vein

Abdominal aorta (cut and removed)

Kidney

Ureter (cut and largely removed)

Abdominal vena cava (removed)

Psoas muscle

Iliolumbar vein

Common iliac vein

Caudal vein

Internal iliac vein

External iliac vein

Rectum (cut)

Femoral vein

Deep femoral vein

Bladder (reflected and pinned)

FIGURE 40-4 Veins of the cat. Abdomen, ventral view.

B. CARDIOVASCULAR AND LYMPHATIC ANATOMY OF THE FETAL PIG

This activity challenges you to identify the major systemic blood vessels of the fetal pig, features of the heart, and lymphoid organs inside the fetal pig's body. To find these structures, you must cut open your specimen's thoracic and abdominopelvic cavities. Assuming you have already removed the skin (Exercise 10), you can simply cut through the ventral aspect of the thoracic and abdominal musculature. Do this by inserting your scissors into the ventral abdominal wall (without damaging any internal organs), lifting up the scissors, and cutting along the midline toward the head and tail. You will need to cut through the costal cartilage that connects the ribs to the sternum. Transverse cuts from this initial cut will produce "doors" to the internal body cavities that can be pulled back to expose the viscera. You may have to cut the ribs to see the thoracic viscera. Carefully move the viscera out of the way (without cutting or removing them) to see the structures indicated in this activity.

> **Hint** In double-injected specimens, *arteries* are filled with red latex and *veins* are filled with blue latex. This makes these vessels easy to identify. In specimens that are not injected, you can often distinguish veins and arteries by the thickness of their walls—veins often have thinner walls than arteries. Veins and arteries can also be distinguished by their *locations*—systemic veins lead toward a vena cava, and systemic arteries branch from the aorta. •

☐ 1 Identify the **aorta** extending from the **heart.** Distinguish these regions of the aorta:
  ☐ **Ascending aorta**
  ☐ **Aortic arch**
  ☐ **Thoracic portion of descending aorta**
  ☐ **Abdominal portion of descending aorta**

> **Hint** **Figures 40-5 through 40-7** illustrate many of the structures of the fetal pig listed in this activity. •

☐ 2 Identify these branches of the **ascending aorta** (Figure 40-5):
  ☐ **Coronary arteries**

☐ 3 Identify these branches of the **aortic arch:**
  ☐ **Brachiocephalic artery** (on right side only)
  ☐ **Subclavian arteries**
  ☐ **Axillary arteries**
  ☐ **Brachial arteries**
  ☐ **Common carotid arteries**

☐ 4 Identify these branches of the **thoracic aorta:**
  ☐ **Intercostal arteries**

☐ 5 Identify these branches of the **abdominal aorta** (Figure 40-6):
  ☐ **Celiac artery**
  ☐ **Splenic artery**
  ☐ **Anterior mesenteric artery**
  ☐ **Renal arteries**
  ☐ **Gonadal (testicular or ovarian) arteries**
  ☐ **Posterior mesenteric artery**
  ☐ **Umbilical arteries**
  ☐ **External iliac arteries**
  ☐ **Internal iliac arteries**
  ☐ **Femoral arteries**

☐ 6 Identify the large **anterior vena cava,** which corresponds to the *superior vena cava* in the human. Identify these tributaries of the anterior vena cava in the fetal pig (Figure 40-7):
  ☐ **Internal mammary vein**
  ☐ **Brachiocephalic vein**
  ☐ **Axillary vein**
  ☐ **Subclavian vein**
  ☐ **Internal jugular vein**
  ☐ **External jugular vein**

☐ 7 Identify the large **posterior vena cava,** which corresponds to the *inferior vena cava* in the human. Identify these tributaries of the posterior vena cava in the fetal pig (see Figure 40-6):
  ☐ **Renal vein**
  ☐ **External iliac vein**
  ☐ **Internal iliac vein**
  ☐ **Femoral vein**

☐ 8 Examine the **heart** of the fetal pig. Identify as many features as you can, using the information in Exercise 35 as a guide.

☐ 9 Locate the **spleen,** a lymphoid organ near the stomach. Try to find one or more **lymph nodes** or **lymphatic vessels.**

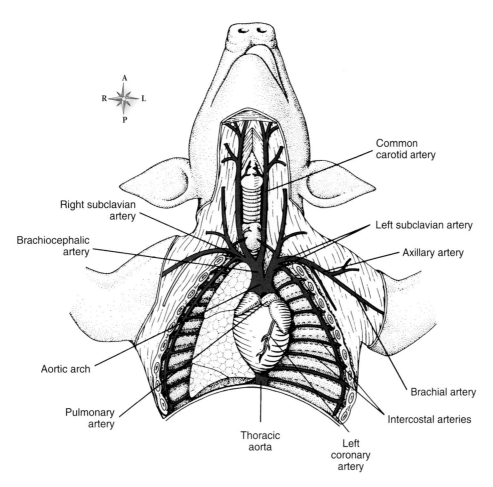

FIGURE 40-5 Arteries of the fetal pig. Neck and thorax, ventral view.

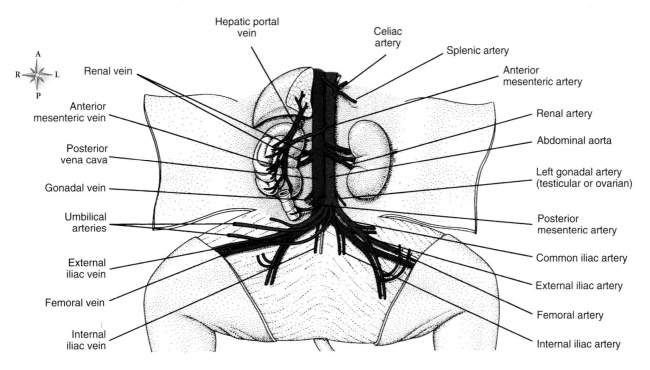

FIGURE 40-6 Arteries and veins of the fetal pig. Abdomen, ventral view.

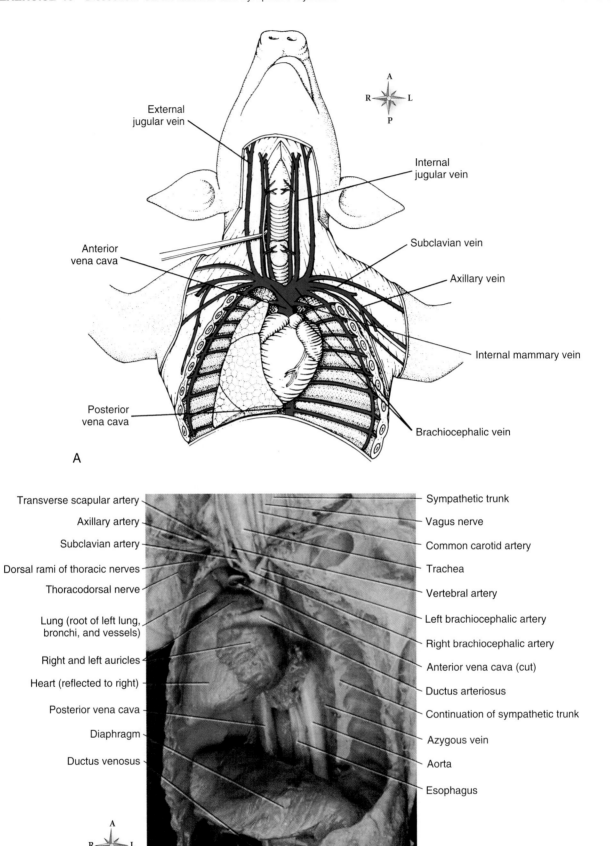

External
jugular vein

Internal
jugular vein

Subclavian vein

Anterior
vena cava

Axillary vein

Internal mammary vein

Posterior
vena cava

Brachiocephalic vein

A

Transverse scapular artery

Axillary artery

Subclavian artery

Dorsal rami of thoracic nerves

Thoracodorsal nerve

Lung (root of left lung,
bronchi, and vessels)

Right and left auricles

Heart (reflected to right)

Posterior vena cava

Diaphragm

Ductus venosus

Sympathetic trunk

Vagus nerve

Common carotid artery

Trachea

Vertebral artery

Left brachiocephalic artery

Right brachiocephalic artery

Anterior vena cava (cut)

Ductus arteriosus

Continuation of sympathetic trunk

Azygous vein

Aorta

Esophagus

B

FIGURE 40-7 **A,** Veins of the fetal pig. Neck and thorax, ventral view. **B,** Vessels of the fetal pig. Neck and thorax, ventral view.

Name: _____ Date: _____ Section: _____

LAB REPORT 40
Dissection: Cardiovascular and Lymphatic Systems

A. Cat Dissection Checklist

☐ **Arteries**

☐ aorta

☐ ascending aorta

   ☐ coronary arteries

☐ aortic arch

   ☐ brachiocephalic artery (on right side only)

   ☐ subclavian arteries

   ☐ axillary arteries

   ☐ brachial arteries

   ☐ vertebral arteries

   ☐ costocervical arteries

   ☐ common carotid arteries

☐ thoracic portion of descending aorta

   ☐ intercostal arteries

   ☐ anterior phrenic arteries

☐ abdominal portion of descending aorta

   ☐ posterior phrenic arteries

   ☐ celiac artery

   ☐ splenic artery

   ☐ anterior mesenteric artery

   ☐ suprarenal arteries

   ☐ renal arteries

   ☐ gonadal (testicular or ovarian) arteries

   ☐ lumbar arteries

   ☐ posterior mesenteric artery

   ☐ external iliac arteries

   ☐ internal iliac arteries

   ☐ femoral arteries

☐ **Veins**

☐ anterior vena cava

   ☐ azygous vein

   ☐ internal mammary vein

   ☐ brachiocephalic vein

   ☐ axillary vein

   ☐ subclavian vein

   ☐ subscapular vein

   ☐ transverse scapular vein

   ☐ brachial vein

   ☐ long thoracic vein

   ☐ internal jugular vein

   ☐ external jugular vein

   ☐ transverse jugular vein

   ☐ posterior facial vein

   ☐ anterior facial vein

   ☐ submental vein

☐ posterior vena cava

   ☐ adrenolumbar vein

   ☐ renal vein

   ☐ common iliac vein

   ☐ external iliac vein

   ☐ internal iliac vein

   ☐ femoral vein

   ☐ greater saphenous vein

☐ **Other organs**

   ☐ heart

   ☐ spleen

   ☐ lymph nodes

   ☐ lymphatic vessels

B. Fetal Pig Dissection Checklist

☐ **Arteries**

☐ aorta

☐ ascending aorta

    ☐ coronary arteries

☐ aortic arch

    ☐ brachiocephalic artery (on right side only)

    ☐ subclavian arteries

    ☐ axillary arteries

    ☐ brachial arteries

    ☐ common carotid arteries

☐ thoracic portion of descending aorta

    ☐ intercostal arteries

☐ abdominal portion of descending aorta

    ☐ celiac artery

    ☐ splenic artery

    ☐ anterior mesenteric artery

    ☐ renal arteries

    ☐ gonadal (testicular or ovarian) arteries

    ☐ posterior mesenteric artery

    ☐ umbilical arteries

    ☐ external iliac arteries

    ☐ internal iliac arteries

    ☐ femoral arteries

☐ **Veins**

☐ anterior vena cava

    ☐ internal mammary vein

    ☐ brachiocephalic vein

    ☐ axillary vein

    ☐ subclavian vein

    ☐ internal jugular vein

    ☐ external jugular vein

☐ posterior vena cava

    ☐ renal vein

    ☐ external iliac vein

    ☐ internal iliac vein

    ☐ femoral vein

☐ **Other organs**

    ☐ heart

    ☐ spleen

    ☐ lymph nodes

    ☐ lymphatic vessels

41
Respiratory Structures

This exercise is the first of three that deal with the **respiratory system.** In the activities presented here, you explore the essential structure of the *respiratory tract.* Lab Exercise 42 deals with some aspects of respiratory function.

The respiratory tract is comprised of the **nose** and **nasal cavity, pharynx, larynx, trachea, bronchi,** and **lungs.** During **ventilation,** a process that includes *respiratory cycles* of **inspiration** and **expiration,** air moves in and out of the respiratory tract. During inspiration air moves through the tract to the lungs; during expiration it moves out. While in the lungs, air and blood exchange oxygen and carbon dioxide in a process called **gas exchange.** Keep these important functions of the system in mind as you explore the gross and microscopic structures presented in this exercise.

BEFORE YOU BEGIN

☐ Read the appropriate chapter in your textbook.
☐ Set your learning goals. When you finish this exercise, you should be able to:
  ☐ describe the major organs of the respiratory system
  ☐ locate respiratory structures on a chart or model
  ☐ demonstrate the structure of respiratory organs in a preserved specimen
  ☐ trace the movement of air through the respiratory tract
  ☐ locate structural features of the trachea in a microscopic specimen
  ☐ locate structural features of lung tissue in a microscopic specimen
☐ Prepare your materials:
  ☐ chart or model of the human respiratory system
  ☐ dissection tools and large tray
  ☐ preserved specimen: *sheep pluck*
  ☐ microscope
  ☐ prepared microslide: *mammalian trachea c.s.*
  ☐ prepared microslide: *human lung c.s.*
☐ Read the directions and safety tips for this exercise *carefully* before starting any procedure.

Study TIPS

Develop a schematic diagram that illustrates the pathway of air as it enters the body and travels to the alveoli. You may want to note on your diagram what happens to the air as it passes each structure (warms, humidifies, filters, etc.). Obtain an unlabeled diagram of both the upper and lower respiratory tracts. Complete this diagram after this lab activity.

A. GROSS ANATOMY

Using a chart or model of the respiratory tract (perhaps a dissectible human head and torso), locate the structural features of the respiratory tract listed **(Figure 41-1).**

☐ 1 *Nose* is the term often reserved for the external cartilage and bone forming the anterior wall of the nasal cavity, but it also may refer to the entire cavity. Identify these nasal features:
  ☐ **Nasal septum**—Wall dividing the nasal cavity into right and left portions
  ☐ **Nares**—*External nares,* or the *nostrils,* and the *internal nares,* or openings, from the posterior nasal cavity into the pharynx (singular of nares is *naris*)
  ☐ **Hard palate**—Floor of the nasal cavity
  ☐ **Conchae**—Three curved ridges extending from each lateral wall of the cavity: the *superior nasal conchae, middle nasal conchae,* and *inferior nasal conchae* (singular of conchae is *concha*)
  ☐ **Paranasal sinuses**—Air-filled, mucus-lined spaces in the skull that communicate with the nasal cavity: *maxillary, frontal, ethmoid,* and *sphenoid* sinuses
  ☐ **Nasolacrimal duct**—Tube that conducts tears from the conjunctiva over the eyes and empties into the nasal cavity

☐ **2** Identify these features of the **pharynx**, or throat **(Figure 41-2)**:

☐ **Nasopharynx**—The upper of three regions of the pharynx, this one is posterior to the nasal cavity. The **uvula** is an extension of the floor of the nasopharynx, or **soft palate**, and serves as the inferior boundary landmark of the nasopharynx. *The pharyngeal tonsils* are on the posterior wall, and the lateral walls have the inferior opening of the *auditory (eustachian) tube* from the middle ear.

☐ **Oropharynx**—The middle portion of the pharynx, it is posterior to the oral cavity. The *palatine* and *lingual tonsils* are found here.

☐ **Laryngopharynx**—The most inferior portion of the pharynx, it is posterior to the larynx.

☐ **3** Identify these features of the voice box, or **larynx**:

☐ **Laryngeal cartilages**—Nine pieces of cartilage (6 in pairs and 3 single pieces) that fit together to form the wall of the larynx: **thyroid, cricoid, epiglottis, cuneiforms** (pair), **corniculates** (pair), and **arytenoids** (pair)

☐ **Vestibular folds** (false vocal cords)—Superior of two pairs of ligaments stretched across the lateral portions of the larynx cavity

☐ **Vocal folds** (true vocal cords)—Inferior of two pairs of laryngeal ligaments

FIGURE 41-1 Midsagittal section of the head, showing respiratory structures. Label the structures indicated on the lines provided and on the blanks in the Lab Report at the end of this exercise.

Coloring Exercises: Respiratory Anatomy

Use colored pens or pencils to shade in both the figure and the labels. Each red numeral in the figure corresponds to a matching red numeral following the appropriate label.

NASAL CAVITY₁
NASOPHARYNX₂
OROPHARYNX₃
LARYNGOPHARYNX₄
LARYNX₅
TRACHEA₆
PRIMARY BRONCHI₇

SECONDARY BRONCHI₈
TERTIARY BRONCHI₉
BRONCHIOLE₁₀
TERMINAL BRONCHIOLE₁₁
RESPIRATROY
   BRONCHIOLE₁₂
ALVEOLAR DUCT₁₃
ALVEOLUS₁₄

Lobes (Shade Lightly)
RIGHT SUPERIOR LOBE₁₅
RIGHT MIDDLE LOBE₁₆
RIGHT INFERIOR LOBE₁₇
LEFT SUPERIOR LOBE₁₈
LEFT INTERIOR LOBE₁₉

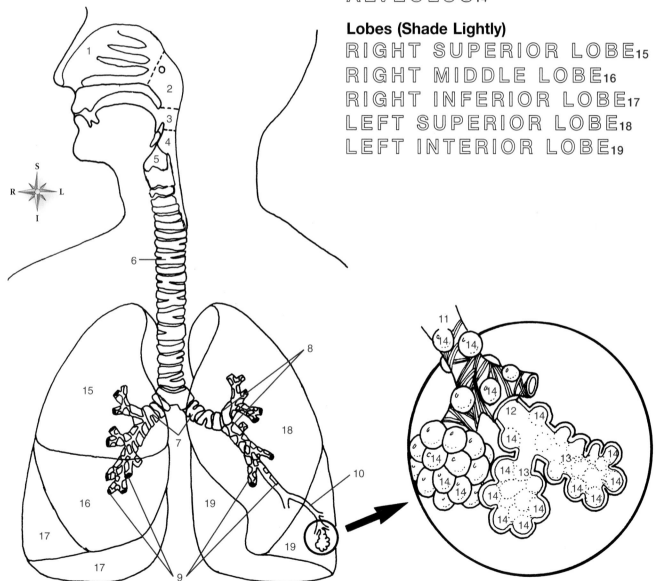

FIGURE 41-2 Structural plan of the respiratory system.

□ 4 The **trachea,** or windpipe, conducts air between the larynx above and the bronchi below. It has C-shaped cartilage rings embedded in its anterior and lateral walls for support. At its inferior end, the trachea divides into the left and right **primary bronchi,** each of which enters a lung at a **hilum.**

□ 5 The **lungs** are divided, on a gross level, into **lobes,** which can be subdivided into **lobules.** The left lung has a *superior lobe* and an *inferior lobe.* The right lung has *superior, middle,* and *inferior lobes.* The lungs are found in the *pleural cavities* in the left and right portions of the thorax. A serous membrane called the **pleura** covers each lung (*visceral pleura*), then folds back to line the pleural cavity (*parietal pleura*). The thin space between the visceral and parietal layers is filled with serous **pleural fluid.**

□ 6 Once in a lung, each primary bronchus branches to form a **bronchial tree.** The successive levels of bronchial branching include:
   □ **Secondary bronchi**—Each serves a separate lobe.
   □ **Tertiary bronchi**—Each is a branch of a secondary bronchus; each tertiary bronchus serves a lobule.
   □ **Bronchioles**—Several levels of small branches of the airway exist within each lobule. Near the end of the branching, **terminal bronchioles** give rise to **respiratory bronchioles,** which in turn subdivide to form **alveolar ducts** that end as groups of air sacs called **alveoli.** The smaller bronchioles are not represented in many models but can be found in some charts and figures.

□ 7 The **diaphragm** is a sheet of skeletal muscle just inferior to both lungs. The diaphragm contracts during inspiration to reduce pressure inside the thorax, drawing air into the respiratory tract.

Study TIPS

As you progress through this dissection, it might be helpful to reference labeled diagrams or illustrations of the human respiratory tract. For reference, you can use your textbook or the *A&P Survival Guide.*

B. DISSECTION

This activity calls for individual dissection or a demonstrated dissection of a *sheep pluck.* The pluck is a portion of the respiratory tract and other organs removed from an animal when it is slaughtered. Notice that the heart and diaphragm are still intact. This is a good opportunity to reinforce your understanding of their anatomical relationship to each other.

safety first

Remember to observe the standard precautions for dissecting a preserved specimen. Use safety goggles to avoid injury during dissections. •

□ 1 Identify the larynx, trachea, primary bronchi, lungs, heart, and diaphragm.

□ 2 Examine the lungs. Can you distinguish the lobes? How many lobes are in each lung? Is it the same number as in the human?

□ 3 Use scissors to cut along the dorsal wall of the respiratory tract to open the larynx and trachea. What features can you identify? Continue your cut through a primary bronchus and into the bronchial tree. How many levels of branching can you see? Can you name the different branches?

C. MICROSCOPIC ANATOMY

safety first

Use the microscope and prepared slides with caution. Do not forget about the electrical hazards and the possibility of cuts from broken slides. •

□ 1 Examine a prepared cross section of a mammalian trachea. Identify these features:
   □ **Lining**—It is composed of pseudostratified columnar epithelium. Locate cilia and goblet cells if you can.
   □ **Outer wall**—It is composed of smooth muscle and assorted connective tissues. Locate portions of the C-shaped cartilage supports in the wall of the trachea. What type of cartilage is it?

□ 2 Examine a prepared cross section of human lung tissue. Identify this feature:
   □ **Alveolus**—It is an air sac that communicates with a respiratory bronchiole. Try to locate the *alveolar epithelium,* the simple squamous epithelium forming the wall. Is any of the connective tissue between alveoli visible in your specimen?

□ 3 Try to locate *pulmonary capillaries* that surround the alveoli. In a cross section, they appear as circles of simple squamous epithelium (and sometimes have blood cells within them).

Name: _____   Date: _____   Section: _____

LAB REPORT 41
Respiratory Structures

Use this table as a checklist for your study of the human model and the sheep pluck. Use your textbook for help with the section that asks for functions.

STRUCTURE	HUMAN	PLUCK	FUNCTION(S)
Nasal cavity	☐	☐	
Nasal septum	☐	☐	
Nares: internal, external	☐	☐	
Hard palate	☐	☐	
Soft palate	☐	☐	
Conchae: superior, middle, inferior	☐	☐	
Paranasal sinuses: maxillary, frontal, ethmoid, sphenoid	☐	☐	
Nasopharynx	☐	☐	
Oropharynx	☐	☐	
Laryngopharynx	☐	☐	
Laryngeal cartilages	☐	☐	
Vestibular folds	☐	☐	
Vocal folds	☐	☐	
Trachea	☐	☐	
Primary bronchi	☐	☐	
Secondary bronchi	☐	☐	
Tertiary bronchi	☐	☐	
Lungs: lobes, lobules	☐	☐	
Pleurae: visceral, parietal	☐	☐	
Bronchioles	☐	☐	
Terminal bronchioles	☐	☐	
Respiratory bronchioles	☐	☐	
Alveolar ducts	☐	☐	
Alveoli	☐	☐	

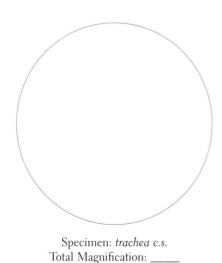

Specimen: *trachea c.s.*
Total Magnification: _____

Specimen: *human lung c.s.*
Total Magnification: _____

Figure 41-1 (from p. 394)

1. _____
2. _____
3. _____
4. _____
5. _____
6. _____
7. _____
8. _____
9. _____
10. _____
11. _____
12. _____
13. _____
14. _____
15. _____
16. _____
17. _____
18. _____
19. _____
20. _____
21. _____
22. _____
23. _____
24. _____

Sketch and label the sheep pluck specimen:

Put in Order

1. _____
2. _____
3. _____
4. _____
5. _____
6. _____
7. _____
8. _____
9. _____

Put in Order (rearrange these structures in the order through which air passes during inspiration)

   larynx
   nasal cavity
   pharynx
   primary bronchi
   respiratory bronchioles
   secondary bronchi
   terminal bronchioles
   tertiary bronchi
   trachea

42

Dissection: Respiratory System

In this exercise, you continue your study of respiratory anatomy by dissecting a whole preserved specimen.

Activity A provides directions for studying the respiratory anatomy of the cat. Activity B is an alternate activity, providing directions for studying the respiratory anatomy of the fetal pig. Activity C is also an alternate activity that asks you to dissect a sheep pluck, or lower respiratory tract and heart of a sheep.

BEFORE YOU BEGIN

☐ Read the appropriate chapter in your textbook.
☐ Set your learning goals. When you finish this exercise, you should be able to:
   ☐ dissect the respiratory anatomy of a preserved cat, fetal pig, or sheep
   ☐ identify the following in a dissected mammalian specimen:
      ☐ larynx
      ☐ trachea and bronchial tree
      ☐ lungs
      ☐ diaphragm
☐ Prepare your materials:
   ☐ preserved cat, fetal pig, or sheep pluck
   ☐ dissection tools and trays
   ☐ storage container (if specimen is to be reused)
   ☐ dissection microscope (optional)
☐ Read the directions and safety tips for this exercise *carefully* before starting any procedure.

> **!** ***safety first***
> Observe the usual precautions when working with a preserved specimen. Heed the safety advice accompanying preservatives used with your specimen. Use protective gloves while handling your specimen. Avoid injury with dissection tools. Use safety goggles to avoid injury during dissections. Dispose of or store your specimen as instructed. •

Study TIPS

As you progress through this dissection, compare your specimen with a diagram or illustration of the human respiratory tract. For reference, use your textbook or the *A&P Survival Guide*. You may want to use your cell phone to take a picture of your specimen and use it later to identify the respiratory structures.

A. RESPIRATORY ANATOMY OF THE CAT

This activity challenges you to identify the major respiratory structures of the cat. Assuming you have already removed the cat's skin (Exercise 10) and opened the thoracic cavity (Exercise 40), you simply have to cut through the muscles of the neck and head to expose internal features of the anterior airway (equivalent to the upper respiratory tract in humans). Be careful as you do this to avoid damaging the specimen to the point that you really cannot tell where the structures are normally located in relation to one another. Remember to carefully move the viscera out of the way (without cutting or removing them) to see the structures indicated in this activity.

☐ 1 Identify the **external nares,** the openings of the **nasal cavity.** Notice that a **nasal septum** divides the nasal cavity into two air passages. If your instructor directs you to do so, cut into the nose and mouth of the cat to expose the nasal cavity and **pharynx.** In the nasal cavity, try to identify the nasal **turbinates** *(conchae)* projecting from the lateral walls. Can you identify the three major regions of the pharynx: *nasopharynx, oropharynx,* and *laryngopharynx?*

☐ 2 Locate and identify the **larynx,** or voice box, deep in the neck. The **epiglottis, thyroid cartilage,** and **cricoid cartilage** of the larynx are easily visible on the ventral aspect.

☐ 3 Identify the **trachea** extending posteriorly from the larynx. Notice the cartilage rings that support this structure.

> **Hint** **Figure 42-1** illustrates many of the structures of the cat listed in this activity. •

☐ 4 Identify the right and left **primary bronchi.** Notice that each extends to a different **lung,** where it splits to form several **secondary bronchi.**

☐ 5 Each secondary bronchus serves a distinct **lobe** of a lung. Identify the following lobes in each of your specimen's lungs:
   ☐ **Anterior lobe** (left and right)
   ☐ **Middle lobe** (left and right)
   ☐ **Posterior lobe** (left and right)
   ☐ **Mediastinal lobe** (right only)

☐ 6 If your instructor directs you to do so, slice into the tissue of one of the lobes and remove a small section of tissue. Examine the internal structure of this tissue with a dissection microscope or hand lens to reveal air passages that constitute distal elements of the **bronchial tree** and gas-exchange tissues. You may make a deeper cut into the lobe to reveal other elements of the bronchial airways.

☐ 7 Locate the following structures of the wall of the thoracic cavity:
   ☐ **Intercostal muscles**
   ☐ **Thoracic inlet**
   ☐ **Parietal pleura**
   ☐ **Visceral pleura**
   ☐ **Pleural space**
   ☐ **Diaphragm**
   ☐ **Phrenic nerve (innervates diaphragm)**

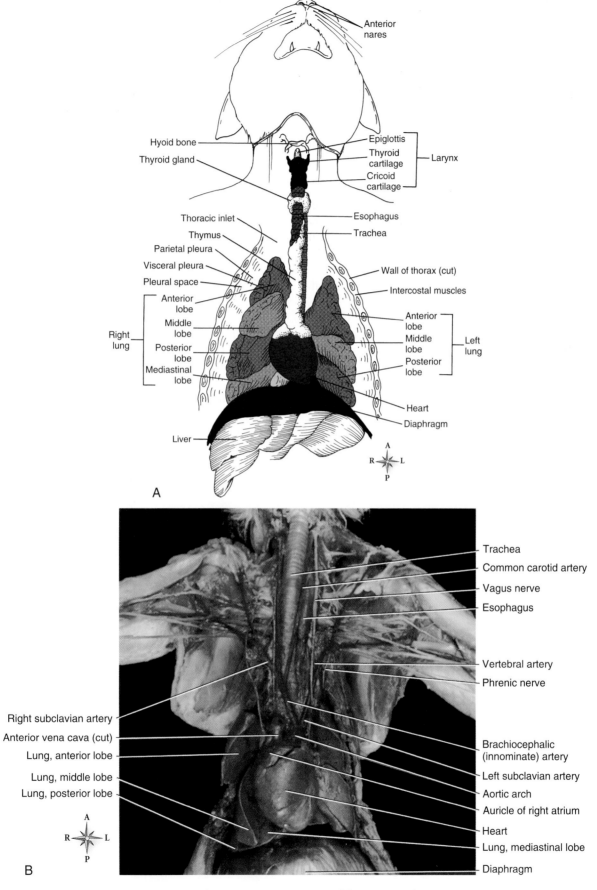

FIGURE 42-1 Respiratory anatomy of the cat. Ventral view.

B. RESPIRATORY ANATOMY OF THE FETAL PIG

This activity challenges you to identify the major respiratory structures of the fetal pig. Assuming you have already removed the animal's skin (Exercise 10) and opened the thoracic cavity (Exercise 40), you simply have to cut through the muscles of the neck and head to expose internal features of the anterior airway (equivalent to the upper respiratory tract in humans). Be careful as you do this to avoid damaging the specimen to the point that you really cannot tell where the structures are normally located in relation to one another. Remember to carefully move the viscera out of the way (without cutting or removing them) to see the structures indicated in this activity.

☐ 1 Identify the **external nares**, the openings of the **nasal cavity**. Notice that a **nasal septum** divides the nasal cavity into two air passages. If your instructor directs you to do so, cut into the nose and mouth of the fetal pig to expose the nasal cavity and **pharynx**. In the nasal cavity, try to identify the nasal **turbinates** *(conchae)* projecting from the lateral walls. Can you identify the three major regions of the pharynx: *nasopharynx, oropharynx,* and *laryngopharynx?*

☐ 2 Locate and identify the **larynx**, or voice box, deep in the neck.

☐ 3 Identify the **trachea** extending posteriorly from the larynx. Notice the cartilage rings that support this structure.

Hint ▸ **Figure 42-2** illustrates many of the structures of the fetal pig listed in this activity. •

☐ 4 Identify the right and left **primary bronchi.** Notice that each extends to a different **lung,** where it splits to form several **secondary bronchi.**

☐ 5 Each secondary bronchus serves a distinct **lobe** of a lung. Identify the following lobes in each of your specimen's lungs:
☐ **Anterior lobe** (left and right)
☐ **Middle lobe** (right only)
☐ **Posterior lobe** (left and right)

☐ 6 If your instructor directs you to do so, slice into the tissue of one of the lobes and remove a small section of tissue. Examine the internal structure of this tissue with a dissection microscope or hand lens to reveal air passages that constitute distal elements of the **bronchial tree** and gas-exchange tissues. You may make a deeper cut into the lobe to reveal other elements of the bronchial airways.

☐ 7 Locate the following structures of the wall of the thoracic cavity:
☐ **Intercostal muscles**
☐ **Thoracic inlet**
☐ **Parietal pleura**
☐ **Visceral pleura**
☐ **Pleural space**
☐ **Diaphragm**

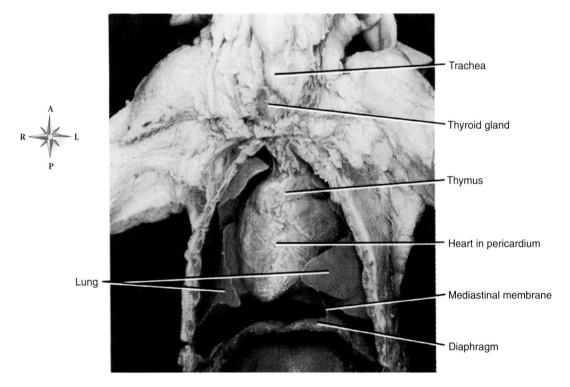

FIGURE 42-2 Respiratory anatomy of the fetal pig. Ventral view.

C. RESPIRATORY ANATOMY OF THE SHEEP

This activity challenges you to identify the major respiratory structures in a *sheep pluck* specimen. This specimen includes a portion of the respiratory system, the heart, and other nearby structures removed from the carcass of a sheep. The organs of the sheep pluck are similar in size to the adult human (depending on the particular sheep and the particular human, of course).

☐ 1 Locate and identify the **larynx**, or voice box, at the anterior end of the sheep pluck.

☐ 2 Identify the **trachea** extending posteriorly from the larynx. Notice the cartilage rings that support this structure.

> **Hint** Figures found throughout Exercises 41 and 42 are useful in identifying many of the structures of the sheep pluck listed in this activity. •

☐ 3 Identify the right and left **primary bronchi.** Notice that each extends to a different **lung,** where it splits to form several **secondary bronchi.**

☐ 4 Each secondary bronchus serves a distinct **lobe** of a lung. Identify the lobes in each of your specimen's lungs. How many are there in each lung? How does this compare to the human?

☐ 5 If your instructor directs you to do so, slice into the tissue of one of the lobes and remove a small section of tissue. Examine the internal structure of this tissue with a dissection microscope or hand lens to reveal air passages that constitute distal elements of the **bronchial tree** and gas-exchange tissues. You may make a deeper cut into the lobe to reveal other elements of the bronchial airways.

Name: _____ Date: _____ Section: _____

LAB REPORT 42
Dissection: Respiratory System

A. Cat Dissection Checklist

❑ external nares
❑ nasal cavity
❑ nasal septum
❑ turbinates (conchae)
❑ pharynx
   ❑ nasopharynx
   ❑ oropharynx
   ❑ laryngopharynx
❑ larynx
   ❑ epiglottis
   ❑ thyroid cartilage
   ❑ cricoid cartilage
❑ trachea
❑ primary bronchi
❑ lung
❑ secondary bronchi
❑ lobes of the lungs
   ❑ anterior lobe (left and right)
   ❑ middle lobe (left and right)
   ❑ posterior lobe (left and right)
   ❑ mediastinal lobe (right only)
❑ wall of the thoracic cavity
   ❑ intercostal muscles
   ❑ thoracic inlet
   ❑ parietal pleura
   ❑ visceral pleura
   ❑ pleural space
   ❑ diaphragm
   ❑ phrenic nerve

B. Fetal Pig Dissection Checklist

❑ external nares
❑ nasal cavity
❑ nasal septum
❑ turbinates (conchae)
❑ pharynx
   ❑ nasopharynx
   ❑ oropharynx
   ❑ laryngopharynx
❑ larynx
❑ trachea
❑ primary bronchi
❑ lung
❑ secondary bronchi
❑ lobes of the lungs
   ❑ anterior lobe (left and right)
   ❑ middle lobe (right only)
   ❑ posterior lobe (left and right)
❑ wall of the thoracic cavity
   ❑ intercostal muscles
   ❑ thoracic inlet
   ❑ parietal pleura
   ❑ visceral pleura
   ❑ pleural space
   ❑ diaphragm

C. Sheep Pluck Dissection Checklist

❑ larynx
   ❑ epiglottis
   ❑ thyroid cartilage
   ❑ cricoid cartilage
   ❑ other features visible?
❑ trachea
❑ primary bronchi
❑ lung
❑ secondary bronchi
❑ lobes of the lungs
   ❑ how many (left lung)? _____
   ❑ how many (right lung)? _____

43
Pulmonary Volumes and Capacities

The use of instrumentation to determine the basic pulmonary volumes and **pulmonary capacities** is called **spirometry.** Pulmonary volumes, or *lung volumes,* are the amounts of air moved in and out of the respiratory tract during different phases of the respiratory cycle. Pulmonary capacities are combinations of pulmonary volumes, as you will see. Spirometry is important in many applications such as research, clinical situations, and exercise training.

In this exercise, you use a **spirometer** to measure pulmonary volumes and capacities. Activities D and E present a computer-based spirometry technique that can be used as an alternate method.

BEFORE YOU BEGIN

❏ Read the appropriate chapter in your textbook.
❏ Set your learning goals. When you finish this exercise, you should be able to:
   ☐ define the volumes and capacities of the respiratory tract and explain their functional significance
   ☐ demonstrate the use of a spirometer to determine pulmonary volumes and capacities
   ☐ understand the effects of exercise on pulmonary volumes and capacities
❏ Prepare your materials:
   ☐ wet or dry (handheld) spirometer
   ☐ one-way valve and mouthpiece (for wet spirometer) or disposable mouthpieces (dry)
   ☐ series of bowls of disinfectant
   ☐ noseclip
   ☐ BIOHAZARD bag
   ☐ stopwatch or timer
   ☐ your institution's available spirometer tool (check with your instructor to see what is being provided)
   ☐ computer system (if computerized version is used)
❏ Read the directions and safety tips for this exercise *carefully* before starting any procedure.

Study TIPS

Before you begin this lab, review pulmonary ventilation capacities. For reference, use your lab manual, textbook, or the *A&P Survival Guide.*

A. PULMONARY VOLUMES AND CAPACITIES

Inspiration, or **inhalation,** is one of two major phases of the respiratory cycle. **Expiration,** or **exhalation,** is the other. The movement of air into and out of the respiratory tract during these phases is termed **ventilation** and is critical to the normal functioning of the entire body. As mentioned in the introduction, a spirometer is an instrument that measures the volume of air moved during the different phases of the respiratory cycle. This activity calls for the use of a *wet spirometer,* which is a vessel inverted in a container of water. A breathing tube communicates with the inverted vessel, which rises in the water as it fills with air. The rise of the inverted vessel is proportional to the volume exhaled into the instrument. A recording spirometer, as shown in **Figure 43-2**, produces a wavy **spirogram.** You will probably use a spirometer that shows the rise on a dial or linear scale. You may instead use a handheld *dry spirometer,* which is a gauge that measures air volume as you exhale into it.

Before using the spirometer, you should practice breathing normally while wearing a noseclip (or while pinching your nostrils shut). The noseclip is needed to prevent the natural tendency to breathe through your nose, which invalidates the spirometry results.

> **!** ***safety first***
> A one-way valve and mouthpiece used with a wet spirometer prevent inhalation of potentially contaminated air from inside the spirometer's air passages; however, be certain that the valves and mouthpieces are disinfected thoroughly by soaking them in a series of alcohol baths before reusing them. If a handheld spirometer is used, be sure to use a *new* disposable mouthpiece *and* disinfect the spirometer itself between uses (see Figure 43-2). ●

☐ 1 Tidal volume (TV) is the volume of air moved into or out of the respiratory tract during normal breathing. Measure your TV as follows **(Figure 43-3):**
If a one-way valve is used:
   ☐ Place your mouth on the tube
   ☐ Inhale normally
   ☐ Exhale normally
   ☐ Read the result and reset the apparatus to zero
If a one-way valve is not used:
   ☐ Inhale normally
   ☐ Place your mouth on the tube
   ☐ Exhale normally
   ☐ Read the result and reset the apparatus to zero

FIGURE 43-1 A recording arrangement using an electronic spirometer. A recording spirometer yields a wave-form spirogram.

FIGURE 43-2 Insert a disposable mouthpiece over the stem of a handheld spirometer. Dispose of used mouthpieces in a BIOHAZARD container.

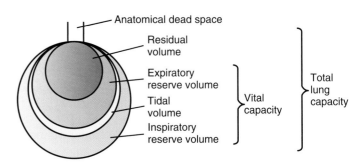

FIGURE 43-3 Diagram of pulmonary volumes and capacities.

 Hint Pulmonary volumes are reported in either milliliters (ml) or liters (L). Remember that milliliters are a thousandth the size of liters. Therefore, a typical TV might be reported as 500 ml or 0.5 L. Be sure to indicate which units you are using when reporting your results.

- Perform each test three times and average your results.
- Typical volumes and capacities are given in the table on the facing page.

☐ **2** Expiratory reserve volume (ERV) is the volume of air that can be expired forcefully after a normal expiration. Measure the ERV as follows:

If a one-way valve is used:
☐ Place your mouth on the tube
☐ Inhale normally
☐ Exhale forcefully (to the maximum)
☐ Read the result and subtract your TV—the difference is ERV; reset the apparatus to zero

If a one-way valve is not used:
☐ Inhale and exhale normally
☐ At the end of the normal expiration, place your mouth on the tube and exhale forcefully
☐ Read the result as ERV and reset the apparatus to zero

☐ **3** Vital capacity (VC) is the volume of air that can be expired after a forceful inspiration. Determine your vital capacity as follows.

If a one-way valve is used:
☐ Place your mouth on the tube
☐ Inhale forcefully (to the maximum)
☐ Exhale forcefully (to the maximum)
☐ Read the VC value and reset the apparatus to zero

If a one-way valve is not used:
☐ Inhale forcefully (to the maximum)
☐ Place your mouth on the tube
☐ Exhale forcefully (to the maximum)
☐ Read the VC value and reset the apparatus to zero

☐ **4** Inspiratory reserve volume (IRV) is the volume of air that can be inspired forcefully after a normal inspiration. Because your spirometer is not really set up to do this, determine the IRV by subtracting TV and ERV from the vital capacity:

$$IRV = VC - (TV + ERV)$$

❏ 5 Analyze and interpret your results. Compare TV, ERV, VC, and IRV to the "textbook" values given in the box. How do you account for any differences?

Pulmonary Volumes and Capacities

VOLUME	DEFINITION	TYPICAL VALUE
Tidal volume (TV)	Volume moved into or out of the respiratory tract during a normal respiratory cycle	0.5 L
Inspiratory reserve volume (IRV)	Maximum volume that can be moved into the respiratory tract after a normal inspiration	3.0 L
Expiratory reserve volume (ERV)	Maximum volume that can be moved out of the respiratory tract after a normal expiration	1.1 L
Residual volume (RV)	Volume remaining in the respiratory tract after maximum expiration	1.2 L
Capacity	Formula	Typical Value
Vital capacity (VC)	TV + IRV + ERV	4.6 L
Inspiratory capacity (IC)	TV + IRV	3.5 L
Functional residual capacity (FRC)	ERV + RV	2.3 L
Total lung capacity (TLC)	TV + IRV + ERV + RV	5.8 L

B. FORCED EXPIRATORY VITAL CAPACITY

The **forced expiratory vital capacity (FVC)** test is useful in determining the nature of pulmonary conditions. In the FVC test, the subject maximally inhales, then maximally exhales as rapidly as possible. The event is timed and a reading taken at exactly 1 second after the beginning of expiration. The 1-second volume is called the **forced expiratory volume** at 1 second, or **FEV₁**. The total amount expired, however long it takes, is the FVC **(Figure 43-4)**. If the FEV₁ is much less than 80% of the FVC, then airway obstruction is suspected. For example, airway constriction in asthma produces a low FEV₁/FVC percentage. The increased resistance to airflow in constricted airways prevents air from being expired rapidly.

The spirometry apparatus used here is not the best for measuring FEV₁ values; however, a rough estimate can be made by following the procedure described.

❏ 1 Designate a SUBJECT, a TIMER, and a RECORDER in your lab team. As the SUBJECT prepares to exhale into the spirometer tube,

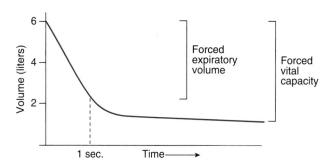

FIGURE 43-4 Spirogram of the forced expiratory vital capacity (FVC) test. In normal subjects, about 80% of the total FVC is exhaled during the first second of forced rapid expiration.

the TIMER stands ready to call "time" at exactly 1 second. The RECORDER will mark the spirometer scale at (or take note of) the volume indicated when "time" is called.
If a one-way valve is used:
❏ Have the SUBJECT place his or her mouth on the tube
❏ Exhale as forcefully and rapidly as possible until the maximum expiration is reached
If a one-way valve is not used:
❏ Have the SUBJECT inhale maximally
❏ Have the SUBJECT place his or her mouth on the tube
❏ Have the SUBJECT exhale as forcefully and rapidly as possible until maximum expiration is reached
❏ 2 The TIMER calls "time" at 1 second after the beginning of exhalation, and the RECORDER marks or makes note of the spirometer volume at exactly that point. This volume is FEV₁. Record the volume at the end of forceful expiration. This volume is FVC.

> **Hint** This method is very inaccurate, but a reasonable approximation of FEV₁ can be obtained if you practice the procedure a few times. More accurate results can be obtained with recording spirometers or spirometers with FEV timing devices. •

❏ 3 Determine the FEV₁/FVC percentage by using this equation:

$$FEV1/FVC\% = (FEV1 \div FVC) \times 100$$

Is the result 80% or above? Try the test on a subject with a known obstructive pulmonary condition. What are your results?

C. EFFECTS OF EXERCISE

Try repeating Activity A, the determination of pulmonary volumes and capacities, using a subject who has just exercised. After determining resting values, have the subject exercise heavily for 2 to 5 minutes. Immediately after exercise has stopped, measure the pulmonary volumes again. How have they changed? How do you account for the changes? Try measuring the volume after about 20 minutes of rest. Explain your results.

D. USING AVAILABLE SPIROMETRY DEVICE

The previous activities present some basic determinations of pulmonary volumes and capacities using traditional equipment. Activities D and E present a method that uses a traditional wet spirometer with computer-assisted data acquisition.

Computer-assisted techniques have become the norm in clinical and research settings (see **Figure 43-1**). The following activities are based on Intelitool's SPIROCOMP apparatus for use with personal computers. (Your institution may use another spirometry device. Ask your instructor for the appropriate information.) The SPIROCOMP program has the feature of collecting and saving group results so that they can be compared later. Your lab section may want to design an experiment to test a hypothesis. You can then use the program's built-in group data collection to gather your results.

safety first

Heed the safety advice given previously in this exercise and in the SPIROCOMP manual. •

The instructions given here parallel the tests outlined in the previous activities.

☐ 1 Use the arrow keys to select RUN SPIROCOMP or EXPERIMENT MENU at the main menu. If the spirometer has not been calibrated, or if the chain has slipped and recalibration is required, the CALIBRATE SPIROCOMP routine will appear. When instructed by the program, lift the spirometer chain off the pulley by pulling up on the *weighted* side of the chain. Turn the pulley knob until the calibration number on the screen reads "0 (±5)." Replace the chain, making sure the pointer is at 0 L. Press any key. Inflate to 5 L *exactly* and press any key.

☐ 2 Answer the question about group records as you wish by pressing the key indicated on the screen. Next you will be asked information about the subject: initials (for identification), gender (M or F), age (in years), and height (in centimeters). Enter each value as asked, pressing ENTER after each entry. The data acquisition screen appears after you are finished. *Windows users* enter data by clicking on FILE and NEW; then type in the name of the new database and save it. Click on ACQUIRE and press CTRL R and enter the data.

Hint Each test should be done with a subject but operated by a separate lab partner. The subject should not look at the computer operator or the computer screen during the tests, or the results might be biased. The subject should rest for several minutes before undertaking the tests. •

☐ 3 Perform the ERV test: Put the mouthpiece in the subject's mouth (do not forget the noseclip). Press E while the subject inhales. The subject should follow these instructions, which appear on the screen:
   ☐ "Breathe normal (tidal) cycles" until told to stop.
   ☐ "Stop after (next) normal exhale"—wait for the next message.
   ☐ "Exhale fully (maximally)"—you will hear a bell sound.
   ☐ The ERV is automatically calculated for you.

Hint The SPIROCOMP manual contains additional information regarding control keys. Any test may be repeated, but only the last test is saved in the memory. Pressing the space bar will abort a test, and the system will try to use the data already collected. Select P or click on FILE and PRINT. •

☐ 4 Perform the TV test: Press T while inhaling and "breathe normal (tidal) cycles" as directed. The system automatically determines average TV after several cycles. If TV is high enough to fill the spirometer before the end of three cycles, press the space bar during inhalation of the second cycle.

☐ 5 Perform the VC test: Press V and follow the instructions telling the subject to inhale maximally, then exhale maximally. Continue exhalation until a VC graph begins to appear on the screen. This maneuver takes some practice.

Hint Notice that the program automatically calculates VC, IRV, FEV_1, and other values. The next section of this exercise explains the meaning of the graph's elements. Press P at any data screen to obtain a printout of the graph. •

☐ 6 When you are ready to test the next subject, press CTRL R and proceed as before. Continue until all subjects have been tested.

☐ 7 After the last test, press the ESC key to return to the main menu. Click the GRAPH AVERAGES button. A graph of averaged data will appear. Obtain a hard copy printout by clicking on FILE and PRINT. Press ESC to return to the main menu or REVIEW/ANALYZE MENU and select DATA REVIEW (SPREADSHEET) or VIEW SPREADSHEET. Click the SUMMARY TABLE button instead and then click on FILE and PRINT to obtain a printed copy.

E. GRAPHING YOUR RESULTS

Figure 43-5 approximates what is seen in the SPIROCOMP data screen. It is a bar chart representing these values:

☐ **cIRV**—Computed inspiratory reserve volume; recall that IRV is calculated by the equation:

$$cIRV = VC - (TV + ERV)$$

❏ **TV**—Tidal volume (averaged from three cycles)
❏ **ERV**—Expiratory reserve volume (value in liters is printed below this and other bars)
❏ **VC**—Vital capacity (computed); recall that VC is calculated by the equation:

$$VC = ERV + TV + cIRV$$

❏ **VC**—Vital capacity (measured); this is the result from the VC test; the forced expiratory volumes (FEVs) at 1 second (FEV$_1$),

2 seconds (FEV$_2$), and 3 seconds (FEV$_3$) are given—actually, they are not volumes but are FEVx/FVC percentage.

☐ **pVC**—Predicted vital capacity; this value is based on research data from subjects of the same size, age, and gender. (Use this value rather than the expected average VC given in the first table in Lab Report 43.)

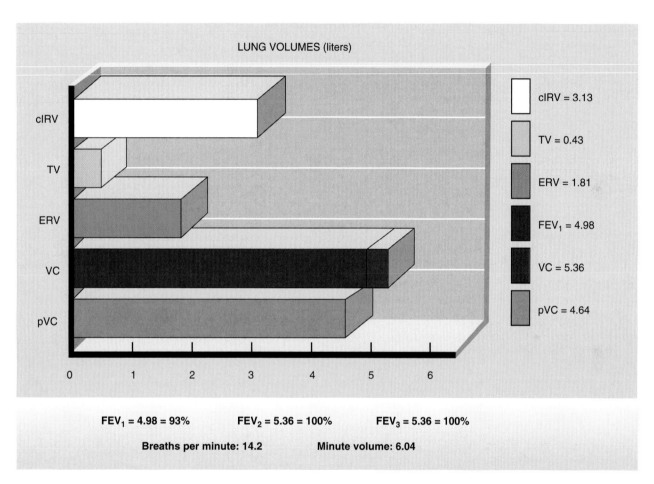

LUNG VOLUMES (liters)

cIRV = 3.13
TV = 0.43
ERV = 1.81
FEV$_1$ = 4.98
VC = 5.36
pVC = 4.64

FEV$_1$ = 4.98 = 93%   FEV$_2$ = 5.36 = 100%   FEV$_3$ = 5.36 = 100%

Breaths per minute: 14.2   Minute volume: 6.04

FIGURE 43-5 Data graph similar to that in the SPIROCOMP screen.

Name: _____ Date: _____ Section: _____

LAB REPORT 43
Pulmonary Volumes and Capacities

Resting:

VOLUME OR CAPACITY	EXPECTED VALUE*	ACTUAL VALUE†	DIFFERENCE	INTERPRETATION
Tidal volume (TV)				
(Average)	0.5 L (500 ml)			
Expiratory reserve volume (ERV)				
(Average)	1.1 L (1100 ml)			
Vital capacity (VC)				
(Average)	4.6 L (4600 ml)			
Inspiratory reserve volume (IRV)				
(Average)	3.0 L (3000 ml)			

*Predicted values are general approximations. Factors such as body surface area, sex, age, and athletic conditioning affect predicted values. If a "predicted vital capacity chart" is available, use the figure from that rather than the figure given here.

†Be sure to indicate units for each reported value (ml or L).

TRIAL	FEV$_1$	FVC	FEV$_1$/FVC %	INTERPRETATION
1				
2				
3				
4				
Best value				

After exercise (0 min):

VOLUME OR CAPACITY	EXPECTED VALUE*	ACTUAL VALUE	DIFFERENCE	INTERPRETATION
TV				
ERV				
VC				
IRV				

*Use the results from the first table on the previous page as your expected results. Be sure to use the correct units of volume when reporting your values.

VOLUME OR CAPACITY	EXPECTED VALUE*	ACTUAL VALUE	DIFFERENCE	INTERPRETATION
TV				
ERV				
VC				
IRV				

*Use the results from the first table on the previous page as your expected results. Be sure to use the correct units of volume when reporting your values.

Discuss your results (comparing resting values with values after exercise):

44
Digestive Structures

The **digestive tract** is a series of hollow organs through which food passes: **mouth, pharynx, esophagus, stomach, small intestine,** and **large intestine.** Each portion is specialized for one or more aspects of the three major functions of the **digestive system:** *secretion, digestion,* and *absorption.* Accessory organs such as the **salivary glands, liver, gallbladder,** and **pancreas** have ducts that lead into the digestive tract and thus support digestive function.

This exercise challenges you to explore the structure and some of the essential functions of the digestive system.

BEFORE YOU BEGIN

☐ Read the appropriate chapter in your textbook.
☐ Set your learning goals. When you finish this exercise, you should be able to:
  ☐ describe the structure of digestive organs and locate them in models and charts
  ☐ identify the principal function of each major digestive organ
  ☐ describe the basic histology of the gastrointestinal wall
☐ Prepare your materials:
  ☐ model of the human torso (dissectible) or chart
  ☐ human skull (with teeth intact)
  ☐ model or specimen of a tooth section
  ☐ microscope
  ☐ prepared microslides:
    ☐ stomach wall c.s.
    ☐ small intestine wall c.s.
    ☐ salivary gland c.s.
☐ Read the directions and safety tips for this exercise *carefully* before starting any procedure.

Study TIPS

Develop a schematic diagram that traces the pathway of food through the entire digestive tract. Include in your design what happens to food as it passes each digestive structure.

A. WALL OF THE DIGESTIVE TRACT

The wall of the digestive tract **(Figure 44-1)** forms a hollow tube continuous with the external environment. Food passes along the tube in a process usually termed **motility.** The wall of the tract is composed of four layers (tunics). They are:

☐ **Mucosa**—Inner lining, consisting of mucous epithelium, connective tissue (*lamina propria*), and a thin layer of smooth muscle (*muscularis mucosae*).

☐ **Submucosa**—Thick layer of connective tissue just superficial to the mucosa; the submucosa includes blood vessels, a network of nerve fibers called the *submucosal plexus,* and *submucosal glands.*
☐ **Muscularis**—Layers of smooth muscle surrounding the submucosa—usually an inner *circular layer* and an outer *longitudinal layer* (the stomach also has a middle *oblique layer*); the muscularis has a network of nerve fibers called the *myenteric plexus.*
☐ **Serosa (adventitia)**—Most superficial layer of the digestive wall, composed entirely of connective tissue (adventitia) or of connective tissue fused to serous epithelial tissue (serosa); the serous membrane extends away from the gastrointestinal wall in folds called *mesenteries;* digestive glands with ducts that lead through the GI wall and into the *lumen* (hollow part) of the GI tract may lie outside the serosa or adventitia.

☐ **1** Locate the digestive tract in a dissectible model of the human torso. Some portions may have the wall cut in a cross section. If so, try to identify each of the four layers previously described. How does each layer differ from organ to organ?

> **! safety first**
> Observe the usual precautions when using the microscope and prepared slides. •

☐ **2** Obtain a prepared slide of a sectioned stomach wall and examine it with your microscope. Identify the four layers of the wall. Examine the mucosa. Notice that it is composed of simple columnar epithelium that forms deep **gastric pits.** They are lined with **surface mucous cells,** which you may recognize as goblet cells. Follow a pit's lumen to the base, or **gastric gland.** You may see more goblet cells called **mucous neck cells.** Some of the very darkly stained cells are **chief cells.** The very pale cells are **parietal cells.** What is the function of each of these cells?
☐ **3** Obtain a prepared slide of a small intestine section. Identify the four layers of the wall. In a true cross section, you cannot tell that the simple columnar epithelium forms large **circular folds,** but you may have noticed them in the model. Each circular fold has fingerlike projections called **villi** that are visible in your specimen.
☐ **4** Obtain a prepared slide of a salivary gland section. Identify the mucus-producing glandular cells by their characteristic light appearance that is produced by the transparent nature

of the mucus that fills them. Try to find the cuboidal duct cells that form rings in a cross-sectioned specimen.

> **Hint** Refer to **Figures 44-2, *B* to *D*,** for color micrographs of the specimens observed in this activity. •

Study TIPS

The Swiss army knife is analogous to the dentition of the human mouth. Humans, being omnivores, have a sort of *Swiss army knife* dentition. A Swiss army knife has many gadgets, but they are really tiny. Humans' dentition has a similar construction. We have one of everything found in both herbivore and carnivore dentition, but none of ours are very capable in comparison. For a complete explanation of this analogy, see the *A&P Survival Guide*.

B. UPPER DIGESTIVE TRACT

Use a dissectible model or other aid to identify the digestive structures indicated.

☐ 1 The **mouth,** or **oral cavity,** is the beginning of the one-way human digestive tract (Figure 44-2, A). Locate these features:
   ☐ **Lips**
   ☐ **Buccinator muscle**—Muscle that forms most of the cheek walls
   ☐ **Tongue**—Mass of muscle covered with mucous epithelium containing *taste buds;* the frenulum is a fold of tissue anchoring its underside to the floor of the mouth
   ☐ **Hard palate**—Anterior bony portion of the mouth's roof
   ☐ **Soft palate**—Posterior soft portion of the mouth's roof (it ends in the conelike uvula)
   ☐ **Palatine tonsils**—Lymphatic structures on the posterior, lateral aspect of the mouth cavity

☐ 2 The 32 **teeth** of the normal adult are special features of the mouth cavity **(Figure 44-3)**. Identify these tooth types in a skull or model. Each type has a representative on each side (left and right) of each jaw (upper and lower):
   ☐ **Incisors**—Central and lateral cutting teeth
   ☐ **Canine**—Tearing tooth
   ☐ **First and second premolars**—Tearing and cutting teeth, each with two points, or *cusps*
   ☐ **First, second, and third molars**—Grinding teeth with three flattened cusps
Find each of these features on a sectioned tooth or tooth model:
   ☐ **Crown**—Superior portion of the tooth
   ☐ **Neck**—Narrow portion, below the crown
   ☐ **Root**—Portion of the tooth within the **alveoli,** or spaces, of the mandible and maxillae
   ☐ **Pulp cavity**—Central space of the tooth filled with **pulp,** which is connective tissue with nerves and vessels
   ☐ **Dentin**—Hard calcified tissue that forms most of the tooth shell
   ☐ **Enamel**—Hard, nonliving mineralized substance that covers the dentin of the crown
   ☐ **Gingiva**—Mucous epithelial covering of the *alveolar ridges* of the jaws
   ☐ **Periodontal membrane**—Fibrous lining of the alveolar walls (**periodontal ligaments** project from this membrane to the root of the tooth, keeping it in place)

☐ 3 The **salivary glands** are exocrine glands whose ducts empty into the mouth cavity. **Saliva** produced by the glands is a watery solution containing mucus, mineral ions, and digestive enzymes. Identify these pairs of salivary glands in **Figure 44-4** and in a model:
   ☐ **Parotid glands**—The largest pair, just anterior to each ear; each secretes a serous (watery) solution that flows through a **parotid duct** leading to the cheek wall across from the second upper molar.

Coloring Exercises: **Wall of the GI Tract**

Use colored pens or pencils to shade in both the figure and the labels. Each red numeral in the figure corresponds to a matching red numeral following the appropriate label.

Serosa
VISCERAL PERITONEUM₁
CONNECTIVE TISSUE OF
   SEROSA₂

Muscularis
LONGITUDINAL LAYER₃
CIRCULAR LAYER₄

Submucosa
SUBMUCOSA₅

Mucosa
LAMINA PROPRIA₆
MUCOUS EPITHELIUM₇

Related Structures
LYMPH NODULE₈
SUBMUCOSAL GLAND₉
MUCOSAL GLAND₁₀
SUBMUCOSAL PLEXUS₁₁
MYENTERIC PLEXUS₁₂
NERVE₁₃
BLOOD VESSEL₁₄
MESENTERY₁₅
GLAND OUTSIDE OF
   TRACT₁₆

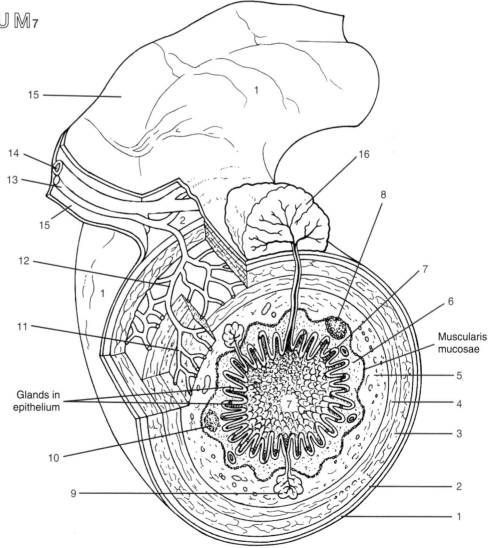

Muscularis mucosae

Glands in epithelium

FIGURE 44-1 Wall of the GI tract.

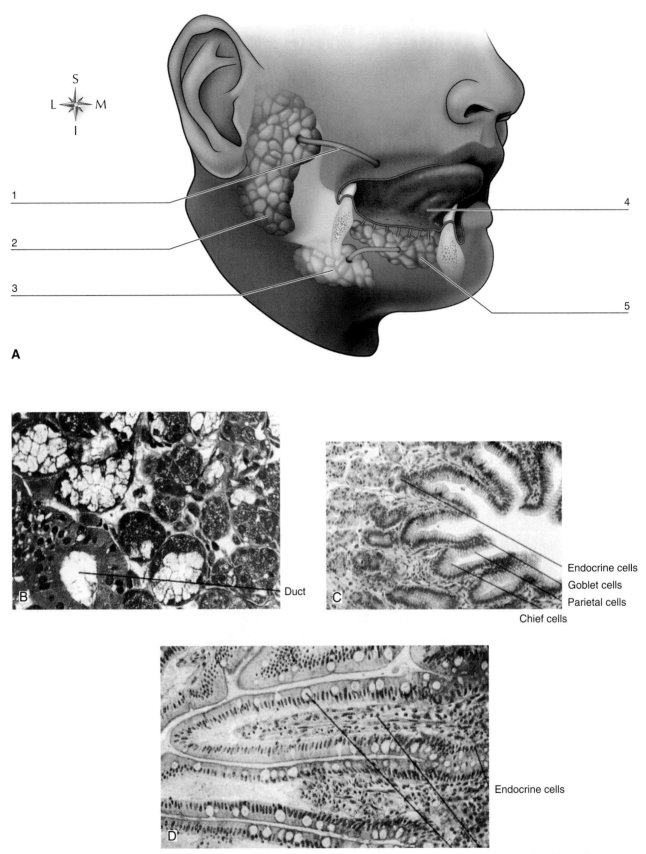

S
L — M
I

1

2

3

4

5

A

B — Duct

C
Endocrine cells
Goblet cells
Parietal cells
Chief cells

D
Endocrine cells

Goblet cell   Blood vessel and lacteal

FIGURE 44-2 **A**, Identify the features of the mouth indicated on the lines provided and on the blanks in the Lab Report at the end of this exercise. **B**, Salivary gland tissue. **C**, Epithelium of the stomach. **D**, Epithelium of the small intestine.

Coloring Exercises: Mouth and Teeth

Use colored pens or pencils to shade in both the figure and the labels. Each red numeral in the figure corresponds to a matching red numeral following the appropriate label.

Mouth

LIPS₁
BUCCINATOR MUSCLE₂
TONGUE₃
HARD PALATE₄
SOFT PALATE₅
UVULA₆
PALATINE TONSILS₇
OROPHARYNX₈

Teeth

Tooth Types

CENTRAL INCISOR₉
LATERAL INCISOR₁₀
CANINE₁₁
FIRST PREMOLAR₁₂
SECOND PREMOLAR₁₃
FIRST MOLAR₁₄
SECOND MOLAR₁₅
THIRD MOLAR₁₆

Tooth Features

CROWN₁₇
NECK₁₈
ROOT₁₉
PULP CAVITY₂₀
PULP₂₁
DENTIN₂₂
ENAMEL₂₃
GINGIVA₂₄
PERIODONTAL
    MEMBRANE₂₅
PERIODONTAL
    LIGAMENTS₂₆
ALVEOLAR RIDGE₂₇

FIGURE 44-3 A, Structure of the oral cavity. **B,** Structure of a tooth.

☐ **Submandibular glands**—Medial to the angle of the mandible, these glands produce mostly serous fluid and some mucous fluid. Their ducts empty onto the mouth floor, just lateral to the frenulum.

☐ **Sublingual glands**—Smallest pair of salivary glands in the floor of the mouth, they produce mostly mucous fluid, which flows into the mouth through 10 or more small ducts in the mouth's floor.

☐ 4 The **pharynx**, or throat, is divided into three regions:

☐ **Nasopharynx**

☐ **Oropharynx**

☐ **Laryngopharynx**

☐ 5 The **esophagus** is a long muscular tube connecting the pharynx to the stomach. Upper and lower **esophageal sphincters** may be represented in the model you are using. The *lower esophageal sphincter* is also sometimes called the *cardiac sphincter*.

☐ 6 The **stomach** is an enlargement of the digestive tract just inferior to the diaphragm, at the end of the esophagus. Locate these stomach features in a model or chart:

☐ **Cardiac opening**—Opening from the esophagus into the stomach region called the **cardiac region**. The size of the cardiac opening is regulated by a ring of muscle called the **cardiac sphincter** (lower esophageal sphincter).

☐ **Fundus**—Region of the stomach superior to the cardiac opening.

☐ **Body**—Main portion of the stomach, forming a **greater curvature** and a **lesser curvature**.

☐ **Pyloric region**—Portion of the stomach near the **pyloric opening** into the small intestine and the **pyloric sphincter** that surrounds the opening.

☐ **Rugae**—Large folds of the mucosa.

C. LOWER DIGESTIVE TRACT

☐ 1 The **small intestine** is a long, narrow tube that folds to fill a large portion of the abdominal cavity (see Figure 44-4). Find these features of the small intestine:

☐ **Duodenum**—Short (±25 cm), C-shaped beginning of the small intestine

☐ **Jejunum**—Long (±2.5 m) middle section of the small intestine

☐ **Ileum**—Very long (±3.5 m) end section of the small intestine

☐ **Common bile duct**—Duct that empties into the duodenum

☐ **Ileocecal junction**—Junction of the ileum with the large intestine, featuring an **ileocecal sphincter** and a one-way **ileocecal valve**.

☐ 2 The **liver**, a large gland in the superior right abdominal cavity, produces **bile** that is secreted into the duodenum. Two **hepatic ducts** conduct bile from the liver and fuse to form a **common hepatic duct**. The common hepatic duct joins the two-way **cystic duct** from the **gallbladder** (just inferior to the liver) to form the **common bile duct**. The common bile duct empties into the duodenum.

☐ 3 The **pancreas** is a gland, cradled in the C of the duodenum, that secretes digestive fluids. Exocrine pancreatic secretions flow through the **pancreatic duct** that joins the common bile duct.

☐ 4 The **large** intestine includes these features:

☐ **Cecum**—A blind sac extending inferiorly from the ileocecal junction; attached to the posterior wall of the cecum is a narrow, wormlike, blind sac called the **appendix**.

☐ **Colon**—A long (±1.6 m) portion of the large intestine that is subdivided into **ascending colon, transverse colon, descending colon,** and **sigmoid colon**; the longitudinal layer of the colon's muscularis forms three bands of muscle called the **teniae coli**; the wall of the colon forms **haustra**, or pouches; the exterior aspect of the colon wall has fatty attachments called **epiploic appendages**.

☐ **Rectum**—Short, straight muscular tube at the end of the sigmoid colon.

☐ **Anal canal**—Short (±2.5 cm) muscular canal at the end of the rectum that exits to the outside of the body by way of the **anus**; it features a smooth muscle **internal anal sphincter** at its superior end and a skeletal muscle **external anal sphincter** at its inferior end.

☐ 5 The organs and inner wall of the abdominal cavity are covered with a serous membrane called the **peritoneum**. The portion that covers the organs is called the **visceral peritoneum**, and the portion that lines the cavity walls is called the **parietal peritoneum**. Extensions of the peritoneum, composed of a thin sheet of connective tissue sandwiched between two layers of serous membrane, support the visceral organs. These extensions are called **mesenteries**. Find these mesenteries in your model:

☐ **Lesser omentum**—It is located between the lesser curvature of the stomach and the liver (and diaphragm).

☐ **Greater omentum**—It connects the stomach's greater curvature to the transverse colon and posterior abdominal wall. It has a long, fatty, double fold that forms an apronlike pocket called the **omental bursa** over the front of the viscera.

Coloring Exercises: Digestive System

Use colored pens or pencils to shade in both the figure and the labels. Each red numeral in the figure corresponds to a matching red numeral following the appropriate label.

ORAL CAVITY1
PAROTID GLAND2
SUBMANDIBULAR GLAND3
SUBLINGUAL GLAND4
PHARYNX5
ESOPHAGUS6
CARDIAC OPENING7
FUNDUS8
CARDIAC REGION9
BODY OF STOMACH10
PYLORIC REGION11
PYLORIC SPHINCTER12
DUODENUM13
JEJUNUM14
ILEUM15
COMMON BILE DUCT16
ILEOCECAL VALVE17
LIVER18
COMMON HEPATIC DUCT19
CYSTIC DUCT20
GALLBLADDER21
PANCREAS22
PANCREATIC DUCT23
CECUM24
APPENDIX25
ASCENDING COLON26
TRANSVERSE COLON27
DESCENDING COLON28
SIGMOID COLON29
RECTUM30
ANAL CANAL31

FIGURE 44-4 Organs of digestion. NOTE: Many organs are shown as being separated from one another for illustration purposes only. In reality, many digestive organs overlap one another when viewed from this perspective.

clinical application: fluoroscopy

Fluoroscopy is a type of radiographic imaging that uses a fluorescent screen rather than film. X-rays pass through the patient and are absorbed by the screen's coating. The energy is reemitted by the coating as light energy. Dense tissues cast a dark shadow on the screen. Therefore, continuous radiation allows a continuous moving image in a moving patient.

Fluoroscopy with the contrast medium **barium sulfate** is used to visualize portions of the digestive tract. A *barium swallow*, or **upper GI series**, images the stomach and portions of the esophagus and small intestine. A *barium enema* (**lower GI series**) images the rectum and colon. A **hernia** of the digestive tract, where a portion of the tract is pushed out of a weak spot in the abdominopelvic wall, can be detected this way. **Ulcers**, holes in the digestive wall, can also be assessed in this manner.

Because fluoroscopy allows observation of the body in motion, it can be used to see the muscular movements of the digestive tract as the barium passes through it. A person can push on the abdomen from the outside to see how digestive organs withstand pressure, similar to compression of abdominal muscles during heavy lifting.

Figure 44-5, *A* and *B*, are regular x-ray photographs taken of an upper and lower GI series. A fluoroscope image would be reversed (black on white, not the white on black seen here). Try to identify the labeled parts on the lines provided and on the blanks in the Lab Report at the end of this exercise.

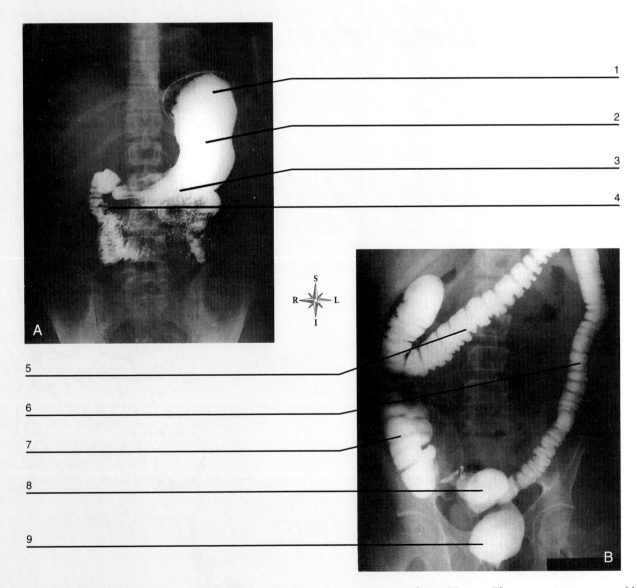

FIGURE 44-5 Radiographs of **A**, a barium swallow, or upper GI and, **B**, a barium enema, or lower GI. NOTE: Fluoroscope images appear black on white, the reverse of the white-on-black images shown here.

Name: _____   Date: _____   Section: _____

LAB REPORT 44
Digestive Structures

Specimen: *stomach wall c.s.*
Total Magnification: _____

Specimen: *small intestine wall c.s.*
Total Magnification: _____

Specimen: *salivary gland c.s.*
Total Magnification: _____

STRUCTURE	MODEL	FUNCTION(S)
Oral cavity	☐	
Buccinator muscle	☐	
Tongue	☐	
Palate: hard, soft	☐	
Uvula	☐	
Palatine tonsils	☐	
Incisors: central, lateral	☐	
Canine teeth	☐	
Premolars: first, second	☐	
Molars: first, second, third	☐	
Parotid glands	☐	
Submandibular glands	☐	
Sublingual glands	☐	
Pharynx	☐	
Esophagus	☐	
Cardiac opening, region	☐	
Fundus	☐	
Body of stomach	☐	
Stomach curvatures: greater, lesser	☐	
Pyloric opening, region	☐	
Rugae	☐	
Duodenum	☐	
Jejunum	☐	
Ileum	☐	
Circular folds	☐	

Continued

STRUCTURE	MODEL	FUNCTION(S)
Common bile duct	☐	
Ileocecal junction: valve, sphincter	☐	
Common hepatic duct	☐	
Cystic duct	☐	
Pancreas	☐	
Pancreatic duct	☐	
Cecum	☐	
Appendix	☐	
Ascending colon	☐	
Transverse colon	☐	
Descending colon	☐	
Rectum	☐	
Anal canal, anus	☐	
Lesser omentum	☐	
Greater omentum	☐	

Figure 44-2 (from p. 418)

1. _____
2. _____
3. _____
4. _____
5. _____
6. _____
7. _____

Figure 44-5 (from p. 422)

1. _____
2. _____
3. _____
4. _____
5. _____
6. _____
7. _____
8. _____
9. _____

Fill-in

1. _____
2. _____
3. _____
4. _____
5. _____
6. _____
7. _____

Fill-in (complete each statement with the correct term)

1. The stomach's mucosa forms large folds called _?_.

2. The two ducts that exit the liver and join to form the common hepatic duct are called _?_ ducts.

3. The colon is divided into _?_ sections.

4. The _?_ duct empties into the duodenum.

5. A substance called _?_ covers the dentin of the tooth's crown.

6. The _?_ is the portion of the pharynx posterior to the mouth cavity.

7. The _?_ sphincter prevents stomach contents from flowing back into the esophagus.

45
Dissection: Digestive System

In this exercise, you continue your study of digestive anatomy by dissecting a whole preserved specimen.

Activity A provides directions for studying the digestive anatomy of the cat. Activity B is an alternate activity, providing directions for studying the digestive anatomy of the fetal pig.

BEFORE YOU BEGIN

☐ Read the appropriate chapter in your textbook.
☐ Set your learning goals. When you finish this exercise, you should be able to:
  ☐ dissect the digestive anatomy of a preserved cat or fetal pig
  ☐ identify the primary organs of the digestive tract in a dissected mammalian specimen
  ☐ identify the accessory organs of digestion in a dissected mammalian specimen
☐ Prepare your materials:
  ☐ preserved cat or fetal pig
  ☐ dissection tools and trays
  ☐ storage container (if specimen is to be reused)
☐ Read the directions and safety tips for this exercise *carefully* before starting any procedure.

> **!** ***safety first***
> Observe the usual precautions when working with a preserved specimen. Heed the safety advice accompanying preservatives used with your specimen. Use protective gloves while handling your specimen. Avoid injury with dissection tools. Use safety goggles to avoid injury during dissections. Dispose of or store your specimen as instructed. •

Study TIPS

As recommended in the other dissections, as you complete this dissection, use a diagram or illustration to compare your specimen with that of the human digestive tract. For reference, use your lab manual, textbook, or the *A&P Survival Guide*. Use the camera on your cell phone to take photos of the specimen and use them later as a resource.

A. DIGESTIVE ANATOMY OF THE CAT

This activity challenges you to identify the major digestive structures of the cat. Assuming you have already removed the cat's skin (Exercise 10) and opened the abdominopelvic cavity (Exercise 40), you simply have to move the viscera out of the way (without cutting or removing them) to see the structures indicated in this activity.

> **Hint** **Figure 45-1** illustrates many of the structures of the cat listed in this activity. •

☐ 1 Identify the **peritoneum,** the serous membrane that lines the wall of the abdominopelvic cavity (*parietal peritoneum*) and covers the organs within the cavity (*visceral peritoneum*). Identify these extensions or folds of the peritoneum:
  ☐ **Greater omentum** and **lesser omentum**
  ☐ **Mesentery**

> **Hint** The *greater omentum* is a large, fatty fold of the peritoneum that lies like an apron over the ventral surfaces of the abdominopelvic organs. You must lift or cut this "apron" out of the way to see most of the digestive organs described in the following steps. •

☐ 2 Identify the **liver** with its *left lobes* and *right lobes*. Locate the **gallbladder** at the posterior surface of the right lobes of the liver. Trace the **cystic duct** from the gallbladder and the **hepatic ducts** from the lobes of the liver. Note where they join to form the **common bile duct.**
☐ 3 Locate the curved **stomach.** Identify these regions of the stomach:
  ☐ **Fundus**
  ☐ **Body**
  Cut the stomach open and identify the mucosal folds called **rugae.**
☐ 4 Identify the **pancreas.** It is composed of two lobes of glandular tissue, one that is embedded in the *mesentery* along the duodenum and one that extends along the edge of the stomach.

☐ 5 The **small intestine** extends posteriorly from the pylorus of the stomach. Identify these portions of the small intestine:
   ☐ **Duodenum**
   ☐ **Jejunum**
   ☐ **Ileum**
☐ 6 The **large intestine** attaches to the distal end of the ileum of the small intestine. Locate these portions of the large intestine:
   ☐ **Cecum**
   ☐ **Ascending colon**
   ☐ **Transverse colon**
   ☐ **Descending colon**
   ☐ **Rectum**
   ☐ **Anus**

B. DIGESTIVE ANATOMY OF THE FETAL PIG

This activity challenges you to identify the major digestive structures of the fetal pig. Assuming you have already removed the animal's skin (Exercise 10) and opened the abdominopelvic cavity (Exercise 40), you simply have to move the viscera out of the way (without cutting or removing them) to see the structures indicated in this activity.

> **Hint** **Figure 45-2** illustrates many of the structures of the fetal pig listed in this activity. •

☐ 1 Identify the **peritoneum,** the serous membrane that lines the wall of the abdominopelvic cavity (*parietal peritoneum*) and covers the organs within the cavity (*visceral peritoneum*). Identify these extensions or folds of the peritoneum:
   ☐ **Greater omentum**
   ☐ **Mesentery**

> **Hint** The *greater omentum* is a large, fatty fold of the peritoneum that lies like an apron over the ventral surfaces of the abdominopelvic organs. You must lift or cut this "apron" out of the way to see most of the digestive organs described in the following steps. •

☐ 2 Identify the **liver** with its *left lobes* and *right lobes*. Locate the **gallbladder** at the posterior surface of the right lobes of the liver. Trace the **cystic duct** from the gallbladder and the **hepatic ducts** from the lobes of the liver. Note where they join to form the **common bile duct.**
☐ 3 Locate the curved **stomach.** Identify these regions of the stomach:
   ☐ **Fundus**
   ☐ **Body**
   ☐ **Pylorus**
   Cut the stomach open and identify the mucosal folds called **rugae.**
☐ 4 Identify the **pancreas,** a mass of glandular tissue that lies within the curve of the duodenum of the small intestine.
☐ 5 The **small intestine** extends posteriorly from the pylorus of the stomach. Identify these portions of the small intestine:
   ☐ **Duodenum**
   ☐ **Jejunum**
   ☐ **Ileum**
   The **large intestine** attaches to the distal end of the ileum of the small intestine. There are two main portions of the large intestine. The proximal portion is a coiled loop called the **spiral colon.** The distal portion is the **rectum,** which terminates at the **anus.**

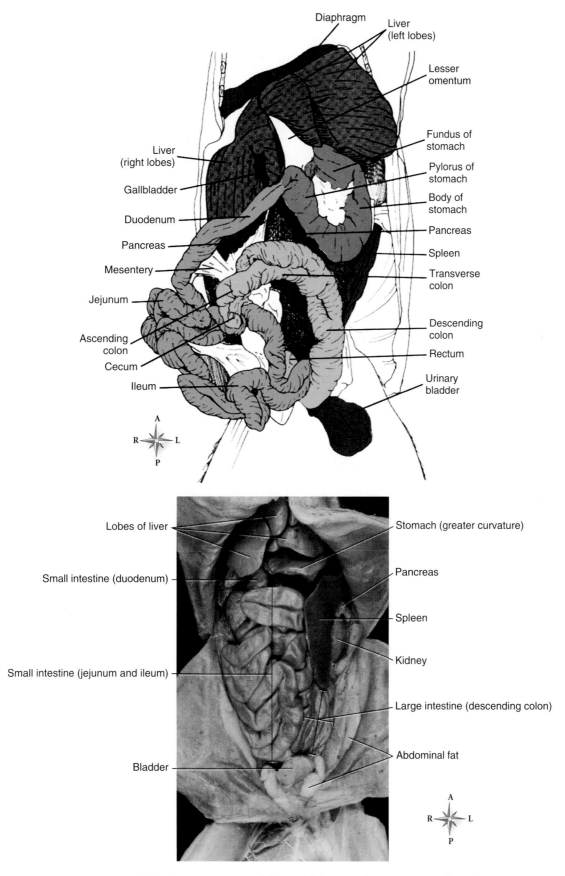

FIGURE 45-1 Digestive anatomy of the cat (abdominopelvic cavity, ventral view).

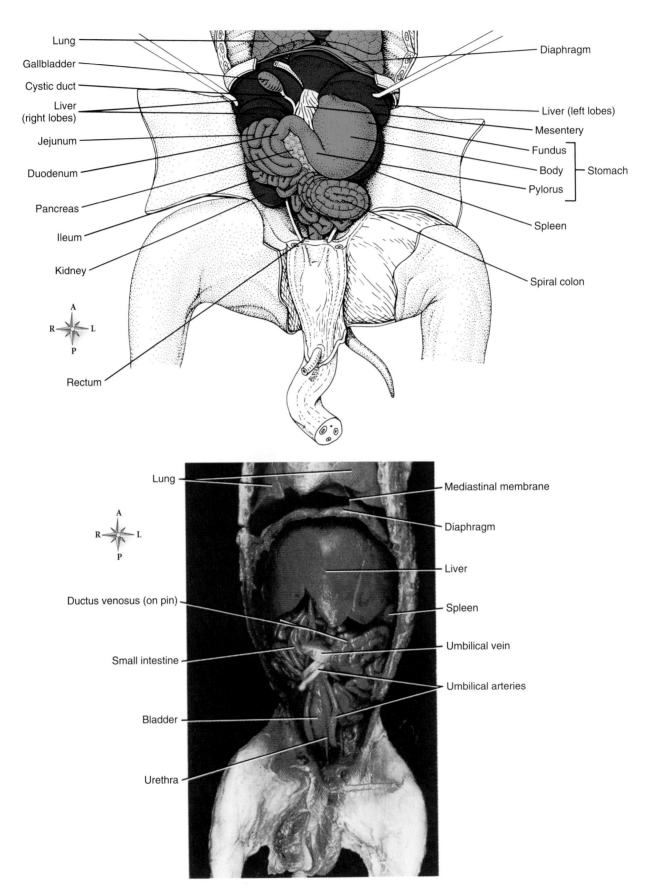

Lung
Gallbladder
Cystic duct
Liver (right lobes)
Jejunum
Duodenum
Pancreas
Ileum
Kidney

A
R — L
P

Rectum

Diaphragm
Liver (left lobes)
Mesentery
Fundus
Body — Stomach
Pylorus
Spleen
Spiral colon

Lung
Mediastinal membrane
Diaphragm
Liver
Spleen

A
R — L
P

Ductus venosus (on pin)
Small intestine
Bladder
Urethra

Umbilical vein
Umbilical arteries

FIGURE 45-2 Digestive anatomy of the fetal pig (abdominopelvic cavity, ventral view).

Name: _____ Date: _____ Section: _____

LAB REPORT 45
Dissection: Digestive System

A. Cat Dissection Checklist

☐ parietal peritoneum

☐ visceral peritoneum

☐ greater omentum

☐ mesentery

☐ mesocolon

☐ liver

    ☐ left lobes

    ☐ right lobes

☐ gallbladder

☐ cystic duct

☐ hepatic ducts

☐ common bile duct

☐ stomach

    ☐ fundus

    ☐ body

    ☐ pylorus

    ☐ rugae

☐ pancreas

☐ small intestine

    ☐ duodenum

    ☐ jejunum

    ☐ ileum

☐ large intestine

    ☐ cecum

    ☐ ascending colon

    ☐ transverse colon

    ☐ descending colon

    ☐ rectum

    ☐ anus

B. Fetal Pig Dissection Checklist

☐ parietal peritoneum

☐ visceral peritoneum

☐ greater omentum

☐ mesentery

☐ liver

    ☐ left lobes

    ☐ right lobes

☐ gallbladder

☐ cystic duct

☐ hepatic ducts

☐ common bile duct

☐ stomach

    ☐ fundus

    ☐ body

    ☐ pylorus

    ☐ rugae

☐ pancreas

☐ small intestine

    ☐ duodenum

    ☐ jejunum

    ☐ ileum

☐ large intestine

    ☐ spiral colon

    ☐ rectum

    ☐ anus

46

Enzymes and Digestion

The term **digestion** refers to the breaking down of complex nutrients into simpler ones. Digestion involves mechanical processes that simply break the nutrients into smaller chunks and chemical processes that split large molecules into smaller molecules. In this exercise, you will look at examples of both types of digestive processes. As an example of a mechanical process, you will use **bile salts** secreted by the liver to break apart lipid droplets. You will use pancreatic **enzymes** to chemically break apart complex carbohydrate and lipid molecules. Enzymes are proteins that catalyze biochemical reactions. **Figure 46-1** shows how enzymes accomplish chemical digestion.

BEFORE YOU BEGIN

❏ Read the appropriate chapter in your textbook.
❏ Set your learning goals. When you finish this exercise, you should be able to:
  ☐ describe the action of pancreatic enzymes on carbohydrates and lipids
  ☐ explain the effects of temperature on enzyme activity
  ☐ perform tests to determine the presence of starch and sugars
  ☐ demonstrate the action of bile on lipids
❏ Prepare your materials:
  ☐ distilled water
  ☐ pancreatin powder (and spatula)
  ☐ 1% starch solution
  ☐ 1% maltose solution
  ☐ Benedict reagent
  ☐ ice water bath (with test tube rack)
  ☐ warm water bath (37°C, with tube rack)
  ☐ hot plate
  ☐ Lugol reagent
  ☐ disposable 1-ml measuring droppers
  ☐ test tubes (approximately 10 ml), tube caps
  ☐ test tube racks and tongs
  ☐ wax pencils
  ☐ beakers (500 ml)
  ☐ bile salt powder (and spatula)
  ☐ vegetable oil (dyed with Sudan B)
  ☐ litmus cream
❏ Read the directions and safety tips for this exercise *carefully* before starting any procedure.

Study **TIPS**

Before you complete this lab activity, review the action of the various enzymes on each of the macromolecules. Remember, the purpose of chemical digestion is to break down these macromolecules into their simplest form. To help you understand this, think of a child's small building blocks. They use these small blocks to construct a larger structure. The large structure represents the macromolecule (polymer). Each of the small blocks represents the monomer. In order for us to use the food we eat, we must break it down to its simplest form (monomer). After we break it down, we can then use these monomers to "build" within our bodies.

A. OBSERVING CARBOHYDRATE DIGESTION

As you know, carbohydrates are molecules composed of carbon, hydrogen, and oxygen arranged in chemical units called **saccharides**. **Polysaccharides** are complex carbohydrates, such as *starch* and *glycogen*, composed of many saccharide units. **Disaccharides** such as *sucrose*, *lactose*, and *maltose* are types of complex sugars composed of two saccharide units. **Monosaccharides** such as the simple sugars *glucose (dextrose)*, *galactose*, and *fructose* are single saccharide units. Because the digestive tract absorbs carbohydrates only in their simplest form (monosaccharides), digestive processes must break polysaccharides and disaccharides into smaller units. **Figure 46-2** presents a simplified scheme of how carbohydrates are digested in the human body. **Amylases,** enzymes that break some of the bonds holding polysaccharides together, are found in the saliva and in pancreatic secretions. The disaccharides formed after the amylases have had their effect are then acted on by **disaccharidase** enzymes to yield monosaccharides that can be absorbed into the blood.

In this exercise, you will use an extract of pancreatic secretions called *pancreatin*. Pancreatin contains pancreatic amylase, as well as pancreatic **lipase** and pancreatic **proteolytic** (protein-digesting) enzymes.

> ⓘ *safety first*
> Ask your lab instructor to demonstrate the proper procedure for handling chemicals and glassware and for dealing with spills and other accidents. Wear protective clothing and eyewear. Never point the open end of a test tube toward a person. Be careful to avoid contaminating chemicals: never use a dropper or spatula for more than one type of substance. •

☐ 1 First, practice the tests used to analyze solutions for the presence of starch and its sugar products. If possible, illustrate major steps.

☐ **Lugol test**—Lugol test uses *Lugol reagent* (an iodine solution) to test for the presence of starch. If Lugol iodine turns from its normal orange color to a deep blue-black, starch is present. Mark a test tube **1a** and put in 2 ml (two full droppers) of starch solution. Add a few drops of Lugol reagent. Notice the color change. Anytime you see this result for Lugol test, you have a positive result (meaning starch *is* present). Mark another tube **1b** and put in 2 ml of distilled water and a few drops of Lugol reagent. The solution should be a shade of orange, which is a negative result (meaning starch *is not* present). Save the tubes and their contents for later reference.

> ⓘ *safety first*
> Be careful of electrical and heat hazards when doing Benedict test. Review safety procedures with the instructor before beginning the test. •

☐ **Benedict test**—Benedict test uses Benedict reagent to determine whether a solution contains certain types of sugar. Mark a test tube **2a** and add 2 ml of maltose solution. To this, add 2 ml of **Benedict reagent**. In a tube marked **2b** put 2 ml of distilled water and 2 ml of Benedict reagent. Place each tube in a beaker of boiling water on a hot plate for 3 minutes **(Figure 46-3)**. At the end of 3 minutes, remove the tubes and place them in your rack. Tube **2a** should show a positive result, or a change from blue to another color, meaning sugar is present. Tube **2b** is an example of a negative result, with the contents remaining blue. Save these tubes for later reference.

☐ 2 Mark eight test tubes: **3a, 3b, 4a, 4b, 5a, 5b, 6a,** and **6b**. To each add 2 ml of starch. Next, simultaneously add a small amount of pancreatin (just enough powder to cover the end of the spatula) to each tube. Immediately:

☐ Place tubes **3a** and **3b** in an ice water bath ($0°C$ to $1°C$)

☐ Place tubes **4a** and **4b** in a rack at room temperature ($20°C$ to $25°C$)

☐ Place tubes **5a** and **5b** in a warm water bath set at body temperature ($37°C$)

☐ Place tubes **6a** and **6b** in a boiling water bath ($100°C$)

☐ Allow each tube to stand in its respective bath for 30 minutes. Remove tubes **6a** and **6b** from the boiling water earlier if they decrease to 0.5 ml or less.

☐ 3 At the end of 30 minutes, place all test tubes in the rack. Test all the **a** tubes for starch by adding a few drops of Lugol reagent to each. Test all the **b** tubes for sugar by adding 2 ml of Benedict reagent to each and boiling them for 3 minutes. Record and interpret your results in Lab Report 46. Did starch digestion occur in any of the tubes? Which ones? How do you know? Did temperature affect digestion? How? Can you explain this result?

Coloring Exercises: Digestive Enzyme Activity

Use colored pens or pencils to shade in both the figure and the labels. Each red numeral in the figure corresponds to a matching red numeral following the appropriate label.

PROENZYME1
ACTIVE SITE2
PROSTHETIC GROUP3
PROTEIN KINASE4
ACTIVATED ENZYME5
NUTRIENT A6
NUTRIENT B7
ENZYME RECYCLING8

FIGURE 46-1 Digestive enzyme activity. Enzymes may be released as inactive *proenzymes*, then activated by another enzyme called a *protein kinase*. Nutrient "AB" fits the enzyme's active site and is split into "A" and "B."

Coloring Exercises: Digestion of Nutrients

Use colored pens or pencils to shade in both the figure and the labels. Each red numeral in the figure corresponds to a matching red numeral following the appropriate label.

CARBOHYDRATE DIGESTION[1]

Complex Nutrients

GLYCOGEN[2]
MALTOSE[3]
SUCROSE[4]
LACTOSE[5]

Simple Nutrients

GLUCOSE[6]
FRUCTOSE[7]
GALACTOSE[8]

Enzymes

AMYLASE[9]
MALTASE[10]
SUCRASE[11]
LACTASE[12]

LIPID DIGESTION[13]

Complex Nutrients

TRIGLYCERIDE[14]

Simple Nutrients

GLYCEROL[15]
FATTY ACID[16]
MONOGLYCERIDE[17]

Emulsifying Agents

BILE[18]

Enzymes

LIPASE[19]

PROTEIN DIGESTION[20]

Complex Nutrients

PROTEIN[21]
PEPTIDE[22]

Simple Nutrients

AMINO ACID[23]

Enzymes

PEPSIN[24]
TRYPSIN[25]
CHYMOTRYPSIN[26]
PEPTIDASE[27]

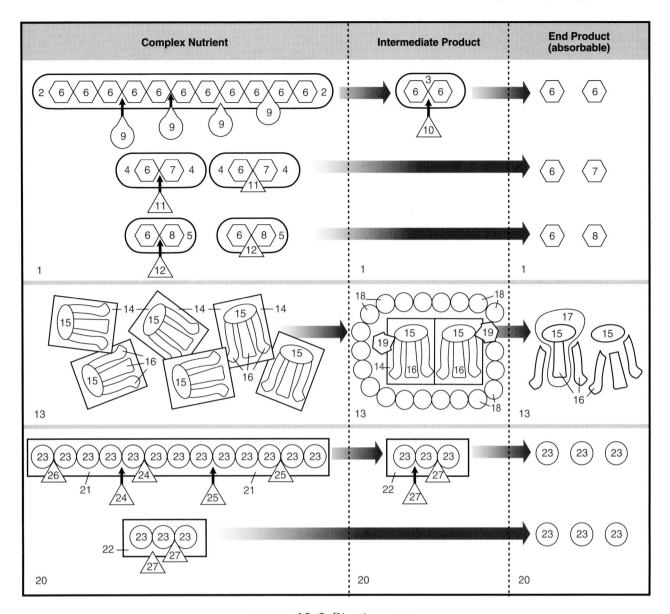

FIGURE 46-2 Digestive processes.

B. OBSERVING LIPID DIGESTION

As described in Figure 46-2, lipids undergo two phases of digestion. The first is a physical process called **emulsification.** Emulsification breaks up large fat droplets into small fat droplets, increasing the fat's surface area and allowing lipase molecules access to the lipid molecules. **Bile salts** secreted by the liver act as *emulsifying agents* in the human digestive tract. The second phase of lipid digestion is a chemical process involving *lipase.* Lipase catalyzes the breakdown of complex lipid molecules into smaller units such as **fatty acid, glycerol, monoglyceride, cholesterol,** and **phospholipids.** Pancreatin, an extract of pancreatic secretions, contains the digestive enzyme pancreatic lipase.

☐ 1 Observe the emulsifying action of bile by performing this demonstration:
   ☐ Mark a test tube **7a** and add 2 ml of distilled water and 2 mL of vegetable oil.
   ☐ Mark a test tube **7b** and add 2 ml of distilled water, 2 ml of vegetable oil, and one spatula of bile salts.
   ☐ Cap the tubes and shake them *simultaneously* for about 30 seconds.
   ☐ Compare the distribution of oil in both tubes. Continue watching them for about 10 minutes. How do you explain the difference between the two tubes?

☐ 2 To observe the results of lipid digestion by pancreatic lipase, follow this procedure:
   ☐ In a tube marked **8a,** put 2 ml of litmus cream, 2 ml of distilled water, and one spatula of pancreatin.
   ☐ In a tube marked **8b,** put 2 ml of litmus cream, 2 ml of distilled water, and one spatula each of pancreatin and bile salts.
   ☐ In a tube marked **8c,** put 2 ml of litmus cream and 2 ml of distilled water.
   ☐ Place all three tubes in a 37° C water bath.
   ☐ Litmus turns from blue to red in the presence of acids. If fatty acids form as a result of lipid digestion, the litmus cream (cream with litmus added) will turn from its original bluish tint to a lavender-pink color and eventually to pink. Observe your tubes for about 1 hour. Do any of the tubes turn pink? How long does it take? How do you explain these results? Report your findings in Lab Report 46.

FIGURE 46-3 A boiling water bath, as used in Benedict test for the presence of sugars.

clinical applications: *enzyme cleaners*

Pancreatin is an extract of pancreatic secretions. It includes pancreatic amylase, lipase, and proteolytic (protein-digesting) enzymes. Wearers of contact lenses sometimes use pancreatin solutions, marketed as enzyme cleaners, to clean their lenses.

Contact lenses float on the tear fluid over the cornea. Over time, components of tear fluid build up on contact lenses. Tear fluid tends to form three layers, as shown in **Figure 46-4**. The top layer is mostly lipids from skin oil (sebum) and other sources. The middle layer is an aqueous solution of salts, proteins, and other substances. The bottom layer is composed mainly of *mucin*, which in turn is composed of combined polysaccharide-protein molecules called *glycoproteins*.

With this background and what you already know about enzymes and digestion, answer the following application questions.

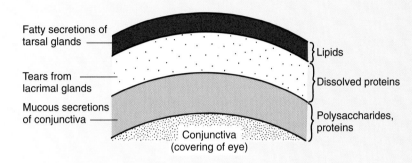

FIGURE 46-4 The three layers of tear fluid on the eye.

1. On which components of the tear fluid can pancreatin act? On what do you base your answer?

2. How would digestion of tear fluid components help a wearer of contact lenses?

3. At what temperature would you recommend using enzymatic contact lens cleaning solutions? Explain.

4. Manufacturers of enzymatic contact lens cleaners recommend that the lenses be soaked in a nonenzyme solution for at least 4 hours after cleaning before wearing them again. What could happen if enzyme remains on a lens when it is put back on an eye?

Name: _____ Date: _____ Section: _____

LAB REPORT 46
Enzymes and Digestion

TUBE	BEGINNING CONTENTS	TEMP	TEST	RESULT	EXPLANATION
1a	Starch	22°C	Lugol (starch)		
1b	Water	22°C	Lugol (starch)		
2a	Maltose	22°C	Benedict (sugar)		
2b	Water	22°C	Benedict (sugar)		
3a	Starch, pancreatin	0°C	Lugol (starch)		
3b	Starch, pancreatin	0°C	Benedict (sugar)		
4a	Starch, pancreatin	22°C	Lugol (starch)		
4b	Starch, pancreatin	22°C	Benedict (sugar)		
5a	Starch, pancreatin	37°C	Lugol (starch)		
5b	Starch, pancreatin	37°C	Benedict (sugar)		
6a	Starch, pancreatin	100°C	Lugol (starch)		
6b	Starch, pancreatin	100°C	Benedict (sugar)		

Discuss the overall meaning of your results by answering the questions posed in Step 3 of Activity A:

TUBE	BEGINNING CONTENTS	TEMP	TEST	RESULT	EXPLANATION
7a	Water, oil	22°C	Visual observation		
7b	Water, oil, bile salts	22°C	Visual observation		
8a	Litmus cream, water, pancreatin	37°C	Litmus (acid)		
8b	Litmus cream, water, pancreatin, bile salts	37°C	Litmus (acid)		
8c	Litmus cream, water	37°C	Litmus (acid)		

Discuss the overall meaning of your results by answering the questions posed in Step 1 and 2 of Activity B:

Fill-in

1. _____
2. _____
3. _____
4. _____
5. _____
6. _____
7. _____
8. _____
9. _____
10. _____
11. _____
12. _____
13. _____
14. _____
15. _____

Fill-in (complete each statement with the correct term)

1. Lipase is an enzyme that digests _?_ molecules.
2. Amylase is an enzyme that digests _?_ molecules.
3. Bile is helpful in preparing _?_ for digestion.
4. The _?_ secretes bile salts.
5. Polysaccharides are broken apart to yield _?_ molecules before being completely digested.
6. Carbohydrates are absorbed into the body in the form of _?_ molecules.
7. The substance _?_ contains several enzymes and is often used to clean contact lenses.
8. _?_ test is used to detect the presence of starch.
9. _?_ test is used to detect the presence of certain sugars.
10. _?_, here used in fatty cream, is a substance used to detect the presence of acids.
11. Enzymes that break apart proteins are termed _?_ enzymes.
12. Glucose is an example of a(n) _?_ type of carbohydrate molecule.
13. Bile _?_ globules of fat.
14. A(n) _?_ is a protein that catalyzes biochemical reactions.
15. Enzymes called _?_ digest sugars such as sucrose and maltose.

47

Urinary Structures

The urinary system is composed of the kidneys, ureters, urinary bladder, urethra, and associated structures. The functions of the urinary system include maintaining extracellular fluid balance, excreting wastes, and maintaining blood pH.

In this exercise, you are challenged to discover the basic anatomy of the urinary system on both the gross and microscopic levels. In Lab Exercise 48, you will have the opportunity to dissect urinary structures in a whole specimen. In Lab Exercise 49, you will analyze the components of the **urine** produced by this system.

BEFORE YOU BEGIN

☐ Read the appropriate chapter in your textbook.
☐ Set your learning goals. When you finish this exercise, you should be able to:
   ☐ identify the major organs of the urinary system and find them in models and charts
   ☐ describe the gross anatomical features of the kidney and identify them in figures, models, and specimens
   ☐ describe the features of the nephron and locate them in figures and models
   ☐ identify the renal corpuscle in a prepared microscopic specimen
☐ Prepare your materials:
   ☐ model of the human torso (dissectible)
   ☐ model of the kidney (frontal section)
   ☐ preserved sheep kidney (double or triple injected, if available)
   ☐ dissection tools and trays
   ☐ model of a nephron and associated structures
   ☐ microscope
   ☐ prepared microslide: *kidney cortex c.s.*
☐ Read the directions and safety tips for this exercise *carefully* before starting any procedure.

Study TIPS

The plan of the urinary system resembles a plumbing system. Smaller-diameter tubes (pipes) lead to larger-diameter tubes (pipes). The small collecting ducts lead to the larger calyces, which lead to the larger ureter.

Develop a schematic diagram that follows the path of urine as it leaves the collecting ducts, enters the bladder, and exits the body. For reference, use your textbook, lab manual or the *A&P Survival Guide*.

A. THE URINARY PLAN

Study the layout of the urinary system by locating these features in a dissectible model of the human torso:

☐ 1 The left and right **kidneys** are located behind the peritoneum, along the posterior abdominal wall **(Figure 47-1, B)**. Locate these kidney features:
   ☐ **Renal fat pad**—Tissue that surrounds and protects each kidney (not shown in all models)
   ☐ **Renal capsule**—The fibrous outer wall of the kidney
   ☐ **Hilum**—An indentation on the medial side of each kidney where vessels and nerves enter or exit
☐ 2 The **ureter** is a muscular tube that exits each kidney at the hilum and extends inferiorly to the pelvic cavity.
☐ 3 The **urinary bladder** is a collapsible, muscular sac for the temporary storage of urine. The two ureters enter on each side of the posterior floor of the bladder.
☐ 4 The **urethra** is a muscular tube that extends from the anterior floor of the bladder to the outside of the body. In the female, it is a short tube that ends just anterior to the vagina. In the male, it is much longer, extending all the way through the penis. In the male, it conducts semen and urine.

Urine is formed in each kidney and is conducted through the ureters to the bladder. When the bladder is full and it is convenient, **urinary sphincters** that control flow through the urethra relax and allow urine to exit the body.

B. THE KIDNEY MODEL

Locate these features of the human kidney on a model (or chart) of a frontal section:

☐ 1 Locate the **hilum** and **renal capsule** from this perspective.
☐ 2 Identify these structures located just within the hilum:
   ☐ **Renal sinus**—A fat-filled cavity
   ☐ **Renal pelvis**—A wide section of the urinary channel, distal to the ureter
   ☐ **Calyces**—Branches of the pelvis that extend from the kidney tissue proper
☐ 3 The kidney tissue proper is divided into an outer **cortex** and an inner **medulla,** as is the tissue of many organs. **Renal pyramids** are cone-shaped sections of tissue lying mostly within the medulla. Each appears as a triangle in a frontal section. Each is composed of collecting ducts that conduct

urine toward its tip (papilla), which is surrounded by the end of a calyx.

Urine formed by the kidney is conducted through the collecting ducts of the renal pyramids to the calyces. The calyces fuse to form the large renal pyramid. As urine is conducted out of the kidney through the hilum, the urinary channel narrows to form the ureter.

☐ 4 Identify these features of the renal arterial supply **(Figure 47-2)**:

- ☐ **Renal artery**—A branch of the abdominal aorta that enters the hilum and extends through the renal sinus
- ☐ **Interlobar arteries**—Branches of the renal arteries that extend outward through the tissue between the pyramids
- ☐ **Arcuate arteries**—Branches of the interlobar arteries that turn to extend between the cortex and medulla
- ☐ **Interlobular arteries**—Branches of the arcuate arteries that extend outward into the cortex
- ☐ **Afferent arterioles**—Small arteries that arise from branches of interlobular arteries, each one extending to a glomerulus
- ☐ **Glomerular capillaries**—Capillaries that arise from an afferent arteriole and form a ball or small capillary bed called a **glomerulus**

☐ 5 After a brief detour, the venous network of the kidney parallels the arterial network, as you may expect:

- ☐ **Efferent arterioles**—Each extending from a glomerulus
- ☐ **Peritubular capillaries**—Small capillary beds that each arise from an efferent arteriole (a network of peritubular capillaries surrounds each *nephron*, the tubular, microscopic unit of the kidney)
- ☐ **Interlobular veins**
- ☐ **Arcuate veins**
- ☐ **Interlobar veins**
- ☐ **Renal veins**—Blood vessels that extend through the renal sinus, out the hilum, to drain into the inferior vena cava

C. THE SHEEP KIDNEY

The sheep kidney is similar to the human kidney and makes an ideal specimen for study.

safety first

Observe the usual precautions when dissecting preserved specimens. Be sure to follow the safety advice that accompanies the preservative used in your specimen. Avoid injury with the dissection tools. Use safety goggles to avoid injury during dissections.   •

☐ 1 Examine the external aspect of your specimen. Identify as many parts of the kidney as you can. Refer to Activities A and B if you have trouble. You may have to remove some of the renal fat pad.

☐ 2 Use a long knife or scalpel to cut a section, dividing the kidney into roughly equal dorsal and ventral portions. Try to identify as many features as you can.

Hint   Double-injected specimens have red latex injected into the arteries and blue latex injected into the veins. Triple-injected specimens also have yellow latex injected into the urinary channels and tubules. You may be able to see some of the finer detail visible in an injected specimen by using a hand lens or a dissection microscope.   •

Coloring Exercises: Urinary System

Use colored pens or pencils to shade in both the figure and the labels. Each red numeral in the figure corresponds to a matching red numeral following the appropriate label.

KIDNEY₁
URETER₂
URINARY BLADDER₃
URETHRA₄
RENAL CAPSULE₅
HILUM₆
RENAL SINUS₇
RENAL PELVIS₈
CALYCES₉
RENAL CORTEX₁₀
RENAL MEDULLA₁₁
RENAL PYRAMIDS₁₂
RENAL ARTERY₁₃
RENAL VEIN₁₄
NEPHRON₁₅

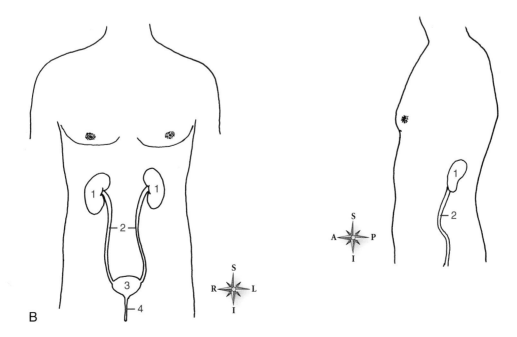

FIGURE 47-1 **A,** Internal structure of the kidney. **B,** Structures of the urinary system.

FIGURE 47-2 Circulation of blood through the kidney. Identify the renal blood vessels indicated on the lines provided and on the blanks in the Lab Report at the end of this exercise.

D. THE NEPHRON MODEL

The functional units of the kidney are the tiny tubules called **nephrons (Figure 47-3)**. The nephrons carry out the three basic processes that accomplish the kidney's function, forming *urine* as they do so: **filtration, tubular reabsorption,** and **tubular secretion.** Material from the blood is filtered into the beginning of the nephron. As the *filtrate* moves along the nephron tubule, some substances are reabsorbed into the blood, and some additional substances are secreted from the blood into the filtrate. The urine thus produced is channeled to collecting ducts, which drain it from the kidney. Locate the main features of the nephron and associated structures in a model or chart.

☐ 1 The **renal corpuscle** is the roughly spherical structure at the beginning of the nephron. The inner portion of the renal corpuscle is the **glomerulus,** a ball of glomerular capillaries. Surrounding the glomerulus is the double-walled **Bowman capsule.** Identify the afferent and efferent arterioles in the model. Can you trace their paths into the renal corpuscle, out, and then to the peritubular capillaries?

☐ 2 The **proximal convoluted tubule** is a narrow channel proceeding from the Bowman capsule of the renal corpuscle. It is *convoluted,* meaning that it is coiled.

☐ 3 Filtrate formed in the Bowman capsule flows through the proximal convoluted tubule and into the **nephron loop** **(Henle loop)**. Anatomically, the loop is a continuation of the proximal tubule. In many nephrons, the **descending limb** of the loop dips far down into the medulla, turns, and returns as the **ascending limb** to the cortex.

☐ 4 Filtrate flows from the ascending limb of the Henle loop into the **distal convoluted tubule.** The filtrate is emptied into a **collecting duct,** a tubule that collects urine from many nephrons and conducts it through a renal pyramid to a calyx. Eventually, the urine is voided during **urination or micturition.**

☐ 5 Your model may represent a nephron whose distal convoluted tubule passes between the afferent arteriole and efferent arteriole, near the renal corpuscle. If so, you may notice that the afferent arteriole wall and distal tubule wall form a specialized structure where they meet. This structure is called the **juxtaglomerular apparatus.**

Juxtaglomerular means "near the glomerulus." The juxtaglomerular apparatus secretes **renin,** an enzyme that catalyzes the conversion of *angiotensinogen* to *angiotensin I*. This begins a series of steps that helps regulate blood pressure.

Study TIPS

The kidneys balance or clean up all the blood that passes through them. An analogy that may help you understand the filtering, reabsorption, and secretion processes of the nephron is one that compares cleaning out your junk drawer. You first "filter" out the drawer by emptying it completely and placing the entire contents on the floor. The next step would be to "reabsorb" all of the items that you want to keep. You would then make final adjustments by removing the items you do not want to retain. Finally, the last step would be to take this "secretion" (urine) and remove it for disposal. For a complete explanation of this analogy, refer to the *A&P Survival Guide*.

FIGURE 47-3 A nephron, the basic functional unit of the kidney. Label the parts of the nephron indicated on the lines provided and on the blanks in the Lab Report at the end of this exercise.

E. MICROSCOPIC SPECIMEN

Obtain a prepared microscopic specimen of a cross section of renal cortical tissue **(Figure 47-4)**. Scan it under low power first and locate one or more renal corpuscles, easily identifiable dark circles. Switch to high power and try to identify these features:

safety first

Observe the usual precautions when using the microscope and a prepared slide. •

☐ **1** The glomerulus is the dark region forming the center of the renal corpuscle. It is a network of glomerular capillaries.

☐ **2** The Bowman capsule is seen as a very thin white or light area surrounding the glomerulus. Actually, the *lumen* of the capsule appears white. The parietal wall of the Bowman capsule is composed of simple squamous epithelium, which can sometimes be distinguished. The visceral wall of the Bowman capsule is composed of specialized epithelial cells called **podocytes.** Podocytes have extensions that wrap around the capillary walls to form a filtration membrane. You will not be able to distinguish podocytes in your specimen.

Hint Figure 47-4 shows a color micrograph of the renal corpuscle. •

☐ **3** The tissue surrounding each renal corpuscle is composed mostly of renal tubules. You will not be able to distinguish which are slices of proximal tubules or distal tubules, but you can appreciate the single-cell structure of their walls. What type of epithelium forms the tubule walls? How is this type of epithelial tissue specialized to perform the functions of the nephron tubule?

Hint If you are using double- or triple-injected sheep kidney specimens in the dissection, you may be able to see renal corpuscles and nephron tubules by examining a sectioned specimen with a hand lens or dissection microscope. •

Proximal tubule   Nephron tubules   Bowman capsule

Glomerulus

Efferent artery   Afferent artery

FIGURE 47-4 Micrograph of a renal cortex cross section. A renal corpuscle and surrounding tubules are visible.

Name: _____ Date: _____ Section: _____

LAB REPORT 47
Urinary Structures

STRUCTURE	HUMAN	SHEEP	FUNCTION(S)
Kidney	☐	☐	
Renal capsule	☐	☐	
Hilum	☐	☐	
Ureter	☐	☐	
Urinary bladder	—	—	
Urethra	—	—	
Renal sinus	☐	☐	
Renal pelvis	☐	☐	
Calyces	☐	☐	
Renal cortex	☐	☐	
Renal medulla	☐	☐	
Renal pyramids	☐	☐	
Renal artery, vein	☐	☐	
Interlobar arteries, veins	☐	☐	
Arcuate arteries, veins	☐	☐	
Interlobular arteries, veins	☐	☐	
Afferent arteriole	☐	☐	
Glomerulus	☐	☐	
Efferent arteriole	☐	☐	
Peritubular capillaries	☐	—	
Renal corpuscle	☐	—	
Bowman capsule	☐	—	
Proximal convoluted tubules	☐	—	
Henle loop: descending limb, ascending limb	☐	—	
Distal convoluted tubule	☐	—	
Collecting duct	☐	—	
Juxtaglomerular apparatus	—	—	

Specimen: *renal cortex c.s.*
Total Magnification: _____

Specimen: *renal cortex c.s.*
Total Magnification: _____

Figure 47-2 (from p. 444)

1. _____
2. _____
3. _____
4. _____
5. _____
6. _____
7. _____
8. _____
9. _____

Figure 47-3 (from p. 445)

1. _____
2. _____
3. _____
4. _____
5. _____
6. _____
7. _____
8. _____
9. _____
10. _____
11. _____
12. _____

Name: _____ Date: _____ Section: _____

Put in Order

1. _____
2. _____
3. _____
4. _____
5. _____
6. _____
7. _____
8. _____
9. _____
10. _____
11. _____

Fill-in

1. _____
2. _____
3. _____
4. _____
5. _____
6. _____
7. _____
8. _____
9. _____
10. _____

Put in Order (rearrange these structures in the order in which substances flow through the urinary system, beginning with the site of filtration)

ascending limb of the Henle loop
Bowman capsule
calyces
collecting duct
descending limb of the Henle loop
distal convoluted tubule
proximal convoluted tubule
renal pelvis
ureter
urethra
urinary bladder

Fill-in (complete each statement with the correct term)

1. The _?_ is a fat-filled cavity just inside the kidney's hilum.

2. The renal _?_ are branches of the renal pelvis.

3. The _?_ is a muscular tube extending from the renal pelvis to the urinary bladder.

4. The three basic processes observed in the nephron are filtration, tubular reabsorption, and tubular _?_.

5. The _?_ conducts blood into the glomerular capillaries.

6. The _?_ conducts blood into the kidney.

7. The _?_ capillaries surround the tubules of the nephron.

8. The inner tissue of the kidney is termed the renal _?_.

9. The _?_ apparatus secretes the enzyme renin.

10. The collecting ducts converge as they extend toward the calyces, forming the renal _?_.

48

Dissection: Urinary System

In this exercise, you continue your study of urinary anatomy by dissecting a whole preserved specimen. Activity A provides directions for studying the urinary anatomy of the cat. Activity B is an alternate activity, providing directions for studying the urinary anatomy of the fetal pig.

BEFORE YOU BEGIN

☐ Read the appropriate chapter in your textbook.
☐ Set your learning goals. When you finish this exercise, you should be able to:
  ☐ dissect the urinary anatomy of a preserved cat or fetal pig specimen
  ☐ identify the organs of the urinary tract in a dissected mammalian specimen
☐ Prepare your materials:
  ☐ preserved cat or fetal pig
  ☐ dissection tools and trays
  ☐ storage container (if specimen is to be reused)
  ☐ dissecting microscope (optional)
☐ Read the directions and safety tips for this exercise *carefully* before starting any procedure.

> **! safety first**
>
> Observe the usual precautions when working with a preserved specimen. Heed the safety advice accompanying preservatives used with your specimen. Use protective gloves while handling your specimen. Avoid injury with dissection tools. Use safety goggles to avoid injury during dissections. Dispose of or store your specimen as instructed. •

Study TIPS

As you proceed through this dissection, it may be helpful to have a diagram or illustration of the human urinary system. Use this to compare your specimen with the structure of the human urinary system. For reference, use your textbook or the *A&P Survival Guide*.

A. URINARY ANATOMY OF THE CAT

This activity challenges you to identify the major urinary structures of the cat. Assuming you have already removed the cat's skin (Exercise 10) and opened the abdominopelvic cavity (Exercise 40), you simply have to move the viscera out of the way (without cutting or removing them) to see the structures indicated in this activity.

> **Hint** ▸ **Figures 48-1** and **48-2** illustrate many of the structures of the cat listed in this activity. •

☐ **1** Move the abdominal viscera out of the way so that you can see the left and right **kidneys** behind the parietal peritoneum. Because they are behind the parietal peritoneum, the kidneys' position is described as being *retroperitoneal*. Notice that each kidney is surrounded by a **renal fat pad** that supports and protects the underlying organ. Notice also that each kidney is capped by an **adrenal gland.** This gland is also known as the *suprarenal gland* in the human.

☐ **2** Expose each kidney by removing the peritoneum and renal fat pad. Identify the **hilum,** or medial notch, of each kidney. Locate these hollow organs that attach to each kidney at the hilum:
  ☐ **Ureter**
  ☐ **Renal artery**
  ☐ **Renal vein**

☐ **3** Remove one of the kidneys and cut it in a longitudinal section as you did with the sheep kidney in Exercise 47, Activity C. Try to identify all the structures listed. You may wish to use a dissecting microscope to examine the detailed structure of the kidney section.
  ☐ **Renal capsule**
  ☐ **Renal cortex**
  ☐ **Renal medulla**
  ☐ **Renal pyramid**
  ☐ **Renal papilla**
  ☐ **Renal pelvis**

☐ 4 Follow the course of each ureter to the point at which it attaches to the **urinary bladder.** Cut the bladder open with a scalpel or scissors and locate the openings of the *left* and *right ureter* and the **urethra.**

☐ 5 Follow the course of the urethra to the outside of the body. How does the course of the urethra differ in the male and female cat?

B. URINARY ANATOMY OF THE FETAL PIG

This activity challenges you to identify the major urinary structures of the fetal pig. Assuming you have already removed the fetal pig's skin (Exercise 10) and opened the abdominopelvic cavity (Exercise 40), you simply have to move the viscera out of the way (without cutting or removing them) to see the structures indicated in this activity.

> **Hint** ▶ **Figures 48-3** and **48-4** illustrate many of the structures of the fetal pig listed in this activity. •

☐ 1 Move the abdominal viscera out of the way so that you can see the left and right **kidneys** behind the parietal peritoneum. Because they are behind the parietal peritoneum, the kidneys' position is described as being *retroperitoneal.* Notice that each kidney is surrounded by a **renal fat pad** that supports and protects the underlying organ. Notice also that each kidney is capped by an **adrenal gland.** This gland is also known as the *suprarenal gland* in the human.

☐ 2 Expose each kidney by removing the peritoneum and renal fat pad. Identify the **hilum,** or medial notch, of each kidney. Locate these hollow organs that attach to each kidney at the hilum:
 ☐ **Ureter**
 ☐ **Renal artery**
 ☐ **Renal vein**

☐ 3 Remove one of the kidneys and cut it in a longitudinal section as you did with the sheep kidney in Exercise 47, Activity C. Try to identify all the structures listed. You may wish to use a dissecting microscope to examine the detailed structure of the kidney section.
 ☐ **Renal capsule**
 ☐ **Renal cortex**
 ☐ **Renal medulla**
 ☐ **Renal pyramid**
 ☐ **Renal papilla**
 ☐ **Renal pelvis**

☐ 4 Follow the course of each ureter to the point at which it attaches to the **urinary bladder.** Note that the *umbilical arteries* run alongside the bladder. Cut the bladder open with a scalpel or scissors and locate the openings of the *left* and *right ureter* and the **urethra.**

☐ 5 Follow the course of the urethra to the outside of the body. How does the course of the urethra differ in the male and female fetal pig?

FIGURE 48-1 Urinary anatomy of the male cat. Ventral view.

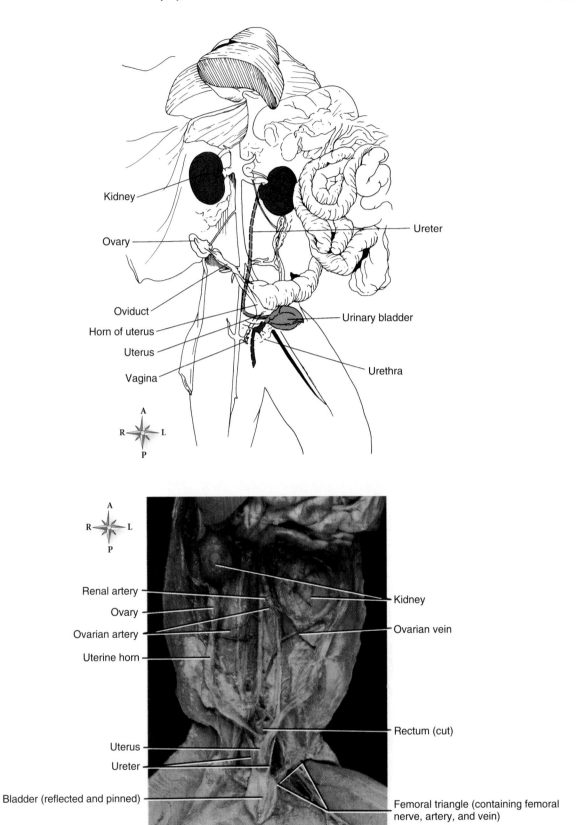

FIGURE 48-2 Urinary anatomy of the female cat. Ventral view.

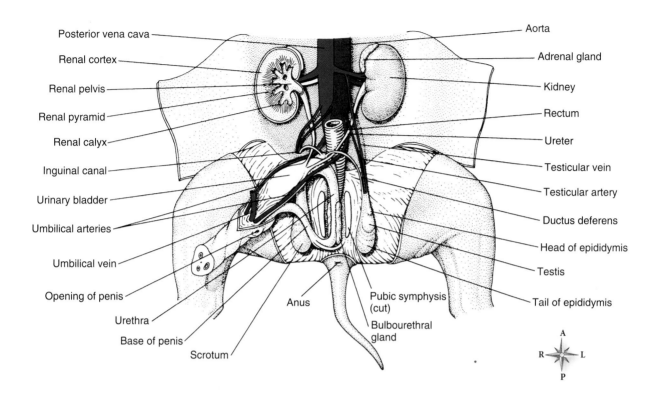

Posterior vena cava — Aorta
Renal cortex — Adrenal gland
Renal pelvis — Kidney
Renal pyramid — Rectum
Renal calyx — Ureter
Inguinal canal — Testicular vein
Urinary bladder — Testicular artery
Umbilical arteries — Ductus deferens
Umbilical vein — Head of epididymis
Opening of penis — Testis
Urethra — Tail of epididymis
Base of penis
Scrotum
Anus
Pubic symphysis (cut)
Bulbourethral gland

A
R ✳ L
P

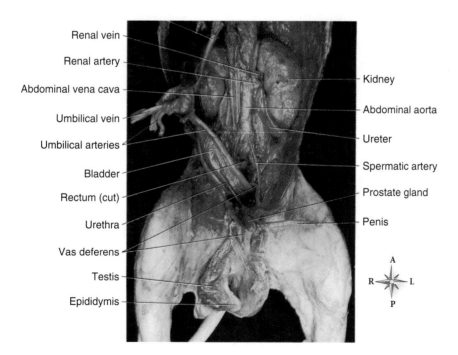

Renal vein — Kidney
Renal artery — Abdominal aorta
Abdominal vena cava — Ureter
Umbilical vein — Spermatic artery
Umbilical arteries — Prostate gland
Bladder — Penis
Rectum (cut)
Urethra
Vas deferens
Testis
Epididymis

A
R ✳ L
P

FIGURE 48-3 Urinary anatomy of the male fetal pig. Ventral view.

455

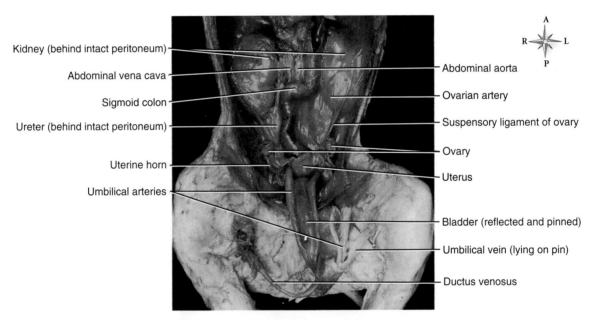

FIGURE 48-4 Urinary anatomy of the female fetal pig. Ventral view.

Name: _____ Date: _____ Section: _____

Dissection: Urinary System

A. Cat Dissection Checklist

- ☐ kidney (left and right)
- ☐ parietal peritoneum
- ☐ renal fat pad
- ☐ adrenal gland
- ☐ hilum
- ☐ ureter
- ☐ renal artery
- ☐ renal vein
- ☐ renal capsule
- ☐ renal cortex
- ☐ renal medulla
- ☐ renal pyramid
- ☐ renal papilla
- ☐ renal pelvis
- ☐ urethra (male)
- ☐ urethra (female)

B. Fetal Pig Dissection Checklist

- ☐ kidney (left and right)
- ☐ parietal peritoneum
- ☐ renal fat pad
- ☐ adrenal gland
- ☐ hilum
- ☐ ureter
- ☐ renal artery
- ☐ renal vein
- ☐ renal capsule
- ☐ renal cortex
- ☐ renal medulla
- ☐ renal pyramid
- ☐ renal papilla
- ☐ renal pelvis
- ☐ urethra (male)
- ☐ urethra (female)

Urinalysis

The examination of urine and its contents is **urinalysis.** Urinalysis can be very comprehensive, testing for dozens of different physical and chemical characteristics. On the other hand, some clinical situations call for urinalysis that tests only one or two urine characteristics. For example, the pregnancy test performed in Lab Exercise 33 was a type of urinalysis that determined the presence or concentration of one particular hormone. In this exercise, you will perform some of the more common clinical urinalysis tests, using the most current methods.

BEFORE YOU BEGIN

☐ Read the appropriate chapter in your textbook.
☐ Set your learning goals. When you finish this exercise, you should be able to:
  ☐ state the normal characteristics of freshly voided urine
  ☐ demonstrate the use of dip-and-read clinical test strips for urinalysis
  ☐ explain the significance of common urine tests
  ☐ prepare and examine a stained urine sediment slide
  ☐ evaluate urinalysis results
☐ Prepare your materials:
  ☐ fresh urine specimen using a packaged substitute in a disposable container
  ☐ dip-and-read multiple test strips (Multistix 10SG are preferred)
  ☐ urine centrifuge and tapered tubes
  ☐ disposable 1-ml droppers
  ☐ Sedistain urine sediment stain
  ☐ paper towels and wipes
  ☐ microscope slides and coverslips
  ☐ microscope
  ☐ full-color urine sediment chart (optional)
  ☐ BIOHAZARD container
  ☐ unknown urine additives (optional)
☐ Read the directions and safety tips for this exercise *carefully* before starting any procedure.

Study TIPS

Urine is a filtrate of plasma. Think of a urinalysis as a "fluid biopsy" of the kidney. A urinalysis is used to evaluate or monitor body homeostasis and detect many metabolic diseases. As you perform this lab activity, understand how certain diseases may affect the characteristics of urine. Table 31-2 in your textbook describes the normal and abnormal characteristics of urine.

A. EXAMINATION OF URINE

Urine reflects the overall status of extracellular fluid because it is derived from blood, and its contents have been adjusted to some extent on the basis of homeostatic balance. Additionally, the health of the kidney and urinary tract in particular affect the characteristics of urine. Observe the urinalysis tests described or perform them yourself on a packaged substitute provided by your instructor.

> **!** *safety first*
> Use artificial or prepackaged sterile human urine. You should still protect yourself and others from contamination by wearing protective lab apparel, gloves, and eyewear. Disinfect all surfaces that have, or *could have,* come into contact with urine. Put all disposable urine containers, droppers, towels, wipes, slides, and coverslips in a BIOHAZARD container *immediately* after use. Handle the sample as if it was nonsterile, freshly collected urine in an effort to practice good laboratory technique. •

☐ 1 Examine these physical characteristics of urine after placing some of the sample in a transparent container:
  ☐ **Transparency**—Normal urine is clear to slightly cloudy (especially after standing). Cloudy urine may contain fat globules, epithelial cells, mucus, microbes, or chemicals.
  ☐ **Color**—Normal urine is amber, straw, or transparent yellow, resulting from the presence of **urochromes** such as *urobilinogen* (a bacterial product derived from *bilirubin*). Yellow-brown to greenish urine may occur when a high concentration of bile pigments is present. Urine that is red to dark brown may have blood present. These or other abnormal colors may also result from the presence of food pigments (e.g., carotene), drugs, or other chemicals.

☐ 2 Many characteristics of urine are determined by the use of paper that is impregnated with test reagents. The paper is dipped into a sample, and a color change indicates the presence (and sometimes the concentration) of a particular substance. You may have used pH test paper in your aquarium or in another lab course. In this step, you will use a plastic strip on which 9 or 10 test papers have been placed. Each paper is impregnated with different reagents. Shake or stir the sample so that any sediment on the bottom of the container becomes suspended. With gloved hands, dip the papered end of one test strip into your sample. Lift it out and tap the excess urine onto the inside rim of the container. You may need to transfer some urine to a test tube so that you can immerse all the paper pads. Read the results by comparing the test papers with standard charts as instructed. Usually, certain tests *must* be read at certain times. A 10-test strip tests for these urine components:

> **Hint** Carefully read the instructions provided by the distributor of your test strips. Follow the instructions exactly, especially those dealing with times at which test strips are to be read. •

- ☐ **Leukocytes**—The occasional presence of white blood cells (WBCs) is normal, but values increase in urinary infections.
- ☐ **Nitrite**—A positive nitrite result indicates the presence of large amounts of bacteria, as in an infection. This test is useful if one has a cloudy urine sample but no microscope to determine whether bacteria are causing the cloudiness.
- ☐ **Urobilinogen**—A derivative of bilirubin, high levels may indicate excessive red blood cell (RBC) destruction or liver disease.
- ☐ **Protein**—Specifically *albumin*, a small protein molecule that is normally absent or present only in trace amounts; higher levels may indicate hypertension or kidney disease. Detectable levels are normal just after exercise.
- ☐ **pH**—The relative H^+ concentration, pH is a determinant of acidity. Normal urine pH is 4.6 to 8. Values are lower (more acid) in acidosis, starvation, and dehydration. pH is higher (more alkaline) in urinary infections and alkalosis.
- ☐ **Occult blood** (RBCs or free hemoglobin)—*Occult* means hidden. This strip tests for small amounts of hemoglobin that do not discolor the urine but are still clinically significant. Normally not present, hemoglobin may indicate kidney infection or the presence of stones in the kidney, ureter, or bladder.
- ☐ **Specific gravity**—This is the ratio of urine density to water density. If urine is pure water, the specific gravity is 1.000. Normal urine is 1.001 to 1.030. Lower values may indicate kidney disease. Higher values indicate high solute concentration and may occur during dehydration or diabetes mellitus. (This test is not present in 9-test strips.) An alternate method for determining specific gravity is to float a **hydrometer** in a cylinder containing urine, as in **Figure 49-1**. Read the scale on the hydrometer at the point that it meets the surface of the urine.
- ☐ **Ketone**—A byproduct of fat metabolism, it may be present during fasting, diabetes mellitus, or a low-carbohydrate diet.
- ☐ **Bilirubin**—Normally not present, or trace present only in amounts, this product of RBC destruction in the liver

FIGURE 49-1 The specific gravity of urine may be determined by floating a hydrometer in urine at room temperature.

may indicate liver disease or bile tract obstruction if present in the urine.

- ☐ **Glucose**—Normally, there is no glucose in the urine. Trace amounts may be present after a meal high in carbohydrates. Continued high levels in the urine may indicate diabetes mellitus or pituitary problems.

> *safety first*
> Do not forget to observe the usual precautions when using the microscope and stained, wet-mount slides. •

- ☐ 3 Observe the components of urine sediment by performing this procedure:
  - ☐ Shake or stir the urine sample to suspend any sediment that has settled.
  - ☐ Transfer some of the urine to a tapered centrifuge tube.
  - ☐ After balancing and securing the centrifuge as your instructor demonstrates, spin the sample for about 5 minutes.
  - ☐ Without disturbing the sediment that has collected in the tip of the tube, squeeze the bulb of a disposable dropper and gently lower it into the urine. When the dropper reaches the bottom, release the bulb *slightly* to collect only a few drops of sediment-containing urine.
  - ☐ Quickly place a drop of the sample on a clean microscope slide. Add one drop of Sedistain and cover it with

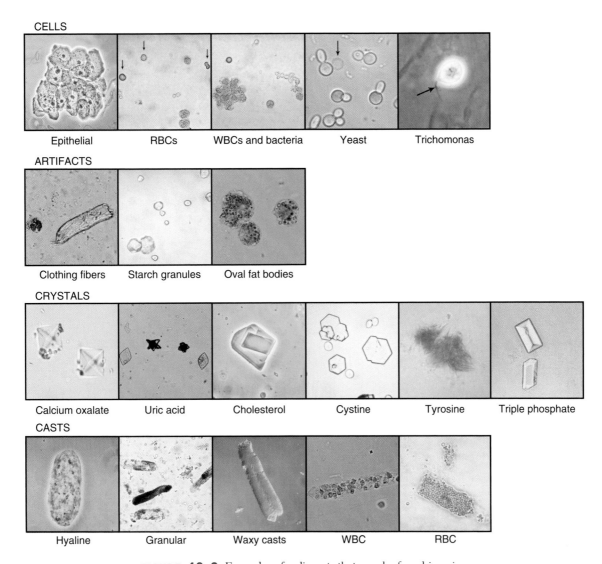

CELLS

Epithelial   RBCs   WBCs and bacteria   Yeast   Trichomonas

ARTIFACTS

Clothing fibers   Starch granules   Oval fat bodies

CRYSTALS

Calcium oxalate   Uric acid   Cholesterol   Cystine   Tyrosine   Triple phosphate

CASTS

Hyaline   Granular   Waxy casts   WBC   RBC

FIGURE 49-2 Examples of sediments that may be found in urine.

a coverslip. Remove excess fluid from the edges with a lab wipe and immediately discard the wipe in the BIOHAZ-ARD container.

☐ Examine the specimen under both low and high power. Move from field to field as you identify different types of sediment.

☐ **4** Your instructor may have a chart of sediment types for you to use in identifying urine solids. **Figure 49-2** presents a minichart of common urine sediment components:

☐ **Cells**—Epithelial cells from the urinary tract lining, blood cells from injury or infection sites, or infectious microbes may be present in sediment. If more than trace amounts of blood or microbial cells are present, a urinary problem is indicated.

☐ **Artifacts**—Artifacts are materials that have accidentally gotten into the sample. These include fabric fibers from underwear, powder used on the skin near the urethral opening, or skin oil droplets.

☐ **Crystals**—Very tiny crystals of normal urine components or drugs may be visible under high power. Small amounts of these crystals may be normal. A large number of crystals are seen in urinary *retention*, the inability to void urine from the bladder. Large masses of crystals are called *stones*, or *calculi*.

☐ **Casts**—Casts are chunks of material that have hardened somewhere in the urinary channel and sloughed off into the urine. They may be roughly cylindrical masses of cells, granules, or other substances.

☐ **5** Your instructor may opt to offer unknown urine additives. Add the additive to your sample as instructed and test the sample as if it were a new urine specimen. The additive will have altered the sample's characteristics in a way that mimics an abnormal condition. Your instructor may choose instead to give you a new sample, one that is abnormal in some respect. Test the new sample in the same way you tested the first sample. Report your results in Lab Report 49.

Name: _____ Date: _____ Section: _____

LAB REPORT 49
Urinalysis

CHARACTERISTIC	NORMAL VALUE	OBSERVED VALUE	INTERPRETATION
Transparency			
Color			
Leukocytes			
Nitrite			
Urobilinogen			
Protein			
pH			
Occult blood			
Specific gravity			
Ketone			
Bilirubin			
Glucose			

Summary and evaluation of this sample:

Sketch (and label) examples of urine sediment found in your sample:

Use this table for the results of the test on the "unknown" sample:

UNKNOWN CODE _____

CHARACTERISTIC	NORMAL VALUE	OBSERVED VALUE	INTERPRETATION
Transparency			
Color			
Leukocytes			
Nitrite			
Urobilinogen			
Protein			
pH			
Occult blood			
Specific gravity			
Ketone			
Bilirubin			
Glucose			

Summary and evaluation of this sample:

50

The Male Reproductive System

Humans, as a species, have two **reproductive systems:** a male system and a female system. The primary function of both is sexual reproduction of offspring. Sexual reproduction in humans requires successful fusion of two **gametes,** or sex cells. Human gametes, or **sperm** and **ova,** are formed by means of *meiosis,* so each has 23 chromosomes. When a sperm cell from the male parent unites with an ovum from the female parent, a cell with 46 chromosomes is formed. This offspring cell has a unique mix of DNA from both parents, providing the variation essential to the survival of the human species.

In this exercise, you are invited to explore the structure and function of the male reproductive system. In Lab Exercise 51, the female reproductive system is presented.

BEFORE YOU BEGIN

☐ Read the appropriate chapter in your textbook.
☐ Set your learning goals. When you finish this exercise, you should be able to:
  ☐ describe the plan of the male reproductive tract
  ☐ describe the organs of the male reproductive system and their principal functions
  ☐ locate male reproductive organs in charts and models
  ☐ identify major features in a microscopic specimen of the testis
  ☐ identify the features of mature sperm in figures and in a prepared smear
☐ Prepare your materials:
  ☐ models and charts of the male reproductive system
  ☐ microscope
  ☐ prepared microslide: *human testis c.s.*
  ☐ prepared microslide: *human sperm smear*
☐ Read the directions and safety tips for this exercise *carefully* before starting any procedure.

Study TIPS

Use the following mnemonic to help you understand the pathway of sperm/semen through the male reproductive tract.

Some	Seminiferous tubules
Real	Rete testis
Energetic	Efferent ductules
Earthworms	Epididymis
Divide	Ductus (vas) deferens
And	Ampulla
Even	Ejaculatory duct
Unite	Urethra

A. HUMAN MODEL

Find the major features of the male reproductive system in models and charts (and in **Figure 50-1**).

☐ 1 The primary sex organs of the male reproductive system are the two **testes.** The testes are located within the **scrotum,** a sac of skin and other tissues on the outer wall of the anterior trunk. A thin layer of smooth muscle called the **dartos muscle** forms part of the scrotum's wall. Find these structures associated with the testes:
  ☐ **Capsule**—A connective tissue outer wall, the capsule has inward extensions that divide each testis into **lobules.**
  ☐ **Seminiferous tubules**—These are long, coiled tubules in which sperm cells are produced. Tissue in between the tubules contains **interstitial cells (Leydig cells)** that secrete *testosterone.*
  ☐ **Rete testis**—This is a network of tubules into which the seminiferous tubules empty. The rete testis, in turn, empties into 15 to 20 **efferent ductules** that leave the testis.

☐ 2 The **epididymis** is a set of coiled tubules on the outside of the testis (but still within the scrotum). Sperm cells formed in the testis move into the epididymis, where they continue to mature.

☐ 3 The **vas deferens,** or **ductus deferens,** conducts sperm cells from the epididymis out of the scrotum and into the pelvic cavity. Trace its path in your model. As the ductus deferens enters the abdominopelvic cavity through the *inguinal canal,* it is associated with nerves, vessels, and a connective tissue covering. Together these structures form the **spermatic cord.** Near its end, each ductus deferens has an enlarged section called the **ampulla.**

☐ 4 Joining the ductus deferens at the ampulla is a duct from a **seminal vesicle.** Each seminal vesicle is a gland that produces fluid that becomes part of **semen.** Semen is the fluid medium containing sperm that is *ejaculated* during the male sexual response. The ductus deferens and seminal vesicle duct unite to form the **ejaculatory duct** that extends to the urethra, just inferior to the bladder.

☐ 5 Surrounding the urethra and ejaculatory ducts below the bladder is the **prostate gland.** This gland, like the seminal vesicles, contributes to the seminal fluid.

☐ 6 Sperm-containing semen is conducted through the **urethra** during the male sexual response. Near the base of the penis, ducts from the **bulbourethral glands** join the urethra.

These small glands contribute a small amount of fluid to the semen.

☐ 7 The **penis** is the erectile structure through which the urethra conducts semen out of the body during ejaculation. Erection of the penis is essential to insertion into the female tract and depositing the semen there. Three vascular bodies, the left and right **corpora cavernosa** and the **corpus spongiosum,** engorge with blood during the sexual response and stiffen the penis. The tip of the corpus spongiosum forms the head of the penis, or **glans penis.** The glans penis is covered by a fold of skin called the **foreskin,** or **prepuce,** unless it has been removed by means of *circumcision.*

B. MICROSCOPIC STRUCTURE OF THE TESTIS

First in a model or chart, and then in a prepared microscopic specimen, locate the following structures in a cross section of the testis **(Figure 50-2)**:

☐ 1 The major feature of a testis cross section is the presence of numerous **seminiferous tubules.** Identify the **basement membrane,** lumen, and walls of a seminiferous tubule. Locate some of the **interstitial cells** between the tubules.

☐ 2 Examine the cells forming the wall of a seminiferous tubule. Large, pale cells with oval nuclei are supportive **sustentacular cells (Sertoli cells).** They extend all the way to the lumen, but their entire length is often difficult to distinguish. The majority of cells are **germ cells.** The outermost layer of germ cells is **spermatogonia.** Some daughter cells of the spermatogonia, nearer the lumen, become **spermatocytes** that divide by means of meiosis to form **spermatids.** Each spermatid develops to become a **spermatozoan,** many of which are seen in the lumen (see Figure 50-2).

safety first

The remaining activities of this exercise call for the use of a microscope. Be sure to observe the usual precautions. •

Coloring
Exercises: **Male Reproductive System**

Use colored pens or pencils to shade in both the figure and the labels. Each red numeral in the figure corresponds to a matching red numeral following the appropriate label.

SCROTUM₁

TESTIS₂

EPIDIDYMIS₃

VAS DEFERENS₄

SEMINAL VESICLE₅

EJACULATORY DUCT₆

PROSTATE GLAND₇

URETHRA₈

BULBOURETHRAL
   GLAND AND DUCT₉

CORPUS SPONGIOSUM₁₀

GLANS PENIS₁₁

CORPORA CAVERNOSA₁₂

FORESKIN₁₃

URINARY BLADDER₁₄

PUBIS₁₅

RECTUM₁₆

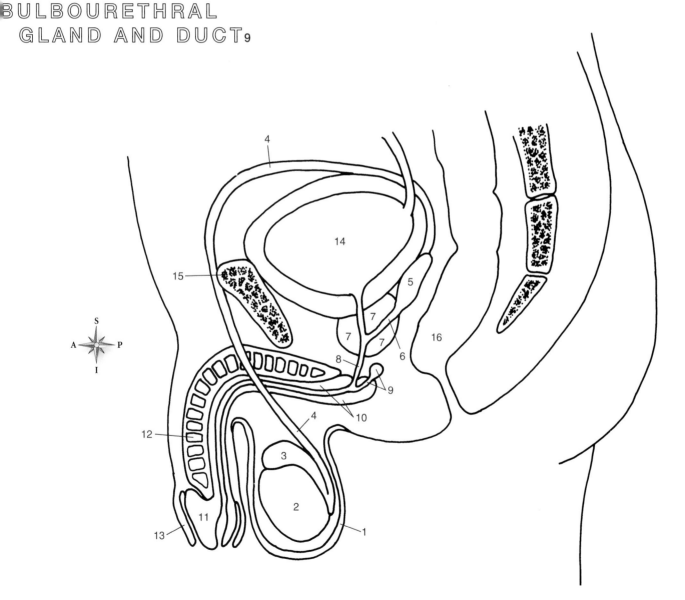

FIGURE 50-1 Male reproductive organs.

Spermatogonia

Spermatids   Spermatocyte   Sertoli cell

FIGURE 50-2 Micrograph of a cross section of a seminiferous tubule in the testis. *T,* Seminiferous tubules; *L,* Leydig interstitial cells.

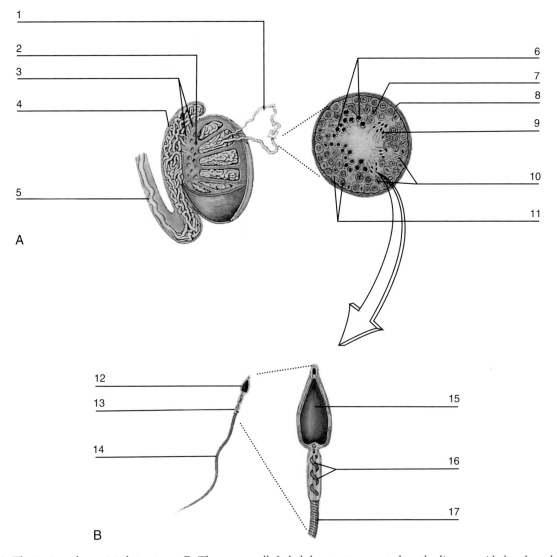

FIGURE 50-3 A, The testis and associated structures. **B,** The sperm cell. Label the structures noted on the lines provided and on the blanks in the Lab Report at the end of this exercise.

C. SPERM CELLS

Examine a prepared microscopic specimen of a sperm (semen) smear under high power **(Figure 50-3, B)**. Notice that each normal sperm has a pear-shaped **head** containing a nucleus. A **midpiece** containing mitochondria is at the base of a **tail,** or *flagellum.*

Up to one-third of the sperm cells in a normal specimen may be deformed. Look for sperm with multiple or misshapen heads or with tail deformities. High ratios of deformed sperm are associated with stress, infection, or high environmental temperatures.

Head

Midpiece

Tail

FIGURE 50-4 Micrograph of a cluster of sperm trapped in mucus.

Name: _____ Date: _____ Section: _____

The Male Reproductive System

STRUCTURE	MODEL OR CHART	FUNCTION(S)
Testis	☐	
Scrotum	☐	
Capsule	☐	
Seminiferous tubule	☐	
Rete testis	☐	
Epididymis	☐	
Vas (ductus) deferens	☐	
Seminal vesicle	☐	
Ejaculatory duct	☐	
Prostate gland	☐	
Urethra	☐	
Bulbourethral gland	☐	
Penis	☐	
Corpora cavernosa	☐	
Corpus spongiosum	☐	
Glans penis	☐	
Foreskin	☐	
Interstitial cell	☐	
Sustentacular (Sertoli) cell	☐	
Germ cell	☐	
Spermatogonium	☐	
Spermatocyte	☐	
Spermatid	☐	
Spermatozoan: head, midpiece, tail	☐	

Specimen: *human testis c.s.*
Total Magnification: _____

Specimen: *human sperm smear*
Total Magnification: _____

Figure 50-3 (from p. 468)

1. _____
2. _____
3. _____
4. _____
5. _____
6. _____
7. _____
8. _____
9. _____
10. _____
11. _____
12. _____
13. _____
14. _____
15. _____
16. _____
17. _____

Multiple Choice

1. _____
2. _____
3. _____
4. _____
5. _____
6. _____

Multiple Choice (select the best response)

1. Semen travels through the male reproductive tract in this order:
   a. ejaculatory duct, vas deferens, epididymis, urethra
   b. epididymis, vas deferens, ejaculatory duct, urethra
   c. urethra, ejaculatory duct, vas deferens, epididymis
   d. vas deferens, epididymis, ejaculatory duct, urethra
2. Sperm cells mature in phases that occur in this order:
   a. spermatogonium, spermatocyte, spermatozoan, spermatid
   b. spermatocyte, spermatozoan, spermatid, spermatogonium
   c. spermatogonium, spermatocyte, spermatid, spermatozoan
3. Erection of the penis is accomplished through increased blood volume in the
   a. corpus spongiosum
   b. foreskin
   c. corpora cavernosa
   d. a and c are correct
   e. none of the above
4. Mitochondria of the sperm cell are found in the
   a. head
   b. midpiece
   c. tail
5. The urethra of the male functions as a part of the
   a. urinary system
   b. digestive system
   c. reproductive system
   d. a and c are correct
   e. all of the above
6. The distal, widened portion of the vas deferens is more specifically known as the
   a. ampulla
   b. ductus deferens
   c. seminal vesicle
   d. prostate gland
   e. proximal tubule

The Female Reproductive System

This exercise continues the study of human reproductive systems begun in Lab Exercise 50. In this exercise, you are invited to explore the essential structure and function of the female reproductive system.

BEFORE YOU BEGIN

☐ Read the appropriate chapter in your textbook.
☐ Set your learning goals. When you finish this exercise, you should be able to:
  ☐ describe the plan of the female reproductive tract
  ☐ describe the organs of the female reproductive systems and their principal functions
  ☐ locate female reproductive organs in charts and models
  ☐ identify major features in a microscopic specimen of a mammalian ovary
  ☐ identify structures of the mammary glands
☐ Prepare your materials:
  ☐ models and charts of the female reproductive system and the breasts
  ☐ microscope
  ☐ prepared microslide: *mammalian ovary c.s.*
☐ Read the directions and safety tips for this exercise *carefully* before starting any procedure.

Study TIPS

There are several female reproductive structures that are homologous to the male reproductive system. Examples include prepuce of clitoris, glans of clitoris, labia minora, openings for the greater vestibular glands, and the labia majora. Develop a table that describes how these female structures are homologous to the male structures. For reference, use your textbook, lab manual, or the *A&P Survival Guide*.

A. HUMAN MODEL

Find the major features of the female reproductive system in models and charts (**Figures 51-1** and **51-2**):

☐ 1 The primary sex organs of the female reproductive system are the two **ovaries.** They are small, rounded organs suspended in the pelvic cavity by ligaments. The ovarian mesentery, or **mesovarium,** attaches the ovaries to the **broad ligament.** The **suspensory ligaments** and **ovarian ligaments** also support the ovaries.

☐ 2 A **uterine tube** is associated with each ovary. Also called a **fallopian tube,** or **oviduct,** this narrow tube with a ciliated lining conducts a mature **ovum** from the area of the ovary toward the uterus. It is the usual site of fertilization. Long processes called **fimbriae** surround the tube's margin at its ovarian end.

☐ 3 The **uterus,** or womb, is a single muscular sac at the midline in the pelvic cavity. Identify these parts of the uterus:
  ☐ **Body of the uterus**—The larger, rounded portion in which is located the main part of the **uterine cavity**
  ☐ **Cervix**—Narrow, inferior portion of the uterus (the **cervical canal** passes through this area to join the vagina)
  ☐ **Serous layer of the uterus**—The portion of the peritoneum that forms the outer uterine wall
  ☐ **Myometrium**—The muscular middle layer of the uterine wall
  ☐ **Endometrium**—The inner layer of the uterine wall

☐ 4 The **vagina** is a muscular canal that receives the male penis during *sexual intercourse*. It functions as the **birth canal** during delivery and as an exit for sloughed-off endometrium during **menses.** The opening of the vagina to the outside may be covered partially or entirely by a thin, membranous **hymen.**

☐ 5 The external genitals of the female are collectively known as the **vulva,** or **pudendum.** Identify these features associated with the vulva:
  ☐ **Vestibule**—The central space of the vulva, into which the vagina and urethra open (openings of **vestibular gland** ducts conduct lubricating fluid into the vestibule)
  ☐ **Clitoris**—The female glans, a small erectile structure in the anterior corner of the vestibule (the clitoris is covered with a fold of skin called the **foreskin,** or **prepuce**)
  ☐ **Labia minora**—A pair of thin longitudinal folds on each side of the vestibule (sing. *labium minus*)
  ☐ **Labia majora**—A pair of thick longitudinal folds lateral to the labia minora (the space between the labia majora is called the **pudendal cleft**) (sing. *labium majus*)
  ☐ **Mons pubis**—A fatty mound, covered with hair, over the pubic bone

Coloring Exercises: Female Reproductive System

Use colored pens or pencils to shade in both the figure and the labels. Each red numeral in the figure corresponds to a matching red numeral following the appropriate label.

OVARY₁
UTERINE TUBE₂
BODY OF UTERUS₃
CERVIX OF UTERUS₄
VAGINA₅
CLITORIS₆
LABIUM MINUS₇
LABIUM MAJUS₈
URINARY BLADDER₉
URETHRA₁₀
PUBIS₁₁
RECTUM₁₂

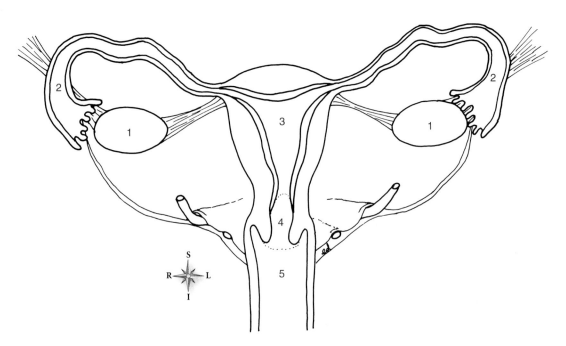

FIGURE 51-1 Female pelvic organs.

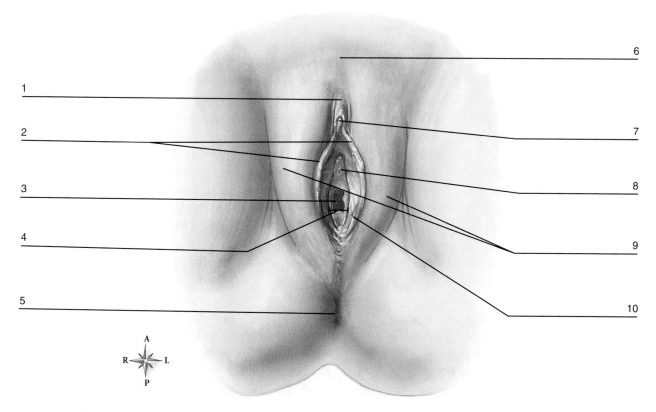

FIGURE 51-2 Female perineum. Label the parts of the vulva on the lines provided and on the blanks in the Lab Report at the end of this exercise.

B. MICROSCOPIC STRUCTURE OF THE OVARY

First, in a model or chart, and then in a prepared microscopic specimen, locate the important structures associated with the ovary **(Figure 51-3)**.

safety first
Be careful of electrical and other hazards when examining your specimen with a microscope. •

☐ 1 Each ovary is covered with a portion of the peritoneum. The outer region of each ovary is composed of dense connective tissue with numerous **ovarian follicles.** Each follicle contains an **oocyte,** the germ cell of the female.

☐ 2 Primary oocytes are oocytes that have developed to a point early in meiosis and then temporarily stopped developing. Each primary oocyte is surrounded by **granulosa cells.** The oocyte and granulosa cells together constitute a **primary follicle.**

☐ 3 When stimulated by hormones, a primary follicle develops into a **secondary follicle.** Each secondary follicle has a central fluid-filled **antrum** and a mass of cells off to the side called the **cumulus mass.** The oocyte is embedded in the cumulus mass.

☐ 4 The follicle eventually develops into a **mature follicle** when the antrum fills with more fluid and the follicle becomes a bump on the ovary's surface. The tissue surrounding the follicle forms a layer called the **theca.** A clear layer, or **zona pellucida,** surrounds the enlarged oocyte. The developing follicle secretes the hormone estrogen.

☐ 5 As more fluid fills the follicle, it bursts open and spills its contents into the peritoneal cavity near the fimbriae of the uterine tube. This process is called **ovulation.** The ruptured follicle then develops into the glandular **corpus luteum,** which secretes **progesterone** and estrogen.

> **Hint** Several ovarian follicles, each in different stages of development, may be found in a single specimen; however, their distribution is rather random. Figure 51-3, *B,* shows a light micrograph of an ovary. •

A

B

FIGURE 51-3 A, Sagittal section of the ovary, showing follicles in different stages of development. **B,** Light micrograph of an ovary. *H,* Hilum; *C,* cortex; *M,* medulla.

C. THE MAMMARY GLANDS

Locate the female breast in a model or chart or **Figure 51-4**. The **mammary glands** are modified sweat glands within the skin of the chest. Although structurally they are components of the integument, they are considered here because of their function of providing nutrition for offspring produced by the reproductive system. Find these features of the breasts:

❑ 1 Both the male and female breast have a pigmented area of skin called the **areola.** The areola surrounds a raised **nipple.**

❑ 2 Normally, only the mammary glands of the female develop. At puberty, adipose tissue develops under the skin of the breast. This tissue supports 15 to 20 glandular **lobes** of the mammary gland.

❑ 3 Each lobe has a single **lactiferous duct** that opens directly onto the surface of the nipple, giving the nipple a total of 15 to 20 openings. Each lactiferous duct has a widened portion called the **lactiferous sinus** near its exit at the nipple. These sinuses act like the bulbs of eyedroppers: when the baby squeezes them with her jaw, the milk in them squirts into the baby's mouth.

❑ 4 Each lobe of the mammary gland is composed of several **lobules.** During *lactation* (milk production), the ends of the lobule ducts form secretory sacs called **alveoli.**

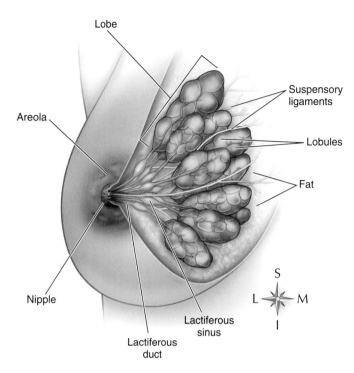

FIGURE 51-4 The female breast.

Name: _____ Date: _____ Section: _____

The Female Reproductive System

STRUCTURE	MODEL OR CHART	FUNCTION(S)
Ovary	☐	
Mesovarium	☐	
Broad ligament	☐	
Suspensory ligament	☐	
Ovarian ligament	☐	
Uterine tube	☐	
Fimbriae	☐	
Body of uterus, uterine cavity	☐	
Cervix, cervical canal	☐	
Serous layer of uterus	☐	
Myometrium	☐	
Endometrium	☐	
Vagina	☐	
Vestibule (of vulva)	☐	
Clitoris	☐	
Prepuce	☐	
Labium minus	☐	
Labium majus	☐	
Mons pubis	☐	
Ovarian follicles	☐	
Areola (of breast)	☐	
Nipple	☐	
Lobes (of mammary gland)	☐	
Lobules (of mammary gland)	☐	
Alveoli (of mammary gland)	☐	

Specimen: *mammalian ovary c.s.*
Total Magnification: _____

Figure 51-2 (from p. 475)

1. _____
2. _____
3. _____
4. _____
5. _____
6. _____
7. _____
8. _____
9. _____
10. _____

Fill-in

1. _____
2. _____
3. _____
4. _____
5. _____
6. _____
7. _____
8. _____
9. _____
10. _____
11. _____
13. _____

Fill-in (complete each statement with the correct term)

1. The fluid-filled space within a follicle is called the _?_.
2. The tissue surrounding a mature follicle is called the _?_.
3. A follicle secretes the hormone _?_.
4. The external genitals of the female are known by the term _?_.
5. The _?_ secrete lubricating fluid into the vestibule.
6. The release of an oocyte from a follicle is termed _?_.
7. The normal site of fertilization of an egg is in the _?_.
8. The narrow portion, or neck, of the uterus is called the _?_.
9. The oocyte in a secondary follicle is embedded in the _?_ mass.
10. The thin membrane covering all or part of the vaginal opening is called the _?_.
11. The _?_ is a structure of the ovary that secretes progesterone.
12. The birth canal is also called the _?_.

52

Dissection: Reproductive Systems

In this exercise, you continue your study of reproductive anatomy by dissecting a whole preserved specimen.

Activity A provides directions for studying the reproductive anatomy of the male cat. Activity B provides directions for studying the reproductive anatomy of the female cat. Activities C and D are alternate activities, providing directions for studying the immature reproductive anatomy of the male and female fetal pig.

BEFORE YOU BEGIN

☐ Read the appropriate chapter in your textbook.
☐ Set your learning goals. When you finish this exercise, you should be able to:
   ☐ dissect the reproductive anatomy of a preserved cat or fetal pig
   ☐ identify the major organs of both the male and female reproductive systems in a dissected mammalian specimen
☐ Prepare your materials:
   ☐ preserved cat or fetal pig
   ☐ dissection tools and trays
   ☐ storage container (if specimen is to be reused)
☐ Read the directions and safety tips for this exercise *carefully* before starting any procedure.

> ! *safety first*
> Observe the usual precautions when working with a preserved specimen. Heed the safety advice accompanying preservatives used with your specimen. Use protective gloves while handling your specimen. Avoid injury with dissection tools. Use safety goggles to avoid injury during dissections. Dispose of or store your specimen as instructed. •

Study TIPS

Obtain a labeled diagram or illustration of the male and female reproductive systems. Use these as you complete this lab. You may also want to use your cell phone camera to take pictures of your specimens and use them later for a study resource.

A. REPRODUCTIVE ANATOMY OF THE MALE CAT

This activity challenges you to identify the major reproductive structures of the male cat. Assuming you have already removed the cat's skin (Exercise 10) and opened the abdominopelvic cavity (Exercise 40), you simply have to move the viscera out of the way (without cutting or removing them) to see many of the structures indicated in this activity. You may have to cut some additional skin or muscle tissue to see a few of the structures more clearly.

> Hint ▶ **Figure 52-1** illustrates many of the structures of the male cat listed in this activity. •

☐ 1 Locate the **scrotum,** a sac of skin between the hindlimbs of the animal. Cut the scrotum open with your scissors or scalpel, taking care not to cut the structures inside the scrotum.
☐ 2 Identify the **testes,** the male *gonads* within the scrotum. Remove the connective tissue covering each testis to reveal the coiled **epididymis.** Note that the **vas (ductus) deferens** leads from the epididymis, through the *inguinal canal,* and into the abdominopelvic cavity.
☐ 3 Trace the course of one of the vas deferens into the abdominopelvic cavity to where it meets its partner from the other side. Note that they join together where they meet the **urethra.** At this location, a mass of glandular tissue called the **prostate gland** can be found.
☐ 4 Follow the course of the urethra toward the base of the **penis,** where a pair of small **bulbourethral glands** can be found.
☐ 5 Identify the **glans penis** at the distal tip of the penis.

B. REPRODUCTIVE ANATOMY OF THE FEMALE CAT

This activity challenges you to identify the major reproductive structures of the female cat. Assuming you have already removed the cat's skin (Exercise 10) and opened the abdominopelvic cavity (Exercise 40), you simply have to move the viscera out of the way (without cutting or removing them) to see many of the structures indicated in this activity. You may have to cut some additional skin or muscle tissue to see a few of the structures more clearly.

 Hint ▶ **Figure 52-2** illustrates many of the structures of the female cat listed in this activity. •

☐ 1 Locate the tiny, lightly colored **ovaries**, the female *gonads*, located just posterior to the kidneys.
☐ 2 Identify the **oviduct**, with its distal *fimbriae*, that leads from each ovary toward a **uterine horn**. Each uterine horn is a lateral extension of the superior portion of the uterus.
☐ 3 Locate the main portion of the **uterus** along the midline of the body. The female reproductive tract continues posteriorly from the uterus as the **vagina** toward the outside of the body. The vagina ends at the *urogenital sinus*.

C. REPRODUCTIVE ANATOMY OF THE MALE FETAL PIG

This activity challenges you to identify the major reproductive structures of the male fetal pig. Assuming you have already removed the fetal pig's skin (Exercise 10) and opened the abdominopelvic cavity (Exercise 40), you simply have to move the viscera out of the way (without cutting or removing them) to see many of the structures indicated in this activity. You may have to cut some additional skin or muscle tissue of the scrotum to see a few of the structures more clearly.

Hint ▶ **Figure 52-3** illustrates many of the structures of the male fetal pig listed in this activity. •

☐ 1 Locate the **scrotum,** a sac of skin between the hindlimbs of the animal. Cut the scrotum open with your scissors or scalpel, taking care not to cut the structures inside the scrotum.
☐ 2 Identify the immature **testes,** the male *gonads* within the scrotum. They should have descended into the scrotum late in fetal development. Remove the connective tissue covering each testis to reveal the coiled **epididymis.** Note that the **vas (ductus) deferens** leads from the epididymis, through the *inguinal canal,* into the abdominopelvic cavity.
☐ 3 Trace the course of one of the vas deferens into the abdominopelvic cavity to where it meets its partner from the other side. Note that they join together where they meet the **urethra.** A small, glandular **seminal vesicle** may be observed at the end of each vas deferens. Also at this location is a single mass of glandular tissue called the **prostate gland.**
☐ 4 Follow the course of the urethra toward the base of the **penis,** where a pair of small, elongated **bulbourethral glands** can be located.

D. REPRODUCTIVE ANATOMY OF THE FEMALE FETAL PIG

This activity challenges you to identify the major reproductive structures of the female fetal pig. Assuming you have already removed the fetal pig's skin (Exercise 10) and opened the abdominopelvic cavity (Exercise 40), you simply have to move the viscera out of the way (without cutting or removing them) to see many of the structures indicated in this activity. You may have to cut some additional skin or muscle tissue to see a few of the structures more clearly.

Hint ▶ **Figure 52-4** illustrates many of the structures of the female fetal pig listed in this activity. •

☐ 1 Locate the tiny, lightly colored **ovaries**, the female *gonads* located just posterior to the kidneys.
☐ 2 Identify the **oviduct,** with its distal *fimbriae,* that leads from each ovary toward a **uterine horn.** Each uterine horn is a lateral extension of the superior portion of the uterus.
☐ 3 Locate the main portion of the **uterus** along the midline of the body. The female reproductive tract continues posteriorly from the uterus as the **vagina** toward the outside of the body. The vagina ends at the *urogenital sinus*.

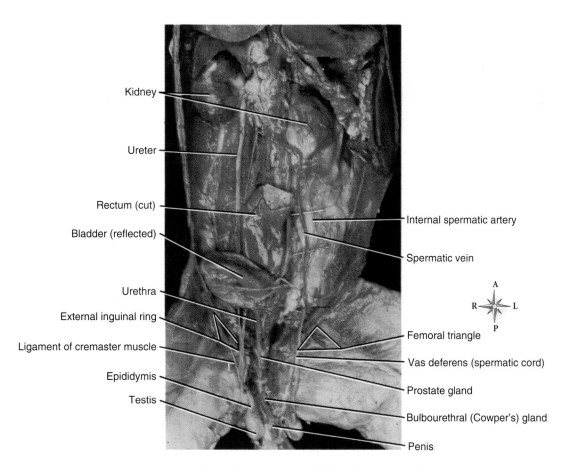

FIGURE 52-1 Reproductive anatomy of the male cat. Ventral view.

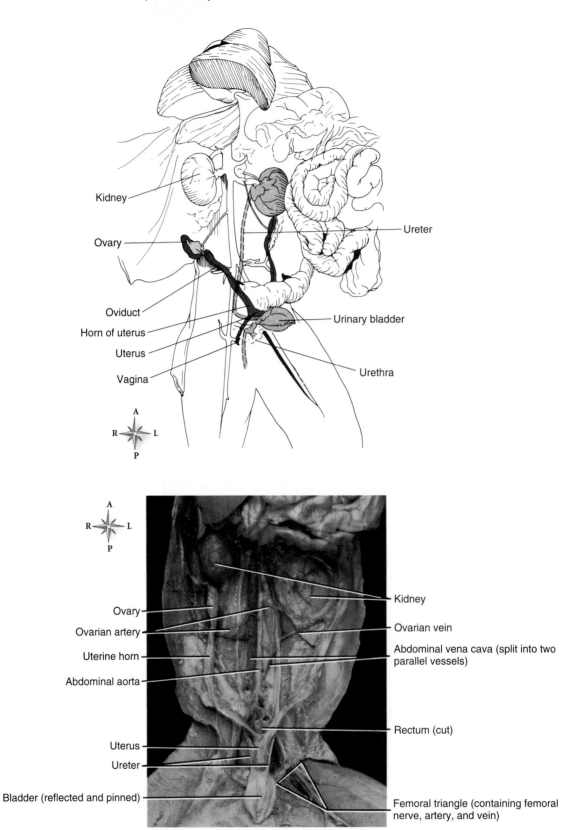

FIGURE 52-2 Reproductive anatomy of the female cat. Ventral view.

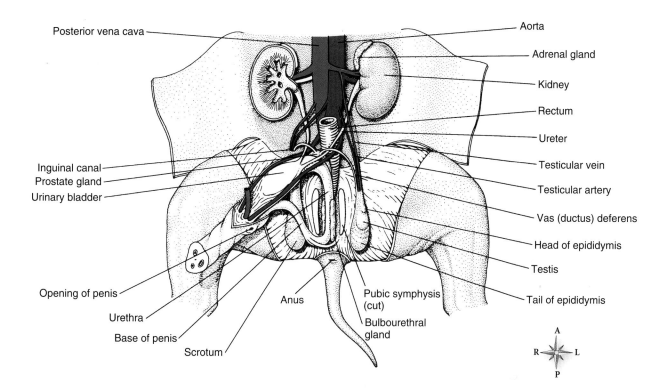

Posterior vena cava

Inguinal canal
Prostate gland
Urinary bladder

Opening of penis

Urethra

Base of penis

Scrotum

Anus

Pubic symphysis
(cut)

Bulbourethral
gland

Aorta

Adrenal gland

Kidney

Rectum

Ureter

Testicular vein

Testicular artery

Vas (ductus) deferens

Head of epididymis

Testis

Tail of epididymis

A
R—L
P

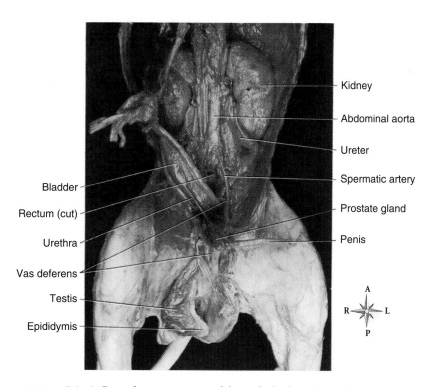

Bladder

Rectum (cut)

Urethra

Vas deferens

Testis

Epididymis

Kidney

Abdominal aorta

Ureter

Spermatic artery

Prostate gland

Penis

A
R—L
P

FIGURE 52-3 Reproductive anatomy of the male fetal pig. Ventral view.

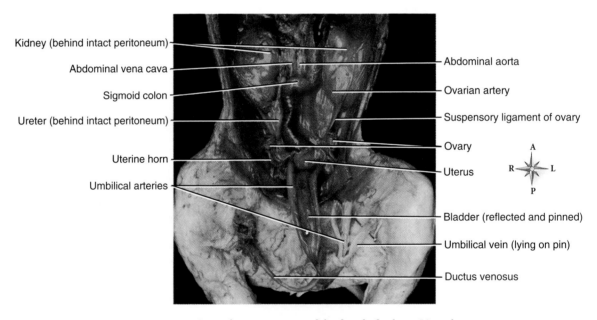

FIGURE 52-4 Reproductive anatomy of the female fetal pig. Ventral view.

Name: _____ Date: _____ Section: _____

LAB REPORT 52
Dissection: Reproductive Systems

A. Male Cat Dissection Checklist

☐ scrotum

☐ testis

☐ epididymis

☐ vas (ductus) deferens

☐ urethra

☐ prostate gland

☐ penis

☐ bulbourethral glands

☐ glans penis

B. Female Cat Dissection Checklist

☐ ovaries

☐ oviduct

☐ uterine horn

☐ uterus

☐ vagina

C. Male Fetal Pig Dissection Checklist

☐ scrotum

☐ testis

☐ epididymis

☐ vas (ductus) deferens

☐ urethra

☐ seminal vesicle

☐ prostate gland

☐ penis

☐ bulbourethral glands

D. Female Fetal Pig Dissection Checklist

☐ ovaries

☐ oviduct

☐ uterine horn

☐ uterus

☐ vagina

53

Development

Human development begins from the moment of fertilization in the female reproductive tract. A sperm cell from the male parent and an oocyte from the female parent unite to form the first cell of the offspring. This cell divides (using mitosis) again and again, forming a mass of cells that will eventually become a mature human. This exercise presents a brief exploration of the stages of human prenatal development.

BEFORE YOU BEGIN

☐ Read the appropriate chapter in your textbook.
☐ Set your learning goals. When you finish this exercise, you should be able to:
   ☐ describe the basic plan of prenatal development
   ☐ identify major features of successive developmental stages in models or charts
☐ Prepare your materials:
   ☐ models or charts of early human development
   ☐ Read the directions and safety tips for this exercise carefully before starting any procedure.

Study TIPS

Develop a concept map that illustrates neonatal development. Include the major events that occur during each developmental period. For reference, use your textbook, lab manual, or the *A&P Survival Guide*.

A. EARLY HUMAN DEVELOPMENT

Obtain a set of models or charts that depict the major stages of early human development. Use the guidance given here and in your textbook to identify the major events of early development and the landmark structures associated with each stage.

☐ 1 The original cell of an offspring is termed the **zygote.** About 18 to 36 hours after being formed by fusion of an egg and sperm, this cell divides. The two daughter cells divide, then their daughter cells divide, and so on, until a ball of cells is formed. Locate a zygote in **Figure 53-1** and in your model.

☐ 2 When the ball has about 32 cells and a fluid-filled cavity called the **blastocele** forms, the offspring becomes a **blastocyst** and continues to grow. Most of the blastocyst is a single layer of cells called the **trophoblast,** but one portion also has an **inner cell mass** several cells thick. The inner cell

mass develops into the embryo. The trophoblast develops into the **chorion,** which later becomes the placenta and the membranes that surround the embryo. Locate this stage in Figure 53-1 and in your model.

☐ 3 Around 7 days after fertilization, the blastocyst begins **implantation** by digesting its way into the endometrium of the mother's uterus. During this stage the chorion (formerly the trophoblast) develops projections (**chorionic villi**) into the maternal blood supply. This close association of the embryonic and maternal tissue is called the **placenta.** Later in development the placenta allows diffusion of substances between the embryo's blood and the mother's blood. Identify this stage in Figure 53-1, then in your model.

☐ 4 By day 11, several features have become visible. Identify these features in Figure 53-1, then in a model or chart:
   ☐ **Connecting stalk**—This narrow piece of tissue connects the inner cell mass to the developing placenta (it will eventually develop into the **umbilical cord**).
   ☐ **Amniotic cavity**—A fluid-filled space within the cell mass, it lies within a layer of cells called the **ectoderm** (this cavity will eventually develop into the **amniotic sac** surrounding the embryo).
   ☐ **Yolk sac**—Another fluid-filled space within the cell mass, this one lies within a layer of cells called the **endoderm.**
   ☐ **Embryonic disk**—This flat sheet of tissue is formed by adjacent layers of endoderm and ectoderm.

☐ 5 By day 14, more features of the developing offspring become apparent, as seen in Figure 53-1:
   ☐ **Primitive streak**—This is a thickened line in the endoderm at the center of the elongated embryonic disk (the embryo will eventually form around the streak; the **notochord** extends from the cephalic end of the streak).
   ☐ **Mesoderm**—This new *germ layer* arises between the ectoderm and the endoderm.

☐ 6 Follow the developmental stages represented in your model or chart, noting that the three germ layers (endoderm, mesoderm, and ectoderm) develop into different tissues and organs. Using your textbook or a reference book, determine which major tissues or organs are derived from each of the three germ layers. Report your findings in Lab Report 53.

☐ 7 After about 60 days, the cartilage and membranous tissue of the embryonic skeleton begin to ossify. From this point onward, the offspring is termed a **fetus.** Examine a model or chart of a full-term fetus. Because its organs and systems have developed sufficiently, the full-term fetus is able to survive outside the uterus. Locate these structures associated with the fetus:

☐ **Amniotic sac**—A fluid-filled space derived from the amniotic cavity, it cushions the developing offspring. At **parturition**, the sac breaks and spills its contents through the birth canal (vagina).

☐ **Placenta**—The organ originally formed by the chorionic villi's implantation into the endometrial lining of the uterus, the mature placenta allows exchange of materials between the fetal circulatory system and the maternal circulatory system. Examine the anatomical relationship of these two sets of vessels.

☐ **Umbilical cord**—Derived from the connecting stalk observed in earlier stages, the umbilical cord includes **umbilical arteries** and an **umbilical vein.** Exercise 38 describes how these vessels fit into the fetal circulatory plan. The umbilical cord serves as a connection between the developing offspring and the mother's body.

FIGURE 53-1 Representative stages of early human development. This figure may also be colored in with colored pens or pencils.

clinical application: *ultrasonography*

Ultrasonography is a method of imaging body parts by using high-frequency sound (ultrasound) waves. Usually a handheld wand that emits ultrasonic waves is placed against the patient's skin. The waves pass through different tissues at different speeds, and some waves are reflected back to the wand. Sensors in the wand detect the reflected ultrasound and relay the information to a computer capable of constructing an image based on the reflections. The image produced by this technique is called a *sonogram.*

An advantage of the technique is that ultrasound energy is not as dangerous as the radiation used in computed tomography (CT) scans and regular radiographs. This is one reason that it has become popular among obstetric physicians. Developing fetal tissue that could be harmed by x-rays is not harmed by ultrasound waves; therefore, the development of a particular embryo or fetus can be monitored by ultrasonography.

Sonograms can be used to determine whether there is a single fetus or multiple fetuses. Abnormally developed structures are sometimes visible. Late in development, male or female genitals can sometimes be seen.

Occasionally, measurements of a fetus at various stages are made. The normal rate of development of organs can then be verified. Usually the age of a fetus is given as the clinical age rather than the developmental age used earlier in this exercise. The clinical age is the time since the mother's last menstrual period, whereas the developmental age is the time since fertilization.

FIGURE 53-2 Sonogram **A** shows the outline of a fetal skull at 153 days (clinical age). Compare it with sonogram **B**, the skull of the same fetus shown at 206 days.

1. The size of the skull has increased by what percentage during the 53 days between sonograms?

2. Which structures in particular do you think are likely to show up well in a sonogram?

3. What other applications for ultrasonography can you think of?

4. What advantages do CT scans, magnetic resonance (MR) images, and regular radiographs have over sonograms?

Name: _____ Date: _____ Section: _____

LAB REPORT 53
Development

Identify

1. _____
2. _____
3. _____
4. _____
5. _____
6. _____
7. _____
8. _____
9. _____
10. _____
11. _____
12. _____
13. _____
14. _____
15. _____
16. _____
17. _____
18. _____
19. _____
20. _____
21. _____
22. _____
23. _____
24. _____
25. _____
26. _____
27. _____

Identify (identify the germ layer from which each of these organs or tissues is derived; write "endo" for endoderm, "ecto" for ectoderm, and "meso" for mesoderm)

1. Adrenal medulla
2. Anterior pituitary gland
3. Bones of the face
4. Bones (except those of the face)
5. Brain
6. Cardiovascular organs
7. Dermis
8. Epidermis
9. Gonads
10. Kidney ducts and bladder
11. Kidneys
12. Lens and cornea of eye
13. Lining of gastrointestinal tract
14. Linings of hepatic and pancreatic ducts
15. Lining of lungs
16. Melanocytes
17. Muscle
18. Nasal cavity
19. Outer ear
20. Parathyroid gland
21. Skeletal muscles of the head
22. Spinal cord
23. Thymus gland
24. Thyroid gland
25. Tonsils
26. Tooth dentin and pulp
27. Tooth enamel

Multiple Choice

1. _____

2. _____

3. _____

4. _____

5. _____

6. _____

7. _____

Multiple Choice (choose the best response)

1. The cell formed by the union of a sperm cell and an oocyte is called a
   a. blastula
   b. morula
   c. zygote
   d. blastocele
   e. b and c are correct
2. The connecting stalk seen early in human development later becomes the
   a. placenta
   b. amniotic sac
   c. umbilical cord
   d. yolk sac
3. The earliest developmental stage at which one can see a fluid-filled extracellular cavity is
   a. morula
   b. blastula
   c. zygote
   d. fetus
   e. 4-cell stage
4. The organ through which maternal and fetal blood exchange materials is the
   a. umbilical cord
   b. umbilical vein
   c. amniotic sac
   d. amniotic cavity
   e. placenta
5. The process by which a baby is born is called
   a. gestation
   b. pregnancy
   c. differentiation
   d. parturition
   e. lactation
6. The chorion is derived from the
   a. trophoblast
   b. blastocele
   c. inner cell mass
7. The embryo develops around a thickened line in the endoderm called the
   a. trophoblast
   b. inner cell mass
   c. notochord
   d. primitive streak

54
Genetics and Heredity

Heredity, or the inheritance of traits, falls into the realm of **genetics.** Genetic information in the form of **genes** is found in the 23 DNA molecules that you inherit from your mother and the 23 that you inherit from your father. This information is passed from generation to generation. Twenty-two pairs of your DNA molecules, or *chromosomes,* are called **autosomes.** The remaining pair is called the **sex chromosomes.** One member of each pair is inherited from one parent, and the other member of the pair from the other parent.

Each autosome in a pair is homologous to the other member of the pair. With this arrangement, a person has two genes for every inherited characteristic. If one gene is always expressed, whether or not its mate is the same gene, geneticists call that gene **dominant.** A gene that is not expressed when its mate is different is termed a **recessive gene.**

All the genes in all the chromosomes taken together are called the **genome.** The study of all the genes in the human species, the *human genome,* is called **genomics.**

BEFORE YOU BEGIN

❏ Read the appropriate chapter in your textbook.
❏ Set your learning goals. When you finish this exercise, you should be able to:
  ☐ identify the phenotype and possible genotypes of selected human characteristics
  ☐ distinguish between the concepts of *dominant* and *recessive* as applied to inherited traits
  ☐ predict probabilities of phenotypes and genotypes in offspring given the parents' genotypes or phenotypes
❏ Prepare your materials:
  ☐ taste papers: control, sodium benzoate, phenylthiocarbamide (PTC), thiourea
  ☐ BIOHAZARD container
  ☐ blood typing materials (if not done previously in Lab Exercise 34)
❏ Read the directions and safety tips for this exercise *carefully* before starting any procedure.

Study TIPS

Review the principles of inheritance. Understand how a Punnett square is used to determine the probabilities of producing offspring with specific gene combinations. For reference, use your textbook or the *A&P Survival Guide.*

A. HUMAN PHENOTYPES AND GENOTYPES

For any particular inherited characteristic, a **phenotype** can be identified. The phenotype is the characteristic actually expressed in an individual. A person's **genotype** is a statement of both genes that influence a particular trait. For example, the phenotype *albinism* is a recessive genetic condition in which a person lacks skin pigmentation. By convention, a gene for normal skin pigmentation, which is dominant, is represented as A. The recessive gene is represented as *a.* A person with normal skin pigmentation may have the genotype AA, meaning that both genes are normal. Geneticists may state that the person's genotype is **homozygous,** meaning that both genes are the same. A person with normal skin color could also have the Aa genotype. Because A is dominant, the abnormal *a* is not expressed. This person has a **heterozygous** genotype, meaning that the two genes are not the same. A person with albinism must have the genotype *aa* because it is the only genotype that allows the recessive abnormal trait to be expressed. Thus, the normal phenotype (normal skin color) may be associated with the genotype AA or the genotype Aa. The abnormal phenotype (albinism) is always associated with the genotype *aa.*

Study TIPS

Skin color is determined by a number of factors, both environmental and genetic. A number of different *A* genes exist in the human gene pool, and genes at other locations in the DNA may influence skin color. The example of albinism is simple when first observed, but the effect of multiple factors complicates things. This is typical of inherited characteristics. Often, many genes influence one particular trait. Also, many environmental factors can affect inherited characteristics.

> ❗ ***safety first***
> The first step of this activity involves tasting test papers. Be sure to use clean procedures in handling the papers before and after you taste them. Used papers are to be placed in a BIOHAZARD container immediately after use. •

☐ 1 The first set of characteristics to be determined involves the sense of taste. It is known that the ability to taste certain compounds depends on the presence of certain genes. You will taste papers that have each been impregnated with a different compound. Before starting, put a piece of CONTROL test paper on your tongue and chew it. If you taste something, you must be sensitive to a compound in the paper itself. Ignore that particular taste in the tests that remain or try to sense *differences* in taste.

- **Sodium benzoate test**—Ability to taste something sweet, salty, or bitter in the paper is dominant
- **PTC test**—Ability to sense a bitter taste is dominant
- **Thiourea test**—Ability to taste something bitter is dominant

2 The next set of determinations involves anatomical characteristics of your hand:

- **Bent little finger (Figure 54-1, A)**—Place your relaxed hand flat on the lab table. If the distal phalanx of the little (fifth) finger bends toward the fourth finger, you have the dominant trait.
- **Middigital hair** (Figure 54-1, *B*)—Dorsal hair on the skin over the middle phalanges of the hand is dominant.
- **Hitchhiker's thumb** (Figure 54-1, C)—If you can hyperextend the distal joint of the thumb noticeably, you have the recessive trait.

3 Determine your phenotype for these facial features:

- **Pigmented anterior of the iris**—If you have pigment on the anterior *and* posterior of the iris, your eyes are green, brown, black, or hazel. If you lack pigment on the anterior aspect of the iris, your eyes are blue or gray. Anterior pigmentation is dominant.
- **Attached earlobes (Figure 54-2, A)**—If the inferior, fatty lobe of the ear is attached rather than free, you have the recessive trait.
- **Widow's peak** (Figure 54-2, *B*)—Assuming you have a hairline, if it is straight across the forehead, you have the recessive trait. If it forms a downward point near the midline, you have the dominant "widow's peak."
- **Tongue roll** (Figure 54-2, C)—Try to curl your tongue as you extend it from your mouth. If you can't curl it, you have the recessive trait.
- **Freckles**—If your face has a scattering of freckles, you have the dominant form of this characteristic. If your face is free of freckles, you have the recessive condition.

4 There are two dominant genes for ABO blood types. One is I^A, which signifies the presence of the A antigen. The other is I^B, signifying the B antigen. The recessive gene is i, signifying neither ABO antigen. A person with the phenotype TYPE A has the genotype $I^A I^A$ or $I^A i$. A person with the phenotype TYPE B has the genotype $I^B I^B$ or $I^B i$. A person with phenotype TYPE AB has the genotype $I^A I^B$. Phenotype TYPE O requires the genotype ii. Record your phenotype (your ABO blood type). What is your genotype?

> **Hint** If you have not already typed your blood (as instructed in Lab Exercise 34), consult your health records or perform the typing now. Refer to Lab Exercise 34 and heed the safety advice given there. •

5 The Rh blood type is also determined by genetics. Presence of the Rh antigen is dominant. What is your Rh blood type? What is your genotype?

Study TIPS

This section instructs you to determine your phenotype for a variety of easily observed characteristics. Once you know your phenotype, you can determine your possible genotypes. For example, if you are an albino, you know that your genotype is *aa*. If you do not have albinism, your genotype is either *AA* or *Aa*. For each characteristic described, record your phenotype and possible genotypes in Lab Report 54.

B. PROBABILITIES OF INHERITANCE

Now that you have a grasp of the concept of phenotype and genotype, you can move on to the concept of **probability**. Probability is the likelihood of a certain outcome in a particular event. As applied to human genetics, probability refers to the likelihood that the offspring of a particular set of parents will have a certain inherited condition. **Genetic counselors** work with prospective parents to determine their possible genotypes for a variety of traits. Then they predict the probability of their children having those traits. In this way, parents can anticipate possible abnormal genetic conditions.

In this exercise, we will use a simple method developed by the English geneticist Reginald Punnett. He devised a simple grid, or **Punnett square,** with which one can easily predict simple ratios of genetic probability.

First, an example:

The father has freckles; the mother does not. The gene for freckles is **f,** *and the gene for no freckles is* **f.** *The father's genotype is either* **FF** *or* **Ff.** *The mother's genotype must be* **ff.** *We must consider two different outcomes in offspring from this couple because the father has two possible genotypes for this trait. First, let's assume that the father's genotype is* **FF.** *Any sperm cell contributed by the father will have the* **F** *gene. Any oocyte contributed by the mother will have the* **f** *gene. We place the possible gene for the father in the left margin of the Punnett square and the mother's in the top margin:*

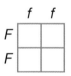

To use the Punnett square, start in the top left square of the grid. Combine the gene from the left margin with the gene from the top margin:

We now have one possible offspring genotype: **Ff**. We then do the same for the other three squares of the grid:

	f	f
F	Ff	Ff
F	Ff	Ff

Our Punnett square predicts a 100% probability that any one off-spring will have genotype **Ff** and therefore have the freckled phenotype. The second possibility is that the father's genotype is **Ff**. We can set up a Punnett square for this possibility:

We can now fill in the grid with possible offspring genotypes, combining the gene from the left margin with the gene from the top margin for each square:

	f	f
F	Ff	Ff
f	ff	ff

Because half the squares have genotype **Ff**, there is a 50% probability that any offspring of this couple will have the **Ff** genotype (and therefore the freckled phenotype). There is also a 50% probability that the genotype will be **ff**, expressed as the nonfreckled phenotype. If the phenotypes or genotypes of the client's parents and grandparents are known, a genetic counselor might construct a **pedigree**, or family tree, to determine the father's likely genotype. If that information is unavailable, the parents will have to deal with the two different probabilities.

Now that you have seen an example, try your hand at the following problems. Draw your Punnett squares and record your results in Lab Report 54.

☐ **1** Huntington disease (Huntington's chorea) is a degenerative nerve disorder with a genetic basis that becomes apparent after about 40 years of age. The abnormal gene that produces this disease, *H*, is dominant. The normal, recessive gene is *h*. One of Heather's parents has Huntington disease, and the other does not. Can you predict the highest probability that Heather will develop Huntington disease later in her life?

☐ **2** Kevin has Rh-positive blood. Christine has Rh-negative blood. Their first child, Andrew, has Rh-positive blood. Both of Kevin's parents have Rh-positive blood. What is the probability that the second child Kevin and Christine are expecting will be Rh negative?

☐ **3** Leo's father has albinism, but Leo does not. Cleo's father has albinism, but she does not. If Leo and Cleo have a child, what is the probability that it will have albinism? What is the probability that their second child will have albinism? Their third child?

☐ **4** In the ABO blood typing system, Mario is type O, and Ana is type AB. What ABO blood types might their children have?

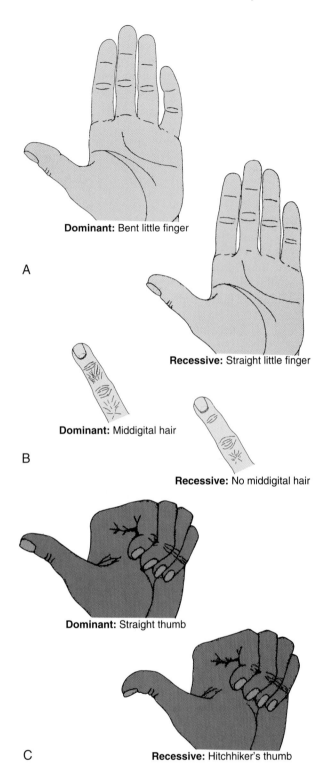

FIGURE 54-1 The dominant and recessive forms of bent little finger (**A**), middigital hair (**B**), and hitchhiker's thumb (**C**).

FIGURE 54-2 Dominant and recessive forms of attached earlobes (**A**), widow's peak (**B**), and tongue roll (**C**).

Name: _____ Date: _____ Section: _____

LAB REPORT 54
Genetics and Heredity

TRAIT	DOMINANT GENE(S)	RECESSIVE GENE	YOUR PHENOTYPE	POSSIBLE GENOTYPES
Sodium benzoate taste	S	s		
PTC taste	P	p		
Thiourea taste	T	t		
Bent little finger	L	l		
Middigital hair	M	m		
Hitchhiker's thumb	H	h		
Pigmented anterior of iris	I	i		
Attached earlobes	A	a		
Widow's peak	W	w		
Tongue roll	R	r		
Freckles	F	f		
ABO blood type	IA, IB	I		
Rh blood type	D	d		

1. What is the highest probability that Heather will develop Huntington disease? ___%

2. What is the probability that Kevin and Christine's second child will have Rh-negative blood? _____%

3. What is the probability that Leo and Cleo's first child will be albino? _____%
   Their second child? _____%
   Their third child? _____%

4. What are the possible ABO blood types of Mario and Ana's children? _____%

55
The Whole Body

This exercise is intended as a possible summary or synthesis activity for the laboratory course. Whether your instructor will invite you to complete this exercise will depend on the course schedule and the availability of the required materials.

The first activity of this exercise suggests that you observe a live or videotaped demonstration of human anatomy using a human body. The second activity presents a special focus on transverse (horizontal) sectional anatomy, which is becoming increasingly important in practical applications of human anatomy.

BEFORE YOU BEGIN

☐ Set your learning goals. When you finish this exercise, you should be able to:
  ☐ describe the overall body plan of the human
  ☐ identify the major organs of the human in a previously dissected cadaver or in a human body model or chart
  ☐ identify structures in selected transverse sections of the human body
☐ Prepare your materials:
  ☐ prosected human cadaver (for demonstration, if available) or human dissection videotape
  ☐ plastinated preparation (or chart): *human thorax, horizontal section (just above heart)*
  ☐ plastinated preparation (or chart): *human abdomen, horizontal section (pancreas level)*
  ☐ demonstration pointers
  ☐ hand lens
☐ Read the directions and safety tips for this exercise *carefully* before starting any procedure.

Study TIPS

The dissection of the human cadaver is a compilation of your study of human anatomy. The chance to learn from a cadaver is invaluable. You may want to obtain an atlas of the human body to use as you proceed through your dissection. This reference will assist you in your identification of the various structures of the cadaver.

A. THE HUMAN CADAVER

Advanced laboratory courses in human anatomy use the human cadaver as the basic dissection specimen. A **cadaver** is an embalmed corpse. If available, view a live or videotaped demonstration using a prosected human cadaver. A prosected specimen is one that has been previously dissected and prepared for anatomical demonstrations.

> ## ! *safety first*
> Do not touch the cadaver unless invited to do so by the demonstrator. If you are invited to touch it, use gloved hands. Cadavers are normally fixed in preservative, which is a toxic substance. Do not inhale the fumes that are immediately above the specimen. Excuse yourself from the demonstration if you feel ill or if you may be sensitive to preservatives such as formalin. Pregnant women should avoid contact with formalin fumes. Use safety goggles to avoid injury during dissections. •

B. TRANSVERSE SECTIONAL ANATOMY

Clinical and research institutions are seeing an increased use of computed tomography (CT) scans, magnetic resonance imaging (MRI), ultrasonography, and other advanced imaging techniques. Each of these techniques requires a basic knowledge of human anatomy as seen in a transverse, or horizontal, section.

Your studies so far have emphasized the sagittal and frontal aspects of anatomy. Now that you are familiar with the essentials of human anatomy from those perspectives, it is time to apply that knowledge to locating structures in transverse preparations.

> ## ! *safety first*
> Plastinated specimens are natural tissues that have been embedded in plastic. Even though they long outlast normal embalmed specimens, they are very fragile. If you handle them at all, be careful not to damage them. Always use a demonstration pointer in pointing to structures, never a pen or pencil. Do not touch the specimen with your pointer; just point at it. •

☐ 1 Obtain a plastinated transverse section of a human torso **(Figure 55-1)** just superior to the heart (at about T4). Try to locate these structures:
  ☐ **Aorta**—If the aorta is present, what section is it (ascending, arch, or descending)?
  ☐ **Superior vena cava**—Can you identify this vein by its position and the thinness of its wall?
  ☐ **Esophagus**—This is a small (and perhaps flattened) muscular tube anterior to a vertebra.
  ☐ **Trachea**—Are any of the C-shaped cartilage rings visible in the tracheal wall?

- ☐ **Thymus**—It is posterior to the sternum.
- ☐ **Lungs**—Can you distinguish any portions of the respiratory tract within the lung tissue? Identify the parietal and visceral pleurae and the pleural cavity.
- ☐ **Sternum**—This structure is in the anterior wall of the thoracic cavity.
- ☐ **Ribs**
- ☐ **Thoracic vertebra**—What features of the vertebra are visible in your specimen?
- ☐ **Spinal cord**—It is inside the vertebral foramen. What features of the spinal cord can you identify?
- ☐ **Skeletal muscles**—They form the wall of the thoracic cavity.
- ☐ **Subcutaneous tissue**—Identify the areolar and/or adipose tissue under the skin.
- ☐ **Integument**—Can you distinguish between the dermis and epidermis? Are there any other organs or structures visible in your specimen? If the upper arms are present in your specimen, identify the humerus and other arm structures.

> **Hint** ▸ Use a hand lens to examine the detail of the structures you have found. Refer to **Figures 55-3 to 55-6**, which show color photographs of transverse sections of human cadavers. •

- ☐ **2** Obtain a plastinated transverse section of the human abdomen **(Figure 55-2)** at the level of the pancreas (about T12). Try to locate these structures:
  - ☐ **Vertebra**—What features are visible in this preparation?
  - ☐ **Spinal cord**—Can you distinguish white and gray matter?
  - ☐ **Kidneys**—Are they the same size? Why or why not? Identify the renal fat pad around each kidney. Can you

distinguish between the renal cortex and the renal medulla?
- ☐ **Aorta**—The abdominal aorta may be present just anterior to the body of the vertebra.
- ☐ **Inferior vena cava**—This large vein is normally next to the aorta.
- ☐ **Pancreas**—This glandular tissue is near the stomach.
- ☐ **Stomach**—This large muscular organ should be present in the left portion of the specimen. Can you identify the rugae (large folds) of the gastric mucosa?
- ☐ **Liver**—This is the dominant feature of your specimen, a large mass of tissue to the right and anterior of the abdominal cavity.
- ☐ **Colon**—Is any portion of the colon visible in your specimen? If so, which section is it?
- ☐ **Peritoneum**—Can you distinguish between the parietal and visceral portions of the peritoneum? Identify the peritoneal cavity. Are any mesenteries distinguishable in your specimen? The lesser omentum?
- ☐ **Ribs**
- ☐ **Abdominal muscles**—Which abdominal muscles could be present in your section?
- ☐ **Subcutaneous tissue**—Is the adipose tissue in this layer of the same thickness all the way around the abdominal wall?
- ☐ **Integument**—Are the dermis and epidermis distinguishable in this section?

> **Hint** ▸ Each specimen is unique, just as every person's body is unique. Therefore, some structures listed may not be present (or identifiable) in your specimen. Refer to Figures 55-5 and 55-6. These plates show transverse sections of a cadaver's abdomen. •

Coloring Exercises: Transverse Thoracic Section

Use colored pens or pencils to shade in both the figure and the labels. Each red numeral in the figure corresponds to a matching red numeral following the appropriate label.

AORTA₁
SUPERIOR VENA CAVA₂
ESOPHAGUS₃
TRACHEA₄
THYMUS₅
LUNG₆
PLEURAL CAVITY₇

STERNUM₈
RIB₉
VERTEBRA₁₀
SPINAL CORD₁₁
SKELETAL MUSCLE₁₂
SUBCUTANEOUS TISSUE₁₃
INTEGUMENT₁₄

FIGURE 55-1 Transverse section of human torso at T4 level.

Coloring Exercises: Transverse Abdominal Section

Use colored pens or pencils to shade in both the figure and the labels. Each red numeral in the figure corresponds to a matching red numeral following the appropriate label.

VERTEBRA₁
SPINAL CORD₂
KIDNEY₃
AORTA₄
INFERIOR VENA CAVA₅
PANCREAS₆
STOMACH₇

LIVER₈
COLON₉
PERITONEAL CAVITY₁₀
RIB₁₁
ABDOMINAL MUSCLE₁₂
SUBCUTANEOUS TISSUE₁₃
INTEGUMENT₁₄

FIGURE 55-2 Transverse section of human torso at T12 level.

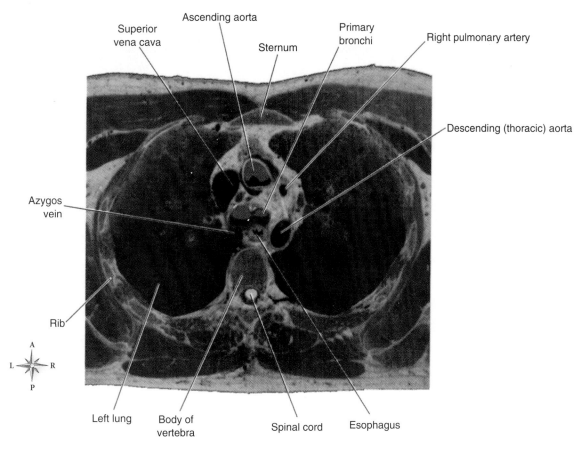

FIGURE 55-3 Transverse (horizontal) section of human thorax at T4 level.

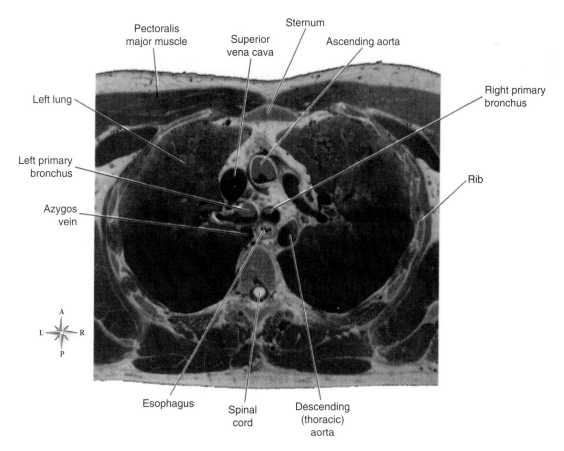

FIGURE 55-4 Transverse section of human thorax at T5 level.

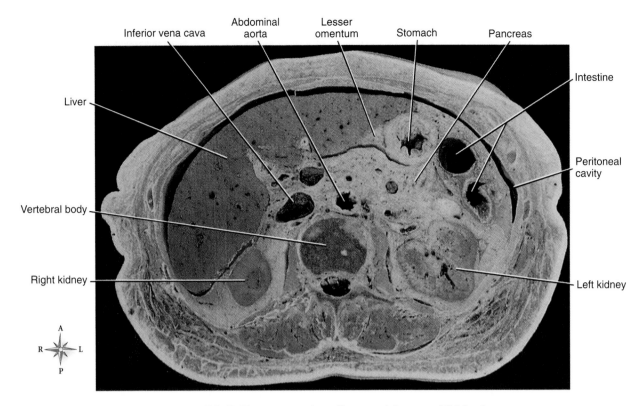

FIGURE 55-5 Transverse section of human abdomen at T12 level.

FIGURE 55-6 Transverse section of human abdomen at L2 level.

Name: _____ Date: _____ Section: _____

LAB REPORT 55
The Whole Body

Sketch and label your thorax (transverse section) specimen:

Sketch and label your abdomen (transverse section) specimen:

Name: _____ Date: _____ Section: _____

LAB REPORT SUPPLEMENT
Microscopic Observations

Specimen: _____
Total Magnification: _____

Specimen: _____
Total Magnification: _____

Specimen: _____
Total Magnification: _____

Specimen: _____
Total Magnification: _____

Notes:

Name: _____ Date: _____ Section: _____

LAB REPORT SUPPLEMENT
Microscopic Observations

Specimen: _____
Total Magnification: _____

Specimen: _____
Total Magnification: _____

Specimen: _____
Total Magnification: _____

Specimen: _____
Total Magnification: _____

Notes:

Name: _____ Date: _____ Section: _____

Microscopic Observations

Specimen: _____
Total Magnification: _____

Specimen: _____
Total Magnification: _____

Specimen: _____
Total Magnification: _____

Specimen: _____
Total Magnification: _____

Notes:

Name: _____ Date: _____ Section: _____

LAB REPORT SUPPLEMENT
Microscopic Observations

Specimen: _____
Total Magnification: _____

Specimen: _____
Total Magnification: _____

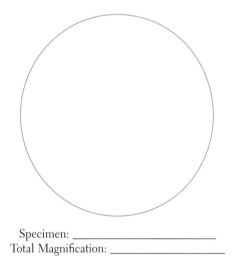

Specimen: _____
Total Magnification: _____

Specimen: _____
Total Magnification: _____

Notes:

Name: _____ Date: _____ Section: _____

Microscopic Observations

Specimen: _____
Total Magnification: _____

Specimen: _____
Total Magnification: _____

Specimen: _____
Total Magnification: _____

Specimen: _____
Total Magnification: _____

Notes:

Name: _____ Date: _____ Section: _____

LAB REPORT SUPPLEMENT
Microscopic Observations

Specimen: _____
Total Magnification: _____

Specimen: _____
Total Magnification: _____

Specimen: _____
Total Magnification: _____

Specimen: _____
Total Magnification: _____

Notes:

Name: _____ Date: _____ Section: _____

Specimen: _____
Total Magnification: _____

Specimen: _____
Total Magnification: _____

Specimen: _____
Total Magnification: _____

Specimen: _____
Total Magnification: _____

Notes:

Name: _____ Date: _____ Section: _____

LAB REPORT SUPPLEMENT
Microscopic Observations

Specimen: _____
Total Magnification: _____

Specimen: _____
Total Magnification: _____

Specimen: _____
Total Magnification: _____

Specimen: _____
Total Magnification: _____

Notes:

Name: _____ Date: _____ Section: _____

LAB REPORT SUPPLEMENT
Microscopic Observations

Specimen: _____

Total Magnification: _____

Specimen: _____

Total Magnification: _____

Specimen: _____

Total Magnification: _____

Specimen: _____

Total Magnification: _____

Notes:

Name: _____   Date: _____   Section: _____

LAB REPORT SUPPLEMENT
Microscopic Observations

Specimen: _____
Total Magnification: _____

Specimen: _____
Total Magnification: _____

Specimen: _____
Total Magnification: _____

Specimen: _____
Total Magnification: _____

Notes:

Name: _____ Date: _____ Section: _____

LAB REPORT SUPPLEMENT
Microscopic Observations

Specimen: _____
Total Magnification: _____

Specimen: _____
Total Magnification: _____

Specimen: _____
Total Magnification: _____

Specimen: _____
Total Magnification: _____

Notes:

Name: _____ Date: _____ Section: _____

Microscopic Observations

Specimen: _____
Total Magnification: _____

Specimen: _____
Total Magnification: _____

Specimen: _____
Total Magnification: _____

Specimen: _____
Total Magnification: _____

Notes:

Name: _____ Date: _____ Section: _____

Microscopic Observations

Specimen: _____
Total Magnification: _____

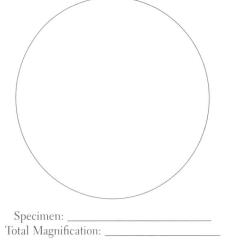

Specimen: _____
Total Magnification: _____

Specimen: _____
Total Magnification: _____

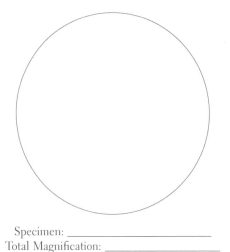

Specimen: _____
Total Magnification: _____

Notes:

Name: _____ Date: _____ Section: _____

Microscopic Observations

Specimen: _____
Total Magnification: _____

Specimen: _____
Total Magnification: _____

Specimen: _____
Total Magnification: _____

Specimen: _____
Total Magnification: _____

Notes:

Name: _____ Date: _____ Section: _____

LAB REPORT SUPPLEMENT
Microscopic Observations

Specimen: _____
Total Magnification: _____

Specimen: _____
Total Magnification: _____

Specimen: _____
Total Magnification: _____

Specimen: _____
Total Magnification: _____

Notes:

Name: _____ Date: _____ Section: _____

LAB REPORT SUPPLEMENT
Microscopic Observations

Specimen: _____
Total Magnification: _____

Specimen: _____
Total Magnification: _____

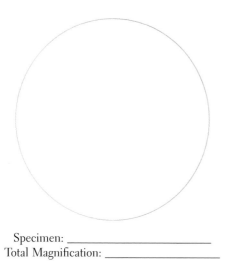

Specimen: _____
Total Magnification: _____

Specimen: _____
Total Magnification: _____

Notes:

Name: _____ Date: _____ Section: _____

Microscopic Observations

Specimen: _____
Total Magnification: _____

Specimen: _____
Total Magnification: _____

Specimen: _____
Total Magnification: _____

Specimen: _____
Total Magnification: _____

Notes:

Name: _____ Date: _____ Section: _____

Specimen: _____
Total Magnification: _____

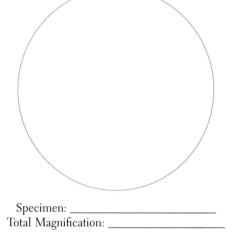

Specimen: _____
Total Magnification: _____

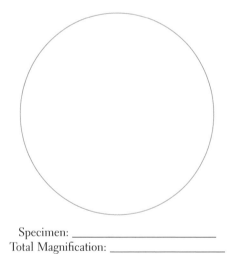

Specimen: _____
Total Magnification: _____

Specimen: _____
Total Magnification: _____

Notes:

Name: _____ Date: _____ Section: _____

LAB REPORT SUPPLEMENT
Microscopic Observations

Specimen: _____
Total Magnification: _____

Specimen: _____
Total Magnification: _____

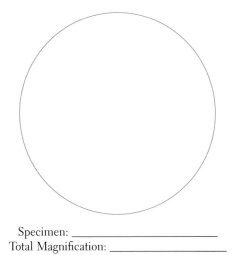

Specimen: _____
Total Magnification: _____

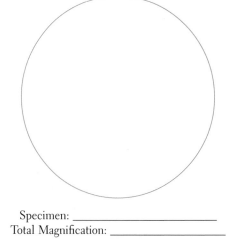

Specimen: _____
Total Magnification: _____

Notes:

Name: _____   Date: _____   Section: _____

LAB REPORT SUPPLEMENT
Microscopic Observations

Specimen: _____
Total Magnification: _____

Specimen: _____
Total Magnification: _____

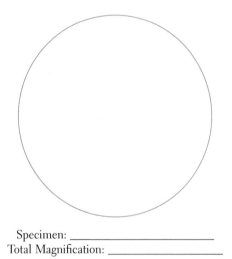

Specimen: _____
Total Magnification: _____

Specimen: _____
Total Magnification: _____

Notes: